NO LONGER THE
PROPERTY OF
ELON UNIVERSITY LIBRARY

D1438741

*INTERNATIONAL SERIES OF MONOGRAPHS IN
PURE AND APPLIED BIOLOGY*

Division: **ZOOLOGY**

GENERAL EDITOR: G. A. KERKUT

VOLUME 37

THE ULTRASTRUCTURE
OF THE ANIMAL CELL

The Ultrastructure
of the Animal Cell

BY

L. T. THREADGOLD, B.A., Ph.D.

DEPARTMENT OF ZOOLOGY,
QUEEN'S UNIVERSITY, BELFAST

THE QUEEN'S AWARD
TO INDUSTRY 1966

PERGAMON PRESS

OXFORD · LONDON · EDINBURGH · NEW YORK

TORONTO · SYDNEY · PARIS · BRAUNSCHWEIG

90248

Pergamon Press Ltd., Headington Hill Hall, Oxford
4 & 5 Fitzroy Square, London W.1

Pergamon Press (Scotland) Ltd., 2 & 3 Teviot Place, Edinburgh 1

Pergamon Press Inc., Maxwell House, Fairview Park, Elmsford, New York 10523

Pergamon of Canada Ltd., 207 Queen's Quay West, Toronto 1

Pergamon Press (Aust.) Pty. Ltd., 19a Boundary Street, Rushcutters Bay, N.S.W. 2011

Pergamon Press S.A.R.L., 24 rue des Écoles, Paris 5^e

Vieweg & Sohn GmbH, Burgplatz 1, Braunschweig

Copyright © 1967
Pergamon Press Ltd.

All Rights Reserved. No part of this publication may be reproduced, stored in a retrieval system, or transmitted in any form, or by any means, electronic, mechanical, photocopying, recording, or otherwise, without the prior permission of Pergamon Press Ltd.

First edition 1967

Reprinted 1969

Library of Congress Catalog Card No. 67–16780

Printed in Great Britain by The Anchor Press Ltd., Tiptree
08 012004 0

To the late Professor J. Bronte Gatenby, a great cytologist, who first showed me the limitless fascination of the cell and who would have revelled in the exciting discoveries of modern cytology.

CONTENTS

FOREWORD

"Yes, I have a pair of eyes", replied Sam, "and that's just it. If they wos a pair o' patent double million magnifin' gas microscopes of hextra power, p'raps I might be able to see through a flight o' stairs or a deal door; but bein' only eyes, you see, my wisdom's limited."
(Sam Weller in *Pickwick Papers*, CHARLES DICKENS)

When writing a text on the cell, an author has, in reality, only two basic approaches open to him. He may either write a general text on "cell biology" or a specialized book on some particular aspect of the cell. Recently, a number of excellent texts on "cell biology" have been published and these give the reader an overall appreciation of the biophysical, biochemical, structural and physiological characteristics of the cell. The adoption of this approach is, however, both the strength and weakness of such books, for in treating everything broadly and nothing in depth, they may leave the reader unsatisfied as to content and with a mistaken impression about certain cellular features.

In the alternative group of special texts, recent books have stressed the biophysical and biochemical aspects of the cell, often to the exclusion of cell structure as generally understood. Biophysical and biochemical researches have led to major and significant advances in cytology, and to a new and fundamental understanding of the functioning of living systems. There has, however, been a tendency to treat these discoveries *in vacuo* and to overemphasize them, as though in themselves they were adequate for a complete understanding of the cell. This is an unbalanced view, for at some point these fundamental and functional aspects must be attached to gross structures existing in the cell. Only by the correlation of function, be it biochemical or morphological, with structure, ranging from the atomic to the cellular, can a comprehensive understanding of the cell be expected to appear.

Among the specialized books, therefore, there is a notable absence of a text which treats in detail ultrastructural morphology and function. During the past twenty years, with the emergence of the electron microscope as a major cytological tool, knowledge of the ultrastructure of the cell has grown at an ever increasing, almost alarming, rate. This accumulated evidence, which has been derived from the study of innumerable and diverse cell types and which has so altered and influenced our concept of the cell as a unit, is unfortunately widely scattered. Consequently, someone coming fresh to the field experiences serious difficulty in readily obtaining the essentials of the subject. It is true that certain ultrastructural features of cells and cellular organoids have been incorporated into available cytology texts, but the descriptions given are often generalized and, because they lack depth and disregard variations, somewhat misleading. Alternatively, reviews of cell ultrastructure which are aimed at the research worker are inevitably intensive, discursive and presuppose a background knowledge of the subject.

The absence of an appropriate text on this particular aspect of the cell has in my experience, and I am sure that of many others, proved a considerable handicap in conducting courses in cytology to undergraduates and graduates. It is my hope, then, that this book will be found sufficiently wide in range and adequate in detail to fill this gap and give the reader an appreciation of the basic ultrastructure of the cell and the variability of particular structures both with function and between cells. In addition the book is intended to act as a bridge between modern biochemical and biophysical cytology and the classical cellular and functional morphology. The reader must, however, always keep in mind that this is intentionally a specialized text not sufficient in itself, and that reference must be made to texts dealing with other fundamental aspects of the cell, so as to obtain a balanced view.†

I have been greatly aided in my task by the numerous excellent reviews of various aspects of the cell which have appeared in recent years. In some sections of the book I have relied heavily on such expert works, paraphrasing them freely, or slightly altering their organization; I hope that authors who recognize their work will accept the compliment that is intended. In other specialized areas of the subject in which I do not consider myself competent to exercise judgement, I have incorporated reported observations into the text very much as the author originally expressed them, avoiding, so I believe, errors of interpretation or accidental misrepresentation.

During the writing of this book, two problems have persistently intruded. The first problem is concerned with content, and the second with the limitations of electron microscopy. As already stated, the accumulated observations on cell ultrastructure now form a vast pool of information, which is rapidly increasing. Expertise over the whole spectrum of this knowledge is beyond the scope of one man or one book, limitations are essential. This text is intentionally confined to the description of structures appearing in the normal animal cell and no evidence is drawn from plant cells, bacteria or viruses, unless unavoidable. Furthermore, only some of the infinite variety of structures which whole cells, or their parts, can assume, are outlined. Of necessity there has been a drastic selection of material, and in many cases a forced decision on the relative significance of some cellular feature or function. Any errors in selection or interpretation are mine alone, but I hope that the reader will look kindly on my mistakes and view omissions as inevitable consequences of the limitations of both author and space.

† A list of references to complementary books is given at the end of each chapter.

The second problem, which arises from electron-microscope techniques themselves, is the result of the predominant use of sections of fixed tissue. The use of sections tends to give a static, two-dimensional picture of the cell, and even changes in structure during cell function are observed only as a severely limited series of stages in an obviously continuous process. I have tried in the text and diagrams to convey a three-dimensional image of the ultrastructure of the cell and to relate individual parts to each other and the whole, and I have attempted to emphasize the dynamic qualities of the cell, the only constant of which is change.

In the last chapter of the book I have speculated and generalized about cell structure, organization and origin, and discussed extent theories in these fields in an uninhibited manner. It was my intention to help the reader take a step back from the previous detail and see all from a distance and in a new light. Observations and knowledge which do not lead to speculation incompletely serve their purpose and fail to pave the way for new attitudes and the redirection of enquiry into new pathways. The reader should realize that observation and speculation go together, and the theories of the day are only transient steps to newer and more comprehensive interpretations of the properties and functions of the living cell.

Queen's University, Belfast   L. T. THREADGOLD

ACKNOWLEDGEMENTS

It is a pleasure to acknowledge my debt to my colleagues Professor G. Owen and Dr. A. Scott for reading the first draft of the manuscript and for making suggestions which have undoubtedly led to improvements in presentation and text. I am especially obliged to Dr. Scott, whose eagle and editorial eye spotted many a slip in both the original text and the proofs.

I am sincerely grateful to all those cytologists who so willingly responded to my requests for photographs, electron micrographs and drawings, for without their generous help this book could not have been so comprehensively illustrated. Their names are too numerous to mention individually, but I hope they will accept this acknowledgement and that beneath the appropriate illustration as an adequate expression of my appreciation.

I should also like to express my genuine appreciation to two other persons. First, Mr. W. Ferguson, for his technical skill with photographic illustrations and for his excellent and unfailing efforts to meet my demands in this field. Finally, but by no means least or last, my wife, Jenny, not only for her practical help with typing chores, but even more for her encouragement and understanding during the many difficult periods involved in the book's long genesis.

I gratefully acknowledge the permission to reproduce published illustrations by the following holders of copyright.

ACADEMIC PRESS LTD.: Fig. 1.10a–c; *Expl. Cell Res.* **5**, 1953; Fig. 3.9c, d; *Expl. Cell Res.* **6**, 1954; Fig. 5.9b; *Expl. Cell Res.* **26**, 1962; Fig. 4.1a; *Expl. Cell Res.* **30**, 1963; Figs. 3.6a; 5.14a; 5.16b, c; 5.17a; *Exp. Molec. Path.* **2**, 1963; Figs. 2.5c–e; 3.16b; 4.11a, b; 4.23b; 5.5a; 6.24a; *5th Int. Congress E.M.,* Philadelphia, 1962; Figs. 4.13d; 6.16d–f; *Int. Rev. Cytol.* **7**, 1958; Fig. 3.18a, b; *J. Ultrastruct. Res.* **1**, 1958; Fig. 3.22a; *J. Ultrastruct. Res.* **5**, 1961; Figs. 3.8b–d; 3.9a, b; *J. Ultrastruct. Res.* **6**, 1962; Fig. 3.15d; *J. Ultrastruct. Res.* **7**, 1962; Figs. 3.1d; 3.2; 3.12e; 3.13a; 3.21b; 4.15c, d; *J. Ultrastruct. Res.* **8**, 1962; Figs. 3.14f; 4.2b; 5.2a; 5.9a; *J. Ultrastruct. Res.* **9**, 1963; Figs. 2.8a; 4.14c; 5.21a–e; *J. Ultrastruct. Res.* **11**, 1964; Fig. 5.9d, e; *J. Ultrastruct. Res.* Suppl. 1, 1959; Fig. 5.8a; *J. Ultrastruct. Res.* Suppl. 4, 1962; Figs. 3.24a; 3.26b; 4.3a, c; 6.20a; 6.21a, b; 7.4d–g; 7.5a, b; 7.6b–e; *The Cell,* I–IV; Fig. 4.10a, b; *Biological Structure and Function* **1**, 1961; Figs. 2.6a–c; 2.7b–d; 4.25c, d; 5.10a; 8.1b; *Interpretation of Ultrastructure* **1**, 1962.

ALMQVIST & WIKSELL: Fig. 4.14a, b; *1st European Reg. Conf. E.M.,* Stockholm, 1956.

ANATOMICAL SOCIETY OF GREAT BRITAIN: Fig. 3.22b; *J. Anat.* **93**, 1959; Fig. 3.22c; *J. Anat.* **95**, 1961.

ELSEVIER PUBLISHING CO.: Fig. 4.11d; *Biochemical Problems of Lipids,* **1**, 1963.

GAUTHIER–VILLARS: Fig. 5.2e; *C.R. Acad. Sci.* **245**, 1957.

AMERICAN HEART ASSOCIATION INC.: Figs. 3.3a; 3.5b; 3.10a, b; 3.28b; *Circulation* **26**, 1962.

S. KARGER, Basel–New York: Fig. 1.5d; *Acta Anat.* **17**, 1953.

LEE & FERBIGER: Figs. 3.13b; 3.28a; 4.5a, b; *Introduction to the Fine Structure of Cells and Tissues,* 1963.

MASSON ET CIE: Fig. 1.10g–i; *Archs. Biol.* **63**, 1952; Fig. 1.10j–m; *Archs. Biol.* **69**, 1958; Figs. 4.21a, b; 5.14b; 5.18a–c; 5.19a–c; *Archs. Anat. microsc. Morph. exp.* **47**, 1958.

MACMILLAN (JOURNALS) LTD.: Fig. 8.3b; *Nature* **188**, 1960; Fig. 3.4; *Nature* **198**, 1963.

P. NOORDHOFF LTD.: Figs. 1.5f, g; 1.10d–f; 1.11g–j; 7.4c; 7.5c, f; 7.6f; *Symposium on the Fine Structure of Cells,* Leiden, 1954.

COMPANY OF BIOLOGISTS LTD., Oxford University Press: Figs. 6.1a–d; 6.2b; 6.3b, c; *J. Embryol. Exp. Morphol.* **10**, 1962.

PAN PACIFIC PRESS: Fig. 8.2a; *Proc. VIII Int. Congr. Haematol.,* Tokyo, 1960.

ROCKEFELLER PRESS: Fig. 3.19a; *J. Gen. Physiol.* **38**, 1955; Fig. 2.9c, d; *J.B.B.C.* **2**, 1956; Figs. 3.24a; 3.29c; 5.3b–f; 5.4a; 6.5b; *J.B.B.C.* **5**, 1959; Figs. 3.23c, d; 4.23a, b; 4.26a; 5.15c–f; 5.16a; 6.18a; *J.B.B.C.* **6**, 1959; Figs. 2.11a, b; 3.25; 3.29b; 6.9b; 6.10a; *J.B.B.C.* **7**, 1960; Figs. 1.8c; 2.8b, c; 2.9a, b; 4.6a–c; 4.24c, d; 4.26d–f; 5.3a; 8.12a–c; 8.13a–c; 8.14a, b; *J.B.B.C.* **8**, 1960; Figs. 1.11a–c; 3.26a; 5.4b, c; *J.B.B.C.* **9**, 1961; Fig. 8.5a; *J.B.B.C.* **10**, 1961; Figs. 3.15a; 4.16; 4.17a–c; 4.22a–c; 5.9c; 8.2c; 8.7a; *J.B.B.C.* **11**, 1961; Figs. 2.3a, b; 4.13a–c; 4.19a–f; 4.25b, c; 5.1a, c; 5.10c; 5.11a; 6.18b–f; 8.14c; 8.15a–c; 8.16a–c; *J. Cell Biol.* **12**, 1962; Figs. 2.8b, c; 2.9e; 2.14b, c; 4.18a, b; 8.9a, b; 8.10a–c; 8.11a–c; *J. Cell Biol.* **13**, 1962; Figs. 2.12a–c; 3.14a, b; 3.23b; 4.7a, b; 4.21c, d; 6.16a–c; 6.17a–c; 6.19a–d; 6.23c, d; 6.24b, c; 6.25a–c; 6.26; 8.5b; 8.6a, b; *J. Cell Biol.* **14**, 1962; Figs. 3.3b; 3.27b; 3.30b; 5.5b, 5.11b; *J. Cell Biol.* **15**, 1962; Figs. 3.15c; 3.16a; 4.9a–c; 5.13a, b; 6.10b; 6.11a; *J. Cell Biol.* **16**, 1963; Figs. 3.7a, b; 3.8a; 3.10c, d; 3.11a–c; *J. Cell Biol.* **17**, 1963; Figs. 3.32a; 4.3c, d; 6.8a, b; 6.9a; 6.22a, b; 6.23a, b; *J. Cell Biol.* **18**, 1963; Figs. 2.13a–c; 4.28b; *J. Cell Biol.* **19**, 1963; Figs. 8.1a; 8.7b–d; 8.10c; *J. Cell Biol.* **21**, 1964; Figs. 6.12b; 6.13a, b; 6.14a–c; 6.15a; *J. Cell Biol.* **22**, 1964; Figs. 4.5c, d; *J.B.B.C.,* Suppl., The Sarcoplasmic Reticulum, 1961.

ROYAL SOCIETY: Figs. 2.12d; 8.2b; *Proc. Roy. Soc.* B, **152**, 1961; Figs. 2.14a; 6.2a, c; 6.3a; *Proc. Roy. Soc.* B, **156**, 1962; Figs. 7.1b, d; *Trans. Roy. Soc.* B, **243**, 1960.

W. B. SAUNDERS & CO.: Figs. 3.30c; 4.2a; 8.3a; *General Cytology,* de Robertis, Nowinski and Salz.

SOCIÉTÉ FRANÇAISE DE MICROSCOPIE: Figs. 3.17; 3.24b, c; 3.31a–c; 4.1d, e; 4.20a–c; 5.6a, b; 5.7a–c; 5.14c, d; 5.20a, b; *J. Microscopie,* **1,** 1962; **2,** 1963.

JAPANESE SOCIETY OF ELECTRON MICROSCOPY: Fig. 3.31d, e; *J. Electron Microsc.* **12,** 1963.

SPRINGER-VERLAG: Figs. 2.3d–f; 2.5a; 3.5c; 5.17b–d; 8.4b, c; *Z. Zellforsch. Mikrosk. Anat.* **48,** 1958; **55,** 1961; *4th Int. Congr. E.M.,* Berlin, 1958.

INTRODUCTION TO
ELECTRON MICROSCOPY

THIS short introduction to the principles and techniques of electron microscopy is for those readers unfamiliar with the method. It was felt that this introduction was necessary in order that such readers might appreciate both the advantages and limitations of the technique, for it is only with an informed appreciation that a reader can make his own critical evaluation of electron microscope studies and their results.

Image Formation

The electron microscope is based on the response of electrons (negatively charged particles) to electromagnetic fields. A metal filament heated in a vacuum emits electrons which can be accelerated by a difference in electrical potential between the filament, at 50–100 kV and the anode, which is positive and at zero potential (Figs. I.1a and I.2). The resulting stream of electrons follows a straight path and has properties similar to those of light, i.e. both corpuscular and wave characteristics at the same time. The beam can, therefore, be focused by means of electromagnetic lenses (Figs. I.1b and I.2). The lenses are coils of wire enclosed in a soft iron casing. When a current flows in the coil, a magnetic field is set up at right angles to the direction of the electron beam. In order to increase and concentrate the magnetic field without excessive increase in current flow, a narrow annular gap is left in the iron casing facing the cavity of the coil and a soft iron pole piece inserted to reduce the diameter of the cavity (Fig. I.1b).

The electron microscope is, therefore, analogous with the light microscope (Fig. I.2). The "light" source is the heated filament which emits a beam of electrons (thermionic emission). This beam is focused on the plane of the object by means of a wire coil (magnetic lens) which acts as a condenser lens. After passing through the object, the beam is deflected by a further magnetic lens which acts as an objective lens. The resulting enlarged image is passed through another lens, the projector or ocular lens, which throws the final magnified image on to a fluorescent screen. A photographic plate may be substituted for the fluorescent screen and exposed. Such photographs are the only permanent record available.

The analogy between a light and electron microscope is not absolute, however, and the two instruments differ in certain essential respects. Although electromagnetic lenses are subject to both spherical and chromatic aberration, as are optic lenses, they do not have a fixed focal length. In electromagnetic lenses the focal length depends on the strength of the magnetic field, which can be varied by alteration of the current passing through the lens coil.

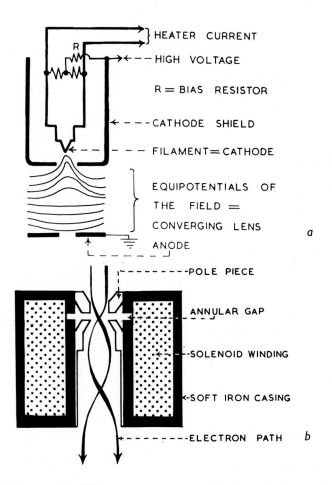

Fɪɢ. I.1. (a) Diagram of a self-biasing electron gun. Electrons produced by the heated filament are accelerated through the gap in the anode by the potential difference (40 to 100 kV) between the cathode and anode. (Original.) (b) Diagram of an electromagnetic lens. The annular gap and pole piece increase the intensity of the magnetic field. The electrons follow a spiral path through the lens. (Original.)

Spherical and chromatic aberration of the magnetic lenses are due to either inherent asymmetrical fields which the lenses form, or to the additional distortion of the field as the result of the lens apertures becoming contaminated by dirt. Lens apertures are metal plates, with holes varying from 25 to 100 μ, which are placed in the bore of the condenser and objec-

tive lenses; they increase the contrast of the image by reducing the aperture
of the lens.

Furthermore, changes in magnification in the electron microscope
require only a change in the focal length of the projector lens; the magnification of the objective lens is fixed. Finally, the electromagnetic lenses
have a considerable depth of field, so that fine changes in focus are not

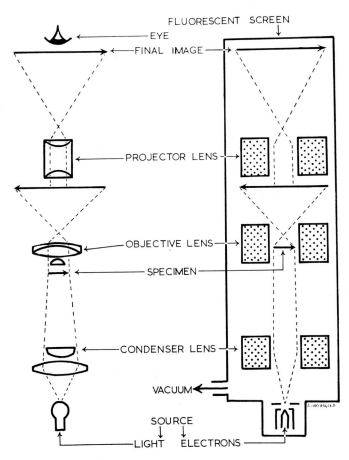

FIG. I.2. A diagram showing the similarities and differences of light and electron microscopes. (Original.)

readily appreciable by direct visual observation; accurate focusing must,
therefore, be carried out by viewing the fluorescent screen with a binocular
microscope.

A further difference between light and electron microscopy is in image
formation. In the former the image is due to differential absorption of light,
which can be accentuated by staining, and results in visible differences in
intensity and wavelength between parts of the image (contrast). In the

electron microscope absorption of the electrons by a specimen of useful thickness is very small. Electrons giving up their energy to the specimen are absorbed. Electrons giving up part of their energy are inelastically scattered and those giving up no energy to the specimen, but which change direction, are elastically scattered. The electron image is due to the scattering of electrons due to their collision with electrons and atoms in the specimen. Those electrons which are strongly scattered are unable to pass through the lens aperture and therefore are lost. This loss of electrons at a particular point of the specimen results in reduced intensity at that point on the fluorescent screen, i.e. it appears dark or electron-dense (adielectronic). The amount of scatter by any area or structure of the specimen depends on its physical density and thickness (its mass density) and not on its atomic number or chemical composition. By the addition of heavy metal or other substances to a particular structure, the scattering power of that structure can be increased and therefore appear more electron-dense on the screen. Such techniques are called electron staining and increase the contrast between the electron-dense (adielectronic) and electron-lucid (dielectronic) parts of the specimen. Contrast of the image, therefore, is due to the accumulative effects of electron scattering which is visualized as variations in intensity over the viewing screen or photograph plate.

Advantages of Electron Microscopy

The major advantage of the electron microscope lies in its resolving power which is much greater than the light microscope. The resolution of a lens is its ability to discriminate as separate two points lying close together. This ability is a function of the wavelength of the light source and the numerical aperture of the lens, as in the following formula:

$$\text{Limit of resolution} = \frac{0 \cdot 61\lambda}{\text{N.A.}},$$

where λ = wavelength of light source, N.A. = numerical aperture of the lens (which is $n \sin \alpha$, where n = the refractive index of the medium and α = the semi-angle of aperture of the lens).

The limit of resolution of a light microscope using monochromatic violet light (4000 Å = λ) is about 1700 Å, because $\sin \alpha$ cannot exceed 1 and the refractive index of most optical materials is 1·6; this gives an N.A. of about 1·4 using an oil immersion lens. The only possibility of increasing resolution, therefore, is to use a "light source" with a shorter wavelength. The wave form of an electron beam is a function of the accelerating voltage

and is approximately $\lambda = \dfrac{12 \cdot 3}{\sqrt{V}}$ Å, where V = accelerating voltage and

λ = wavelength of electrons. With an accelerating voltage of 60,000 V, the wavelength of the electrons would be 0·05 Å. This would give an increase in resolution of 80,000 times over monochromatic violet light of 4000 Å wavelength (4000 ÷ 0·05 Å), e.g. a resolution of about 0·02 Å.

Although theoretically a lens of $1 \cdot 0$ mm focal length could give a resolution below 5 Å, in practice a routine resolution of 10 Å must be considered good because of the inherent astigmatism of lenses and other limiting factors such as aperture angle, specimen preservation, section thickness, and the stability of the accelerating voltage and the lens current.

Limitations and Disadvantages of Electron Microscopy

Although the electron microscope is the only instrument available for the direct observation of cellular ultrastructure and at first appraisal appears to be an ideal instrument for this purpose, it has definite limitations. These limitations fall into three broad interlocking groups, namely (a) inherent physical and mechanical properties of the electron microscope, (b) techniques of specimen preparation, (c) interpretation of results.

The poor penetrating power of electrons in air and the consequent necessity of operating the electron beam in a vacuum are two inherent physical properties of the electron microscope which are the direct cause of a considerable number of limitations to the technique. Operating in vacuum immediately eliminates the study of living cells and tissues and necessitates the fixation and dehydration of the material. Even in vacuum, the power of electron penetration is limited, and it therefore follows that whole specimens or sections of tissue must be thin, in the order of 200–1000 Å, depending on the accelerating voltage of the beam and the mass density of the specimen. In addition, the interaction of the electrons with the specimen and with residual air or organic molecules in the evacuated column, plus the heat produced during operation of the filament and coils, result in damage of the specimen. The organic molecules in the vacuum (mainly organic vapours from the oil and grease of the vacuum system) condense and form absorbed films on the specimen. These films are fixed and transformed to graphite-like material by interaction with the electrons. This contamination layer reduces resolution and may alter dimensional relationships of cellular structures. Similarly, the heat of the column and the heat produced in the specimen by its interaction with electrons, result in changes in the thickness of the whole specimen or of cellular structures and the alteration of the spatial relationship of cellular parts.

The observation of the specimen in vacuum and at an adequate thickness has resulted in complex techniques of specimen preparation. As already noted, fixed and dehydrated tissue is required and these processes lead to changes in molecular organization and chemical composition of cellular structures and in their size, shape and spatial interrelationship. In order to obtain specimens of useful thickness, the tissue must normally be sectioned. This involves giving additional mechanical support to the specimen by infiltrating it with liquid plastic which can subsequently be hardened by polymerization. This process, which is embedding, can result in the expansion or shrinkage of the specimen, or both in succession. Other distortions in ultrastructure similar to those caused by fixation and dehydration can also occur. Indeed, fixation, dehydration and embedding, can bring about alterations in the original structure which are extreme and give an end product which must be considered an artefact. Additionally, some structures are not adequately preserved and consequently are soluble or become extracted by other means, so that they are completely lost as a structural entity. The process of sectioning itself alters ultrastructure and compression, for example, will alter an originally circular outline to an oval one.

A final limit to electron microscopy lies in the interpretation of the electron micrographs and the problem of sampling. The electron micrograph (positive photo) is in reality a map of the mass density of the specimen or tissue slice, with or without enhancement or alteration of relative densities of structures by staining. It is readily conceivable that those features most prominent in photographs are not necessarily those most significant from a functional viewpoint. Indeed, it is probable that the most active components of the cell are the most labile and therefore the most difficult to preserve. As indicated already, some structures of importance may not be preserved at all, so would be absent from the photograph, while others may be altered in small, but significant, aspects. The accuracy of the picture produced and its relationship to actual structures existing in the living cell must always be uppermost when examining the results of electron microscopy.

Additionally, permanence of structure is over-emphasized by the techniques essential for microscopic study of cell structure and leads inevitably to suppression of the functional aspects of the cell. These cytological techniques depend on stabilizing structure by the removal of the time element essential to function. A particular living cell may show permanence of a kind which will distinguish it from other cell types and as an individual among cells of its own kind, but this permanence is in essence false. A continuous flow of matter and energy passes through the cell, and the latter, with the aid of internal or external energy, transforms these materials into its own particular structure. The cell is always in a state of flux, a state which becomes increasingly evident when the cell is investigated at increasingly finer levels of organization. The inevitable penalty paid for stabilizing structure is the loss of the dynamic qualities which characterize living organisms.

The difficulties of interpretation of electron micrographs are increased further by the problem of sampling, in order that a representative or a three-dimensional image of the structure may be formed. Increased magnification and resolution compound detail enormously and emphasize dissimilarities between samples which, in light microscopy, might well appear identical. An added complication results from the thinness of the sections. At 600 Å thickness, 100 sections would be required to section completely a nucleus of 6·0 μ diameter, nearly the whole thickness of which could be observed at one time in the light microscope with a section of normal thickness. The technical skill required to obtain 100 serial sections at 600 Å, not to mention recording them photographically, emphasizes the inherent limits of electron microscopy. This point is more readily appreciated by taking a stated example: if a picture is taken at × 1500 on a 2-in. photographic plate, an area of only 0·001 mm² is recorded. Under these circumstances it is estimated that 1 month would be required to photograph 1·0 mm² and 7·5 years for 1·0 cm². These difficulties in sampling are more pronounced when cyclic phenomena of the cell are investigated, such as secretory or mitotic cycles.

A further consequence of this limitation in sampling is the reconstruction of cellular ultrastructure in three dimensions. For such cell organoids as mitochondria it is possible to reconstruct a tridimensional model from relatively few sections, because the number of mitochondria per cell is large and their random distribution and orientation in the cytoplasm compounds section planes, which is equal to very numerous samples. Such a situation does not readily occur, and becomes more rare with the increasing size of the organoid, until at the level of the whole cell serious difficulties are encountered due to differences in function state between even adjacent cells. Allied to this problem of three-dimensional reconstruction is that of deciding the orientation and relationship of the structure observed in the section plane (or micrograph) to that of the complete structure as it exists in the cell. An adielectronic line seen in a micrograph may represent a section of a fibre or of a sheet or layer (membrane); an oval profile may be a true representation of an oval-shaped tube cut transversely, but might equally well represent an oblique section of a circular tube; two adielectronic lines lying in parallel and joined at their ends may be a longitudinal section of a tube, a cross-section of a closed flattened sac, or a cross-section of a U-shaped narrow boat-like structure.

It is obvious, therefore, that the advantages of resolution in electron microscopy are counterbalanced by its limitations. Many so-called facts or observations are only interpretations of a mass density map, so that observations themselves, as well as conclusions, general theories and propositions of structure and function, must always be critically evaluated.

Further Reading List

1. WISCHNITZER, S., *Introduction to Electron Microscopy*, Pergamon Press, Oxford, 1962.
2. KAY, D., *Techniques for Electron Microscopy*, 2nd Edit., Blackwell, Oxford, 1964.
3. PEASE, D. C., *Histological Techniques for Electron Microscopy*, 2nd Edit., Academic Press, London, 1965.

Part I

THE INTERPHASE CELL

CHAPTER 1

INTRODUCTION TO THE ANIMAL CELL

THIS chapter is an introduction to the structure and function of the animal cell as revealed by techniques other than electron microscopy. The account is intentionally brief and, consequently, incomplete. Its purpose is to help readers having little or no cytological background to become familiar with terminology and to obtain not only an appreciation of cell structure and function, but also a comprehensive view of the cell as a unit. Readers who already have a knowledge of cytology can either refresh their memories or proceed directly to Chapter 2, as they desire.

Definition of the Cell

The cell is difficult to define. The simplest definition, that the cell is a membrane-bound volume of protoplasm, the nucleus, embedded in another membrane-bound volume of protoplasm, the cytoplasm, is inadequate; it divorces structure from function. A more acceptable statement is that the cell is the primary agent in the organization of animals and the unit of structure and function, but even this definition must be accepted with reservations, because it implies, first that protoplasm organized as nucleus and cytoplasm is the only basic form that living matter assumes, and, second, that the organism is no more than the sum total of its individual cells. The cell thus becomes the independent unit of life.

The first implication is unacceptable, for animals organized on other than the cellular pattern are known. Rotifers, for example, are mainly syncytial, the cytoplasmic areas around individual nuclei being interconnected to a greater or lesser extent. Syncytia also occur in the tissues of higher animals, e.g. striated muscle. During embryogenesis in insects only the nucleus divides during early cleavage, forming a multinucleate mass; cytoplasmic cleavage follows later. Some animal cells do not have a nucleus, for example, the mammalian erythrocyte, and it is questionable whether the chromidia of protozoa are homologous with the metazoan nucleus, especially since protozoa with both nucleus and chromidia occur. Furthermore, it is not unusual for cells in certain tissues to have more than one nucleus. Finally, ciliated protozoa possess within their "single cell' complex structures, gullet, contractile vacuoles and cilia, and, although the point is debatable, protozoa are best thought of as non-cellular animals, rather than single-celled.

3

The idea that cells are the independent units of life is also assailable, and the assumption that the cell is in any way the only legitimate unit of structure and function must be avoided. Even morphologically a cell is dependent on neighbouring cells, e.g. for its shape to some extent, and this interdependence of cells is more pronounced when function is considered. Within the animal body cells are dependent to varying degrees on other cells, some of which may be relatively or actually far distant. For a constant supply of essential chemical substances (oxygen and nutrients), for information and stimulation (nerve impulses, circulatory fluids and hormones), and for the removal of the products of its own activities, the cell is obligated to other cells. Just as the structures within the individual cell are in delicate balance, so that proper function may be attained, so that cell is in balance with its environment and with other cells. Reciprocal interaction between cell and organism occurs, each influencing the other. It must not be forgotten that cells arise from pre-existing cells, *omnis cellula e cellula* of Virchow; this is dependence in its most extreme form.

It is the organism, the whole animal, which is of primary importance. This is the unit of life, and whether its total protoplasmic volume is subdivided into cells, or not, is secondary. The greater the protoplasmic mass, the more necessary is the division of the organism into areas of protoplasm morphologically differentiated and having restricted or specific function. This differentiation of form and function is most readily attained by the division of the whole animal into relatively independent units, the cells, with consequent increased efficiency for the organism.

Nevertheless, the concept of the cell as a physiological and structural unit is convenient, even if the individuality of the cell is not as complete as may be implied on occasion. The living cell has the machinery which is essential for independence and is generally in physico-chemical equilibrium with its environment. If this cellular organization is brought into sufficient imbalance, its function is destroyed and it is no longer significant as a unit, even though some of its parts continue to function; death is inevitable. This latter statement emphasizes two inherent phenomena of the cell which cannot be overstated, namely, the inseparable union of structure and function, and its corollary, the dynamic nature of living cells. Function is the dynamic aspect of structure and must be considered essentially as a change of structure with time. Unending change and adaptation are characteristics of all living matter and therefore of cells also, but these characteristics tend to be overlooked in the fixed and stained tissues used for microscopic study.

The cell has the following characteristics, therefore, morphological, chemical and physical organization, which can be appreciated at a variety of levels; function, evident in the cell's ability to assimilate, grow and reproduce; independence to the extent that it is in equilibrium with its environment by means of its power of self-regulation and its adaptability.

Cell and Nuclear Size

Cell and nuclear size are in many ways interrelated and are further related to cell and nuclear shape. Separating these characteristics for individual consideration is convenient, but must not obscure the dependence of one cell character upon another or others.

Cell and nuclear size are extremely variable, so that the enumeration of linear dimensions is not very instructive; the range of linear sizes is more useful (Fig. 1.1). The average human tissue cell measures between 10 and 20 μ in diameter, but the range in diameter is between 6·5 μ (small lymphocyte) and 250 μ (oocyte). In the whole animal kingdom the range of cell

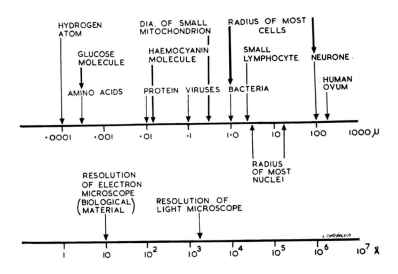

Fig. 1.1. A scale relating the sizes of various living organisms and systems from cells to viruses, with molecules and the limits of resolution of light and electron microscopes. Log scale. (Original, after A. B. Hastings, T. Young and J. R. Hoag.)

size is even greater. The smallest cell is about 4·0 μ (small lymphocyte), while the ostrich egg has been measured at 75,000 μ in diameter.

This great range in cell volume is misleading, however, for cells with the same function, but from different animals, are about the same size, and the range of cell size is similar in different animals, irrespective of that animal's overall size. Nevertheless, cell size is characteristic for any particular group of animals to some extent, e.g. amphibians generally have larger cells than reptiles, birds or mammals, and this seems to be correlated with the active or passive nature of the whole group.

Nuclear size also shows a considerable range, but this is much more restricted than the cell size range. Most nuclear diameters fall between 5 and 25 μ (Fig. 1.1). There is no real knowledge of the absolute range of nuclear size because measurements are not numerous. The difference in nuclear size between animal species may be due to the diploid number of chromosomes of each species. It has been shown that the surface area of the nucleus is proportional to the number of chromosomes within that nucleus. Nevertheless, the proportionality of chromosome numbers and nuclear surface area and the size relationship between the nuclei of polyploid and normal cells, is not universal.

Despite the great variability of cell and nuclear volumes within and between animals, it is possible to isolate factors which influence or control volume throughout the animal kingdom. Some of these factors affect both the cell and the nucleus, others only one of these. The two major common factors are age and function, in its various aspects. Subsidiary influences on cell volume are mechanical factors in the immediate vicinity, and, for the nucleus, interkinetic growth.

A reduction in cell volume due to early cleavage of the large fertilized egg is characteristic of early embryogenesis, and this is followed by cell growth in the post-hatched or post-natal period, the duration of growth depending on species. During cell senescence there is a decrease in cell volume, as one of the processes leading to cell death; the reduction is presumably due to the degeneration of metabolic processes within the cell. The influence of age on nuclear volume is almost identical with its effect on cell volume. During early embryogenesis nuclear volume falls, due to the absence of nuclear synthesis. The opposite effect is seen during later growth which leads to the nucleus attaining the adult volume. A secondary reduction in nuclear volume occurs during ageing and senescence and, accompanied by structural changes, gives rise to pyknotic nuclei.

Undoubtedly function is the most important single factor influencing the size of both cell and nucleus. It influences cell volume in a general way, for obviously eggs, or any cell which has storage as one of its major functions, must inevitably be large. More specifically, the control of cell and nuclear volume depends on surface area considerations. In cells with similar function three factors tend to control size, namely, the nucleo-plasmic ratio, the ratio of cell surface area to cell volume, and the metabolic rate of the cell.

The theory of nucleo-plasmic ratio (N/P) states that the volumes of the nucleus and cytoplasm are related in such a way that if one changes so must the other. In polyploid or haploid cells the volume of the nucleus is altered compared with the normal, and so is the cytoplasmic volume. From the known function of the nucleus as a controlling centre for cellular activity, this N/P ratio is to be expected. A nucleus of a certain volume cannot exert a useful influence over an inordinately large volume of cytoplasm. The surface through which the nucleus must exert its influence, the nuclear membrane, increases only as a square, while the volume of the cytoplasm increases as a cube (Fig. 1.2a). If cell size increases greatly the N/P ratio can be restored either by division of the cell, preceded by nuclear growth, or by an increase in nuclear surface area by changing its shape (Fig. 1.2b).

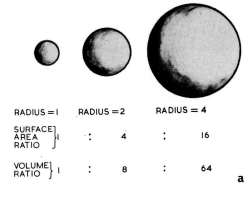

RADIUS = 1   RADIUS = 2   RADIUS = 4

SURFACE
AREA   1   :   4   :   16
RATIO

VOLUME   1   :   8   :   64
RATIO

a

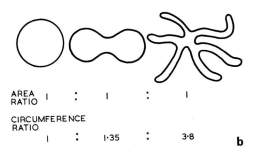

AREA   1   :   1   :   1
RATIO

CIRCUMFERENCE
RATIO
         1   :   1·35   :   3·8

b

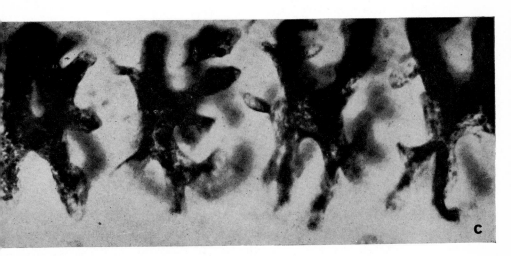

c

FIG. 1.2. (a) An illustration of the changes in surface area and volume ratios with increases in cell diameter. (Original.) (b) Illustration of changes in circumference length without changes in area. Changes of this type are possible in both cell and nucleus. (Original.) (c) Nuclei of the spinning gland of the larva of *Liparis*. Branching nuclei are typical of these cells during active synthesis. (Courtesy Dr. R. A. R. Gresson.)

The above examples illustrate the control of the cytoplasmic volume by the nucleus, but the converse also occurs. In gastropods and annelids cleavage of the fertilized egg results in cells of unequal volume. The nuclei within the larger cells grow so as to restore the N/P ratio to normal. In mature cells, however, the N/P ratio varies within narrow limits, being kept relatively constant until cell division is imminent, when the ratio is upset. For example the nucleus of the amoeba $A.$ *proteus* grows only from about 8 μ^3 ro 12 μ^3 during the first 20 hr of the interkinetic phase, but during the following 4 hr it grows to over 15 μ^3. This increase is presumably due to the reduplication of the chromosomes and is therefore a functional change in volume. This disturbance of the N/P ratio may be one of a number of factors responsible for division. Nevertheless, if the N/P ratio is upset badly, the function of the cytoplasm or nucleus will be greatly disturbed, perhaps irreversibly.

The ratio of cell surface area to cell volume, and nuclear surface area to nuclear volume is the same problem already noted in the relationship of nuclear to cell volume. Surface area increases as the square and volume as the cube. All substances necessary for cell maintenance must pass through the cell membrane in both directions and this limits the possible volume of the cytoplasm. In nuclei a similar situation occurs, for much evidence exists to show the correlation between nuclear size, the extent of its surface area, and the elaboration of material by the cell. In the spinning glands of certain insects, prior to a short period of intense secretory activity, the increase in nuclear volume is paralleled by a great extension of the nuclear membrane (Fig. 1.2c). Similar labyrinthine nuclei occur in the Malpighian tubules, and the nutritive cells of insects.

The surface area of the cell is directly concerned in the rate of cell metabolism. The rate of exchange of gases, metabolites and water, to mention but a few cellular requirements, depends not only upon the volume of the cell, but the rapidity with which they may be exchanged across the cell membrane. Just as the surface to volume ratio of nuclei can be changed by alterations in shape, so too can that of the whole cell. Surface area can be increased, but not volume, by the cell becoming elongated, folded, elliptical, flattened or irregular in form. Another mechanism for overcoming this condition is for the cytoplasm to flow, peripheral cytoplasm becomes central, resulting in substances being carried inwards to supply other areas of the cell. This type of cytoplasmic flow probably occurs in most cells.

Finally, both cell and nuclear size are limited by the mechanical factors inherent in the lipoprotein membranes enclosing them. These membranes are extremely thin and cannot retain large volumes. The cell membrane can be supported by the counter pressure of adjacent cells, by stronger material such as collagen and reticular fibres, or specialized structures of its own, e.g. pellicles, cuticles and capsules. Cell volume, therefore, can be increased by these means which are not available to the nucleus.

Cell and Nuclear Shape

Cell shape is mainly controlled by such internal factors as function, age, cytoplasmic viscosity and structure, the physical characteristics of its enclosing semipermeable membrane and such external factors as applied pressures or tensions. The shape of the nucleus is also influenced by age, function, nuclear membrane characteristics and the external pressures of the surrounding cytoplasm and its inclusions.

Despite differences in shape, cells may be broadly classified into those which have a variable shape (amoeboid cells) and those which have stable shape (fixed cells). In the former group are amoebae, leucocytes, muscle, secretory cells and melanocytes, to mention but a few, and in the latter group are the vast majority of epithelial cells, neurones, erythrocytes and some protozoans.

Function has an important influence on the overall shape of cells and in the alteration of that shape. Neurones are examples of cells peculiarly adapted in their shape to a particular function, but they do not alter that shape significantly when functioning. In contrast, smooth muscle cells have a permanently fusiform shape, but the proportions of that shape alter with function, while melanocytes are starlike when expanded and almost spherical when contracted. Secretory cells show alterations in form during activity, usually one pole only being involved, while epithelial cells in the transitional epithelium of the bladder change shape completely as the organ becomes full and distended.

Many cells alter shape during embryological differentiation, muscle and nerve again being good examples. Even in adult animals however, cellular differentiation occurs and involves extreme alterations; for example, during the development of spermatozoa from spermatogonia (Fig. 1.3a). Age demonstrates its influence in a most pronounced fashion during cell senescence, folding and shrinkage being the phenomena generally observed.

Changes in cytoplasmic viscosity alter cell shape either overall or locally. In cell groups, those cells with a decreasing viscosity will be gradually compressed by adjacent cells. Local changes in viscosity precede invaginations such as pinocytosis and evaginations such as pseudopodia.

Of the formed structures of the cell, the cell membrane and the cell web are concerned in cell shape. The cell membrane is naturally intimately involved in all alterations of cell shape, but may be the active principle in cases like the striated border and the microvilli, both structures being repeated, closely aligned infolds and outfolds of the membrane. Cells may also be surrounded by a product of their own, such as a cuticle or pellicle, thus ensuring permanence of form. The cell net, to be described fully later, appears as a locally fibrous area of protoplasm generally running immediately beneath the cell membrane, but may penetrate deep into the cytoplasm or completely across the cell (Fig. 1.3b, c). The cell web may be mainly

2

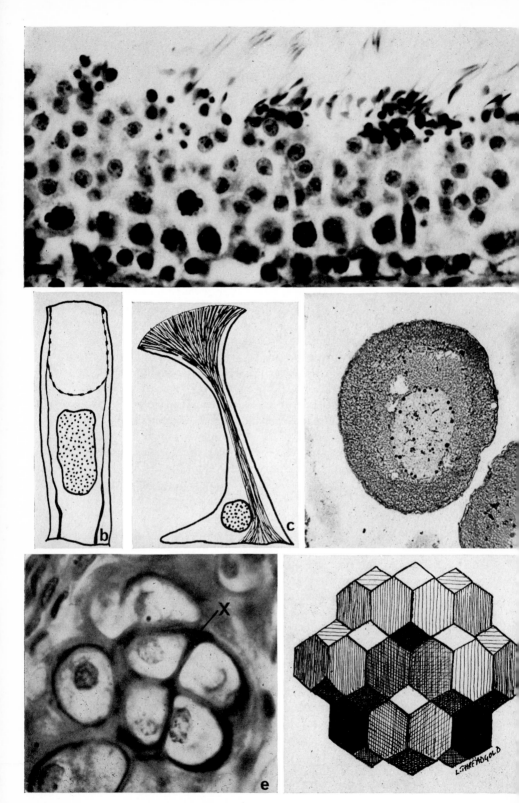

FIG. 1.3. (a) Mouse testis showing the changes in the shape of male germ cells during spermatogenesis. (Orig[inal.] ×1500.) (b) and (c) The appearance of the cell web in a mucous cell and a pillar cell of the cochlea respectiv[ely.] (Original, after C. P. Leblond, H. Puchtler and Y. Clermont.) (d) and (e) Frog egg and cartilage cells to illust[rate] the generally spherical shape assumed by cells not subject to reciprocal pressures. Note effect of reciprocal p[res]-sures in the group of recently divided cartilage cells at X. (Original. (d) ×950. (e) ×950.) (f) Tetrakaidecahed[ron] the packing of fourteen-sided solids without interstices. (Original, after Dr. J. Gray.)

responsible for the total shape in stable cells, or for localized areas of the cell being unalterable.

External factors, though often subordinate to inherent factors, do control cell form to a considerable degree in some cases. When external compression is minimal, for example in a fluid or semifluid medium, the cell should become spherical because protoplasm is viscous and the cell membrane semi-elastic. This condition is met in chondroblasts and osteo-blasts, leucocytes and eggs of aquatic animals; all these cells obey the law of the minimal surface area (Fig. 1.3,d e). Exceptions to this rule are numerous, however, because of the intrinsic cellular features already mentioned.

The influence of external pressures and tensions is more clearly seen in cell communities, tissues and organs. In these circumstances mechanical forces determine shape to a great degree. Dividing eggs are subject to changes in external conditions from that of minimal surface area to that of reciprocal pressures and show an accompanying alteration in cell shape, from the original spherical cell to a cluster with four or more sides, fourteen being about the limit. Four-, six-, twelve- and fourteen-sided solids can be packed without interstices. The tetrakaidecahedron (14-sided solid) best obeys the law of minimal surface, having six quadri-lateral faces and eight hexagonal sides (Fig. 1.3f). Counts on some cell masses have shown that many cells approximate to this number, but in others the number is lower. Some cells are intimately connected by means of terminal bars and desmosomes (attachment points), so that shearing or tension forces are transmitted throughout the mass, e.g. pickle cells of the epidermis.

Cell shape, therefore, depends on surface tension, externally applied pressures and tensions, internal resistance to compression or tension due to protoplasmic viscosity, the cell membrane and associated structures, formed bodies in the cytoplasm, and, not least, the function and functional state of the cell.

Nuclei show as great a variety of shape as cells. Generally, however, nuclei are spherical and ellipsoidal, because they are not subject to stress or tension. Function within the cytoplasm can cause alterations in nuclear shape, for example lipid storage by fat cells, which results in a kidney-shaped nucleus. Nuclear form is most influenced by its own function, however, and this is seen in the hooked, filiform, spiral or other bizarre forms of sperm heads. Changes in the shape of individual nuclei are a response to active metabolism, the branching and ramifying types which occur in the spinning glands of insects having already been mentioned (Fig. 1.2c). These increases in nuclear surface area, which are such a necessary part of active metabolism, results in lobes, sacculations, deep infoldings and incisions, and sometimes even tubular ingrowths forming intranuclear canaliculi. Ageing results in inevitable and irreversible nuclear changes, with reduction in volume resulting in a wrinkled nuclear membrane.

Nuclear shape, therefore, depends on internal characteristics and structure which give permanence, with other internal and external factors tending to change nuclear shape as a consequence of function.

Cellular Morphology

The cell may be considered as a two-phase system, the inner nuclear component having a different function, structure and physico-chemical composition, from the outer cytoplasmic component. The nucleus exercises general control over the growth and development of the cytoplasm and is the residue of the genetic material, the chromosomes. The more heterogeneous cytoplasm carries out the general activities of the cell, absorption and evacuation of materials, anabolism, catabolism and secretion (Fig. 1.4).

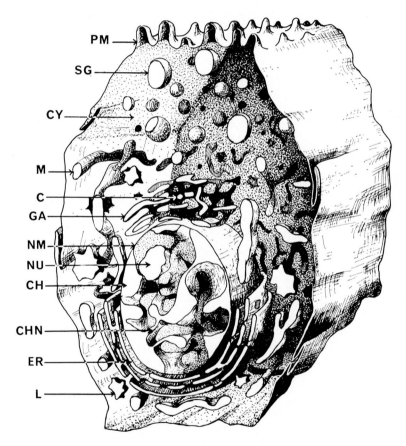

FIG. 1.4. Three-dimensional drawing of a typical cell, as observed by light microscopy. C, centriole; CH, chromocentre; CHN, chromonemata; CY, cytoplasm; ER, endoplasmic reticulum; GA, Golgi complex; M, mitochondrion; NM, nuclear membrane; NU, nucleolus; PM, plasma membrane; SG, secretion granule; L, lipid. (Original.)

This division of the cell into two phases is not absolute, however, from either the morphological or functional viewpoints; the two phases are mutually interdependent. Classical studies have frequently demonstrated the passage of nuclear, usually nucleolar, material across the nuclear membrane into the cytoplasm where it initiates a particular cellular process. The reverse passage of material has not been so often demonstrated, but it must exist, for otherwise the nucleus could not obtain the chemical substances essential for the reduplication of the chromosomes or for growth. Furthermore, the two-phase system breaks down completely during cell division when nucleoplasm and cytoplasm admix.

The Structure of the Nucleus

Usually cells are mononucleate but variations are common. Mammalian red blood corpuscles are of course anucleate and some protozoans may also be considered so if the homology of chromidia and nuclei is denied. Two nuclei per cell is not rare; such nuclei may be either alike, e.g. mammalian liver and mid-intestinal cells of insects (Fig. 1.5a), or unlike, e.g. protozoan micro- and macronuclei, the former having a nutritive function and the latter genetic (Fig. 1.5b). Polynucleate cells also exist. *Paramecium woodruffi* has three or four micronuclei, although the number varies from none to eight. Osteoclasts may have numerous nuclei, and in syncytia such as striated muscle the nuclei may number many hundreds (Fig. 1.5c). In some cases this polynucleate condition may be temporary, as in the early embryogenesis of insects.

The nucleus may be positioned within the cytoplasm in response to a variety of forces. Often it is centrally placed, where it is most able to exert its influence throughout the whole cell, but it may be displaced by vacuoles or inclusions to one side or one pole. The relative density of the cytoplasm in different regions of the cell may also determine nuclear position, because most nuclei have a specific gravity greater than that of the surrounding cytoplasm, although in some eggs it is less. In addition to such physical factors acting on nuclear position, function is again significant in this respect. The nucleus tends to lie in the region of the cell characterized by the most active metabolism. When the nucleus is polarized it usually lies next to the source of food or oxygen, namely, blood vessels, sinusoids and nutritive cells.

Nuclei are usually classified on the basis of structure as (a) chromidial or scattered, (b) massive, and (c) vesicular, although these forms are connected by many intermediates.

Chromidial nuclei are small granular masses of chromatin or a similar substance which stains like chromatin, and are scattered throughout the cytoplasm. They originate by the breakdown of a nuclear-like body and even reform into a single structure at certain phases of the life cycle. They may occur by themselves or co-exist with macro- and micronuclei, and are

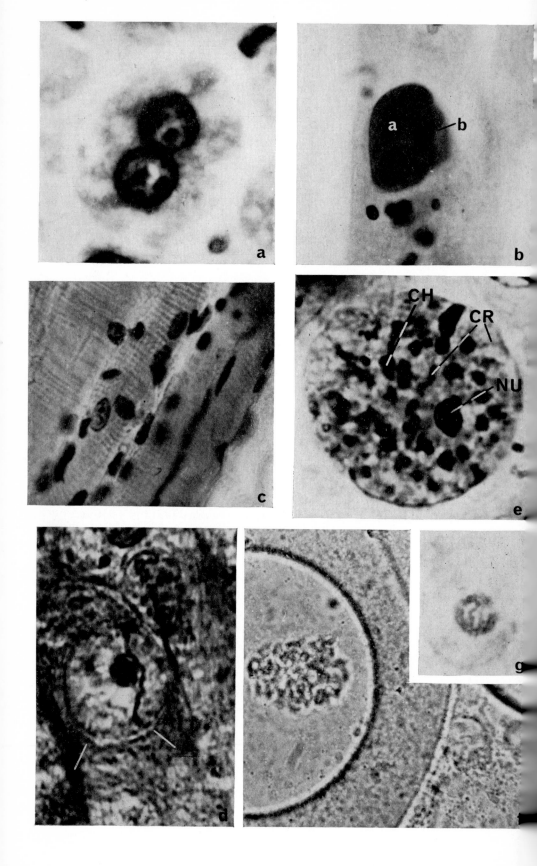

confined to protozoa, mainly the ciliates and rhizopods. The homology of the chromidia with the nuclei of metazoan cells is debatable, but as they do have functions similar to the latter, they probably represent a primitive type of nucleus.

Massive nuclei occur only in germ cells and are derived from vesicular nuclei by a concentration of the chromatin. They are homogeneous, dense, stain intensely, and do not have an obvious nuclear membrane (Fig. 1.3a).

The vesicular nucleus is the type most frequently found in cells of both metazoans and protozoa. It is bounded by a distinct nuclear membrane, which may be thickened locally or throughout by a plastering of chromatin on its internal surface. The membrane is usually assumed to be single but by certain techniques it may appear double, with distinct nuclear and cytoplasmic components (Fig. 1.5d.) This bounding membrane is a very pliable structure which is physiologically active. Enclosed by the membrane is a homogeneous or finely granular material, the nucleoplasm, in which all other nuclear structures are embedded. Reticulating through this nucleoplasm are fine threads, the chromonemata, their number characteristic for each cell type. Larger flakes or masses of chromatin also occur and these chromocentres (false nucleoli) are either connected to, or appear as expanded parts of, the chromonemata (Fig. 1.5e). The chromocentres are often attached to the nuclear membrane. Both the chromonemata and chromocentres are composed of deoxyribonucleic acid (DNA) and are the autonomous and continuing parts of the chromosomes during the interkinetic phase.

Finally, there is within the nucleus one or more bodies which are not connected to the chromatin reticulum and are the true nucleoli. Nucleoli are absent in some cells, and when present may alter in number in any particular cell. Nucleoli are numerous in the imediate post-division stage and later unite into one or more nucleoli. Furthermore, they may be more numerous in the same cell type in different sexes, e.g. they are more numerous in human female cells (mean 4 or 5) than in human male cells (mean 3 or 4). Sometimes nucleoli may number hundreds in one nucleus. Cells in the anabolic state usually possess or form large nucleoli, whereas the onset of catabolism results in the reversible diminution of nucleolar size.

Nucleoli are either homogeneous, round or oval, or filamentous and irregular; the two forms are interchangeable. The smooth round forms

FIG. 1.5. (a) Binucleate cell from the liver of the mouse. (Original. × 1800.) (b) Two unlike nuclei (*a*, macronucleus; *b*, micronucleus) in *Paramecium caudatum*. (Original. × 1500.) (c) Multinucleate muscle cell of the mouse. (Original. × 1500). (d) The nuclear membrane, as observed by light microscopy. The double character of the membrane is evident at the arrows. (Courtesy Dr. C. A. Baud.) (e) A typical vesicular nucleus with chromocentres (CH), chromonemata (CR), nucleolus (NU), and nucleoplasm. (Original. × 1500.) (f) and (g) Nucleolus with nucleolonema and pars amorpha. (f) as observed by phase contrast, oocyte of the armadillo; (g) stained with silver, neurone of cat. (Courtesy Drs. C. Estable and R. J. Sotelo.) (f) × 1500; (g) × 1200.)

are common to young cells or cells immediately after division, while the irregular shape arises as the cell ages. Homogeneity of nucleoli is only apparent, however, for special techniques reveal the nucleolus as bipartite, its major component being amorphous (the pars amorpha), and has embedded in it a filamentous part (the nucleolonema) (Figs. 1.5f, g). The nucleolonema is a coiled thread with expanded areas or nodules, and has a form resembling a loose ball of string. Variations in size, shape and number of the nucleolonema occur during cell growth, division, differentiation and senescence, and during cellular activity. Surrounding the nucleolus is a more or less complete ring of DNA, the nucleolus-associated hetero-chromatin.

Nucleoli are heavier than the rest of the nucleoplasm and contain ribo-nucleic acid (RNA), acid phosphatase, DPN synthesizing and other enzymes and small amounts of lipid. Because the nucleolus is Feulgen negative and is unstained by methyl green, it is considered by biologists not to be of chromosomal material, that is, DNA. The nucleolonema is the permanent part of the nucleolus, continuing to exist during cell divi-sion, when it is closely associated with the chromosomes. The filament grows during cell division, although the pars amorpha disappears, and after division the nucleolonema gives rise to a new pars amorpha. Nucleoli are concerned with the production of RNA and protein synthesis.

The complex nature of the nucleus as described above is derived from the study of stained sections. Nevertheless, the nucleolus, with pars amorpha and nucleolonema, and the chromocentres and chromonemata are visible in living cells when viewed by phase contrast and interference microscopes.

The Chemical Composition of the Nucleus

The major chemical components of the nucleus are the nucleoproteins, and DNA and RNA, and it is to be expected that the nucleus will contain both the precursor substances and the necessary enzymes for their synthesis. The nucleus is, therefore, composed of basic proteins, protamines and histones; non-histone protein and residual protein; nucleic acids (DNA and RNA); lipids; inorganic compounds and enzymes. An estimate of the chemical composition of the mammalian liver nucleus is DNA 9 per cent, RNA 1 per cent, histone 11 per cent, non-histone protein 65 per cent, residual protein 14 per cent.

The nucleic acids, DNA and RNA, are polymers consisting of many units called nucleotides. The nucleotides are made up of one molecule of sugar with a nitrogen base, either purine or pyrimidine, and phosphoric acid, the nucleotides being linked together by phosphoric acid bonds between the sugars (Fig. 1.6). The type of sugar determines the nucleic acid, *d*-ribose in RNA, and deoxyribose in DNA, the former being mainly located in the nucleolus and the latter in the chromosomes. The bases in DNA are the purines, adenine and guanine, and the pyrimidines, cytosine and thymine. RNA has the same bases except for the substitution of uracil for thymine.

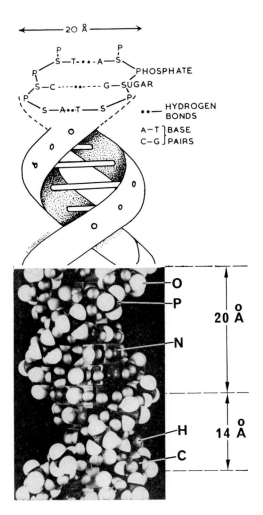

FIG. 1.6. Molecular and structural model of DNA. O, oxygen; P, phosphorus; N, nitrogen; H, hydrogen; C, carbon. (Original.)

The DNA molecule is composed of two polynucleotide chains running in opposite directions and helically coiled about each other (Fig. 1.6). The chains are united by hydrogen bonding of their bases, in such a manner that adenine is only linked with thymine and cytosine with guanine. This arrangement explains the reduplication of DNA, for a single polynucleotide chain acts as a template for a new chain. The species specificity of DNA

2*

and mutations are explained by the great number of different combinations possible.

The Functions of the Interphase Nucleus

The interphase nucleus has a twofold function, namely, self-maintenance and chromosome replication, and control of cytoplasmic activity.

The DNA component of the nucleus appears to be very stable and has a very slow turnover of its components. Some slight breakdown and resynthesis of DNA occurs and is revealed by the rate of incorporation of phosphorus and amino acids. Despite the observation that once formed DNA is stable, this does not mean that it is metabolically inactive. Protein, RNA, DNA and ATP synthesis are part of the activity of the interphase nucleus. An important result of these activities is the reduplication of the genetic material, and the enzymes necessary for this event have already been shown to be present.

The second function of the interphase nucleus is the control of cytoplasmic function and differentiation. This nuclear influence, however, is very indirect and long-term, and a delicate interaction and interdependence exist between the nucleus and cytoplasm; neither can long continue without the other. When cells are enucleated they cease to grow, synthesize and metabolize, and nuclei without cytoplasm are deprived of the oxidative enzymes which are localized in the mitochondria. The nucleus apparently maintains the ATP level in the cytoplasm, perhaps by control of the production of co-enzymes involved in glycolysis. In enucleate cells the ATP level cannot be maintained and its fall interferes with metabolic activities and synthesis, both of which require energy; so growth, movement of the cytoplasm and cell, and other activities eventually cease.

The other mode of nuclear control over the cytoplasm is through the production by DNA of RNA for export to the cytoplasm where it influences cytoplasmic protein production. It is postulated that the DNA molecules have sequences of nucleotides which act as codes for the arrangement of amino acids to form a protein. A triplet of three nucleotides arranged in a certain order signifies a particular amino acid, and a sequence of these triplets in a certain order would combine into a particular protein. This sequence of nucleotides on the DNA molecule replicates an RNA copy (called messenger RNA) by a template mechanism similar to DNA replication, but with uracil replacing thymine (Fig. 1.7). This messenger RNA passes to the cytoplasm where it either forms part of a ribosome (ribosomal RNA) or attaches to an already formed ribosome (Fig. 1.7). This ribosome and its attached messenger RNA now become the template for a specific protein. Amino acids in the cytoplasm become activated by being combined to a high energy phosphorylated nucleotide (transfer RNA plus energy from ATP) and become attached to the template with the help of a specific enzyme, guanosine triphosphate. The amino acids are linked up in a sequence which depends on the coding in the messenger RNA, to give a specific protein. Finally, some release mechanism frees the protein from the template and the transfer RNA (Fig. 1.7). The protein so formed may be utilized by the cell for structural purposes, or for enzymes, or be exported as a secretory product.

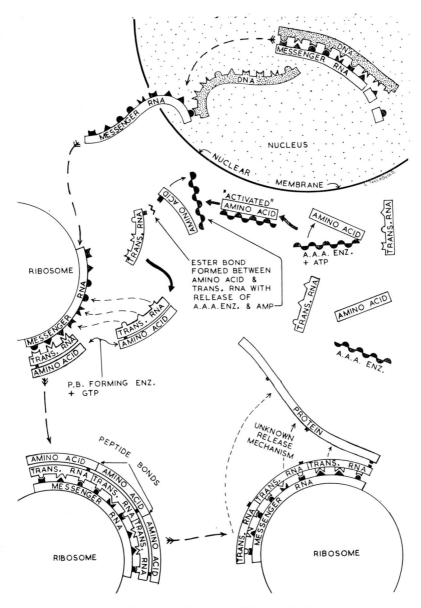

FIG. 1.7. Diagrammatic illustration of the roles of DNA and RNA in protein synthesis. (Original.)

The Cytosomal Phase

The cytosomal phase, which completely surrounds the nucleus, is composed of a ground matrix, the hyaloplasm. Within this is a heterogeneous collection of formed bodies, the universally present organoids (mitochondria, Golgi complex, endoplasmic reticulum and centrosome), the cell net, and the inconstant inclusion bodies (either ingested substances, cell products or by-products of catabolism). Although not visible by light microscopy and classical cytological techniques, a cell membrane must contain and enclose the cytosomal phase. The existence of a true limiting membrane to the cytoplasm is supported by the consistency of cell shape, by micro-dissection experiments in which an elastic and pliable membrane is demonstrated and can be ruptured, and by the selective permeability which cells diplay; for example, potassium can be accumulated within the cytoplasm, sodium cannot; the larger molecules of amino acids and glucose can penetrate cells, some smaller molecules cannot. The cell is able to maintain a relatively constant and definite chemical, ionic and osmotic character, somewhat independent of the immediate environment, a situation which would be impossible if the cytoplasm was not enclosed by a semipermeable membrane. The exact structure and composition of this membrane probably varies with cell function. There has been a tendency to replace the term cell membrane by plasma membrane, mainly because the former term is a morphological one and the major evidence for this cell structure is derived from physiological research, during which the term plasma membrane came into common use. Plasma membrane will be used throughout this text.

Related to the plasma membrane are a number of formed structures such as the brush border, striated border, cilia and flagella. The brush border appears as a distinct layer over the luminal surface of the columnar epithelial cells of the mucous membrane of the alimentary canal and has fine regular striations which were considered to be protoplasmic evaginations cemented together. The striated border of the proximal convoluted tubules of the kidney is similar to the brush border. It consists of hair-like outgrowths with small basal granules and resembles a dense brush. The true structure of both these specializations of the apical membranes of epithelial cells is described in Chapter 3.

Cilia and flagella are motile specializations which fringe the free borders of many cells (Fig. 1.8a, b). The main difference between the two structures is that cilia are short, have a pendular stroke, and beat synchronously, while flagella are few and long, have an undulant motion and beat independently. Cilia and flagella are used for locomotion in protozoans and planarians, for producing currents and counter-currents during respiration, circulation and reproduction in many metazoans, e.g. human trachea, mollusc intestine and spermatozoan movement. These structures also appear in organs and tissues in which they apparently have no function, e.g. chromaffin cells of the adrenal and in the pituitary.

The number of cilia per cell varies from a few to hundreds and some protozoans may have 14,000 per organism. In certain instances the cilia are bound together into twos (membranelles) or into clusters (cirri), but are normally distributed singly over the surface of the cell or organism (Fig.

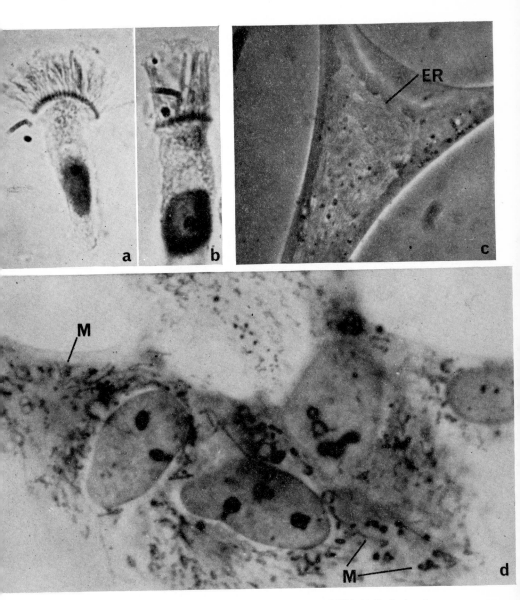

Fig. 1.8. (a) and (b) Ciliated cells. (Original. (a) × 1000. (b) × 1500.) (c) Endoplasmic reticulum (ER) as observed by phase contrast; tissue culture cell. (Courtesy Dr. G. G. Rose.) (d) Mitochondria (M) in tissue culture cells. Note the extensive polymorphism. (Original. × 1200.)

1.8a). Both cilia and flagella consist of two parts, a hair-like shaft which projects free from the surface, and a basal body which is intracellular and is the origin and kinetic centre for the free portion. In some instances additional rootlet fibrils, which act as anchors and supports, penetrate deep into the cytoplasm. The cylindrical shaft tapers at the tip and varies in length from 5 to 10 μ, with a diameter approximately 0·2 μ. In addition to motile cilia there are immotile forms with a sensory function, e.g. the cnidocils of cnidoblasts which "fire" the nematocysts of coelenterates.

The Hyaloplasm

The hyaloplasm or ground substance is by volume the major component of the cytosome, for in it all other formed structures lie. From both the structural and functional viewpoints, this region of the cell is of great importance and all molecules utilized by the cell must pass through it while being moved from one cell organoid to another in the process of attaining temporary or ultimate form and destination. It must be very complex, heterogeneous, and extremely labile. Little is known about the structure of the hyaloplasm, however, despite its importance. This is mainly because of the inability of the classical techniques and the light microscope to deal effectively with this fluctuating mass.

Light microscopy reveals the hyaloplasm as homogeneous and structure-less, or finely granular, depending on previous treatment. Under the most favourable light optical conditions, or with special techniques, small particles with Brownian movement, or fibrillar structures may be observed. Recent research with the phase contrast microscope has shown the presence of a series of approximately parallel lines within the hyaloplasm (Fig. 1.8c). The lines are most conspicuous in the peripheral cytoplasm which is free of other cell organoids. The structures are much thinner than mitochondria and show erratic curves and bends; sometimes the lines resemble a loose ball of string. These lines are undoubtedly endoplasmic reticulum. In certain cells the ground cytoplasm has special properties, staining with basic dyes, very much like the nucleus. This region is called the ergasto-plasm and occurs as flake-like bodies in the basal region in many secretory cells (pancreas, chief cells of the stomach), as the Nissl substance, in neurones, and as basophil clumps in liver cells. The ergastoplasm contains RNA, which accounts for its basophilia.

The hyaloplasm is complex in a physico-chemical sense also. The matrix contains ions, especially potassium, sodium and chloride, amino acids, simple fats, small protein molecules, carbohydrates, and RNA, all in a watery medium. The major part of the protein is globular, but during some physiological processes may take on a fibrillar form. Such fibrillar proteins probably provide a structural foundation for the cytoplasm, forming a network cross-linked by van der Waals forces, by similar valencies, or by hydrogen bonds. Sol–gel transformations and other mechanical properties of the cell, such as elasticity, rigidity, intracellular movement and contractility, are probably due to changes in the strength of the crosslinkages, the form of the protein, and their degree of folding.

The hyaloplasm, therefore, despite apparent lack of structure, is really both structurally and chemically complex and is an area of the cell where processes of physiological importance take place.

Mitochondria

Mitochondria are small polymorphic structures, more or less evenly distributed through the cytoplasm (Fig. 1.8d). The organoids measure between $0.2–3.0$ μ in diameter, and between $7.0–10.0$ μ in length, although in frog oocytes mitochondria may be as long as 40.0 μ. The number of mitochondria per cell varies with the tissue and degree of cellular differentiation, younger cells generally have more mitochondria than older ones, and with function. Rat liver cells have an average of 2500 mitochondria, the eggs of the echinoderm *Strongylocentrotus purpuratus* 14,000, and in the amoeba *Chaos chaos* the number is estimated at 500,000, although this varies with volume. Mitochondrial origin is obscure, but it is suggested that they can rise *de novo* as well as by the fragmentation of existing mitochondria, followed by growth.

Mitochondria occur most commonly in the shape of either rods or granules, the former with a maximum diameter of about 1.0 μ and the latter with a maximum diameter of about 3.0 μ. Shape varies and may result in complex forms, e.g. nets, rings, strings of beads, clubs, racquets and V- or Y-shapes. The rod and granular forms are interchangeable, rods breaking down into granules and granules fusing into rods. Changes in shape are mainly due to changes in hydrogen ion concentration, osmotic pressure and functional activity. The mitochondria of a particular tissue often have a characteristic shape, and this is also true in some cells. Localization of mitochondria with a particular shape in limited areas of the cell may occur, e.g. epithelial cells of the mucous membrane in which basal mitochondria are granular, whereas lateral and apical mitochondria are filamentous. Special distributions or orientations may also occur, as in the primary spermatocytes of most mammals, in which mitochondria are clumped in a polar juxtanuclear position, or in the liver cells of amphibians, in which mitochondria are orientated along the axis between the blood capillaries and the bile canaliculi. Mitochondria tend to cluster wherever cellular activity is most intense, as in the apical pole of ingesting intestinal cells.

In cell function mitochondria are of great importance. They are responsible for the enzymatic (catalytic) activities which together comprise aerobic respiration at the cellular level, and they may also be involved in protein synthesis (by transamination) and fatty acid oxidation. Carbohydrates, proteins, and fats (which have been metabolized to pyruvate, and to amino and fatty acids by enzymatic action elsewhere in the cell), are oxidized by mitochondrial enzymes of the Krebs cycle and the oxidative phosphory-lation chain to CO_2 and water. This process is a stepwise one and releases energy in small quanta, which are "stored" in the energy-rich bonds of adenosine triphosphate (ATP). The Krebs and oxidative phosphorylating processes are, therefore, energy-transmuting cycles and mitochondria are energy transformers. Energy inherent in chemical compounds present in the cell are turned into biologically useful energy and mitochondria release this energy whenever and wherever it is needed for chemical, osmotic, electrical, or mechanical work by the cell.

The chemical composition of mitochondria is now well known. They are composed of lipoproteins, with the protein fraction being the major part, 65–70 per cent of the dry weight. The numerous enzymes associated with the mitochondria probably account for a great amount of the protein. The lipid content is generally about 25 per cent of the dry weight, but is as high as 50 per cent in rat liver mitochondria, and as low as 20 per cent in muscle mitochondria. The lipid is mainly lecithin and phosphatidyl-ethanolamine, and these are probably closely associated with the proteins. The mito-chondria also contains traces of other elements. Sulphur, probably in the form of SH-groups and belonging to the proteins, accounts for up to 1·16 per cent of dry weight, iron for approximately 0·2 per cent and copper for up to 0·35 per cent. RNA is present in some mito-chondria, usually less than 0·1 per cent, but in rat liver the content is as much as 5·0 per cent and DNA has been claimed to be present in some instances.

Lysosomes

Lysosomes are really a biochemical concept and refer to enzyme-rich bodies within cells. They are without structural characteristics, except for being small, approximately spherical bodies, either homogenous or granular (Fig. 1.9a). Their distinguishing characteristic is the presence within them of enzymes such as acid and other hydrolases, catalase, etc., which are revealed by histochemical or biochemical techniques. Nevertheless, they have a significant role to perform in cell metabolism.

Golgi Complex

The so-called Golgi apparatus or Golgi complex is a cytoplasmic organoid whose existence and structure have often been in dispute. Because it was not generally visible in living cells by classical light microscopy, could not be stained *intra vitam,* and was only revealed by reduction of metal salts, the existence of the Golgi complex was denied by some. The evidence from studies with the ultracentrifuge, specialized optical techniques, and histo-chemical techniques such as those which reveal nucleoside diphosphatases

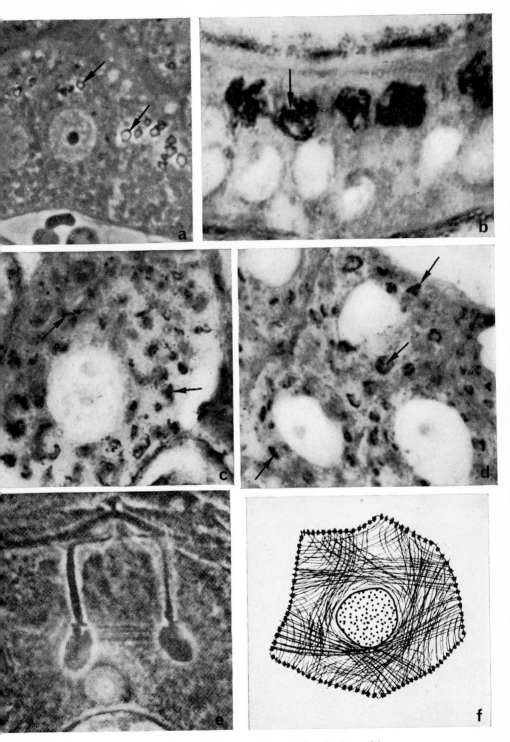

Fig. 1.9. (a) Lysosomes (arrows) in the cells of the kidney tubule epithelium of the mouse. (Original. ×500.) (b) The Golgi complex (arrow) in the epididymis of a mouse, polar, reticular type. (Original. ×800.) (c) The Golgi complex (arrows) in the neurone of the chicken spinal cord, perinuclear, reticular type. (Original. ×1000.) (d) The Golgi complex (arrows) in the neurone of the cockroach, *Blatta orientalis*, dictyosome type. (Original. ×1000.) (e) Centrioles, *Barbulonympha*. (Courtesy Dr. L. R. Cleveland. ×1000.) (f) The cell web in the pickle cell. (Original, after C. P. Leblond, H. Puchtler and Y. Clermont.)

(Fig. 1.9b–d) have demonstrated both the reality and individuality of this organoid. Also in dispute is the homology of the structures which in protozoans, other invertebrates and vertebrates give similar reactions to the classical Golgi techniques. As will be shown however, studies with the electron microscope suggest that the para-basal bodies of protozoa are homologous with the dictysome of invertebrates and the Golgi complex of vertebrates, at least as far as structure is concerned. In view of the controversy, all that can be stated with certainty is that a localized region of the cytoplasm exists in the majority of cells, which has special properties differentiating it from the remainder of the protoplasm. The region has a marked ability to reduce osmic acid and silver salts, and under suitable conditions gives a positive histochemical reaction for lipids and carbohydrates, and the enzymatic responses for nucleoside diphosphate, thiamine pyrophosphate, and alkaline and acid phosphatases in some tissues.

It is difficult to define the structural characteristics of the Golgi complex for this is most controversial, but the accepted classical concept will be given. The complex is a polymorphic structure which is large in active cells, neurones or gland cells, and is small in inactive cells. Within any particular cell the Golgi complex hypertrophies with hyperfunction and atrophies with hypofunction. It also changes with age, being large in young cells. A decrease in size is sometimes accompanied by fragmentation in older cells. Each cell usually has only one Golgi complex, but this may subdivide and become diffuse, when each resulting part may be considered and act as a separate Golgi complex (a dictyosome). In this latter state Golgi complexes may be very numerous (Figs. 1.9d).

The shape of the complex is variously described as a net, or reticulum, as rings, hollow spheres, rods, lamelli, or granules. It is possible that the net-like or reticular forms are due to the union of rings, rods, crescents or other shapes, by over-impregnation with reduced metals. The individual elements of the complex may show a bipartite structure, with an outer dense osmophil or argentophil part and an inner osmophobe or argentophobe part. Vacuoles or secretory granules may also occur among the formed elements. The Golgi complex is therefore made up of bilamellar rods, crescents, rings, etc., in association with granules and vacuoles.

The localized and diffuse forms of the Golgi-complex are interchangeable, but the localized type is general in vertebrates and the diffuse form in invertebrates. When localized, the complex may be perinuclear, as in vertebrate neurones, or polar (Fig. 1.9b, c) between the nucleus and secretory apex of the cell, as in the epididymis. Changes in distribution, shape and size are reflections of the functional changes within the cell. The large size of the complex in secretory cells and the production of the acrosome by this complex in spermatozoa, combined with many other observations on the Golgi complex in relation to secretion, strongly suggest that the complex is a synthesizing or segregating apparatus.

Such researches as have been carried out on the chemical composition of the Golgi complex all lead to the assumption that it is lipoprotein. The complex does not stain for lipids after normal processes because of the masking protein, but after being subjected to proteases, the complex stains positively with Nile blue sulphate, a lipid and fat stain. Furthermore, in cells treated with fat solvents, the Golgi complex cannot be demonstrated by classical cytological methods.

The Centrosome and Centriole

In the interphase cell a clear round area of cytoplasm, the centrosome, lies polar and near the nucleus. Within this clear area lie one or two dense spherical bodies, the centrioles or division centres. In some cells the centrioles appear as short rods with side buds and the pair of rods lie more or less parallel (Fig. 1.9e). The centrioles are the point of convergence and, perhaps, origin for the spindle fibres. The side buds are daughter centrioles whose replication is necessary to provide centrioles for subsequent divisions.

Cellular Inclusions

Cellular inclusions are the inconstant bodies residing temporarily in the cytoplasm. These bodies have their origin either externally or within the cell, and are either food substances, cell products, or the by-products of cell function. Products of the first type are either ingested or absorbed, like fat, or accumulated food reserves, like glycogen or some yolk. The cell products or secretions are manufactured within the cytosome and then secreted for the use of other cells; such products are often mucoproteins such as mucinogen, or mainly proteinaceous, such as insulin or zymogen. The by-products are inert substances which accumulate through catabolism. The group includes crystalloids, such as protein crystals and pigments of various kinds. The pigments may have an exogenous origin, e.g. carotene which is accumulated and transformed into vitamin A by liver cells, haemosiderin, derived from the destruction of erythrocytes, which is ingested by reticular cells, or endogenous, such as the melanins located particularly in the cells of the epidermis.

In addition to the inclusions mentioned above, the majority of cells contain fibrous elements, and these are especially abundant and conspicuous in muscle and nerve cells. These fibrous elements are the cell web, and there is good reason for believing the myofibrils, neurofibrils and the division spindle are modifications of this web. The web shows a variety of forms, depending on the basic function of the cell. In intestinal cells the web is a single layer lying immediately beneath the apical plasma membrane and stretching between the terminal bars (a row of granules on or near the lateral plasma membrane at the apical pole of the cell). In the cells of the striated duct of the salivary gland the cell web is multi-layered; in pillar cells of the organ of Corti it is a dense packed bundle of fibrils extending from cell base to apex (Fig. 1.3c). In liver cells, by contrast, it is circumferential, being attached to the terminal bars which run longitudinally in the wall of the bile canaliculi, while in the pickle cells of the epidermis the web is dispersed, criss-crossing the cytoplasm between the numerous peripheral desmosomes (Fig. 1.9f). The myofibrils of striated, smooth and cardial muscle react to the special staining methods used to demonstrate the cell web, and give an identical response; they may therefore be considered a contractile web. The centrioles and spindle fibres respond, as do the neurofibrils, and must also be considered as related to the cell web.

Visible Evidence of Cellular Activity

The structure of the cell as described in the previous pages is largely derived from a study of cells fixed and stained by a variety of methods, and although changes in structure with function have been emphasized, the resulting picture is of a more or less static polymorphic body. The living cell, on the contrary, is in constant motion, as a whole, and in its individual parts. This aspect is brought out most forcibly by the techniques of microcinematography, time lapse cinematography and phase contrast microscopy. These techniques have revealed not only the activity of particular cell organoids, but the activity of two or more cell structures in relation to each other and the cell as a whole.

In the nucleus, the nuclear membrane alters shape, giving rise to pseudopodia or shallow indentations. These formations are a response to stimuli such as the passage of nutrients into the cell and the migration of nuclear material into the cytoplasm. The shape of the nucleus may vary successively between spherical, ellipsoidal, kidney or other shapes. The whole nucleus may rotate within the cytosome at a rate of about one revolution per 75 sec (Fig. 1.10a–b). The direction of rotation may change frequently between clockwise and anticlockwise. The nucleus may also move through the cytoplasm, either independently, in response to a functional need, or due to intracellular forces or inclusions. Within the nucleus, the nucleolus is particularly amoeboid. It alters shape from smooth and round to irregular and filamentous. In extreme cases the nucleolus becomes a loose skein with marginal structures and granules. The nucleolus moves within the nucleoplasm and frequently makes broad or tenuous contact with the nuclear membrane (Fig. 1.10d–f). Opposite such areas of contact vacuoles may arise in the cytoplasm and mitochondria become associated with them. In addition, some of the amorphous parts of the nucleus, or parts of the nucleolus, may be extruded into the cytoplasm as small droplets.

In the cytoplasm the mitochondria are in continuous movement. These are plastic bodies which unite, or divide transversely, give off lateral branches, or form loops by fusion with themselves, or become beaded. These changes can occur in a matter of seconds only, and as many as 15–20 alterations in 10 min is not unusual (Fig. 1.10g–i). The mitochondria move

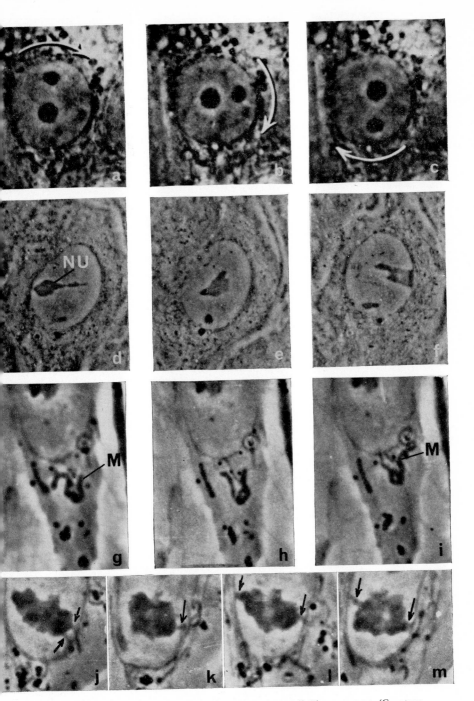

Fig. 1.10. (a)–(c) Rotation of the nucleus in tissue culture cell. Phase contrast. (Courtesy of the late Dr. C. M. Pomerat.) (d)–(f) Nucleolar (NU) movement to and from the nuclear membrane, combined with nuclear rotation in HeLa cell. Phase contrast. (Courtesy Dr. R. Lettre. × 800. 20 min between photographs.) (g)–(i) Mitochondrial (M) movement in tissue culture cells. Phase contrast. (Courtesy Drs. J. Frederic and M. Chevremont. × 3050.) (j)–(m) Nucleolar-mitochondrial association in tissue culture cells (arrows). Phase contrast. (Courtesy Dr. J. Frederic. × 2500.)

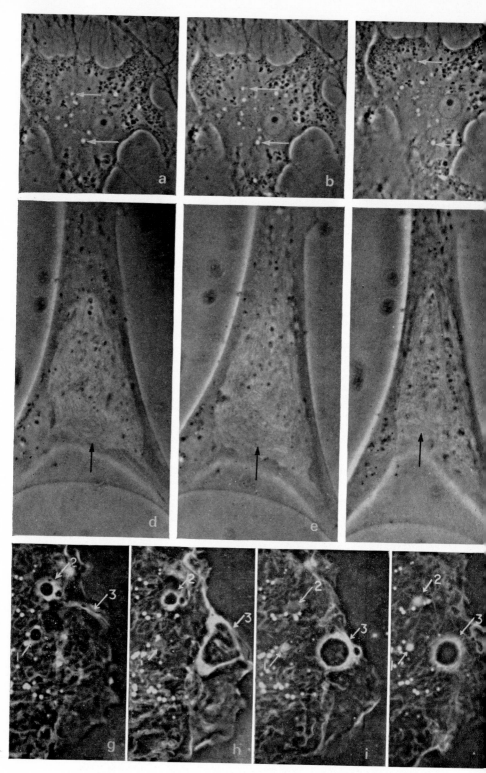

Fig. 1.11. (a)–(c) Secretory activity of the Golgi complex in living osteoblasts. Particular secretory droplets are numbered. (Courtesy Dr. G. G. Rose.) (d)–(f) Changes in the form and distribution of the endoplasmic reticulum (arrows) in living tissue culture cells. (Courtesy Dr. G. G. Rose.) (g)–(j) Pinocytosis in living cultured human chondrosarcoma cells, at arrow No. 3. (Courtesy Dr. G. O. Gey. ×800. (g) 0·0 min. (h) 1·5 min. (i) 2·0 min. (j) 3·0 min.) Photos (a)–(j) phase contrast.

throughout the cytoplasm, most probably as passive bodies in the cytoplasmic streams. In other circumstances they show more positive motion and have been observed to move to and from the nucleus by rapid jerky movements, usually at the time when nucleolar material is apparently migrating to the cytoplasm (Fig. 1–10j–m). Although mitochondria are labile and active in most cells, they are not so in all. They may be anchored in respect to some other cytoplasmic organoid, e.g. surrounding the flagellum of sperm tails, or to inclusions such as fat droplets around which they are wrapped, or to the plasma membrane, as in the kidney tubule cells.

The Golgi complex is another very active cell organoid. It changes form and place within the cytosome, even though it tends to be juxta-nuclear. It may appear as a rough-surfaced flat or discoidal body, or with a spaghetti-like form. Within or upon the complex appear droplets which move slowly within the organoid, coalesce or enlarge, and finally migrate into the cytoplasm (Fig. 1.11a–c). The endoplasmic reticulum is subject to rapid changes in the living cell, altering from a series of parallel lines to crisscrossed, bent or curved arrays of lines in one or two minutes (Fig.1.11d–f).

During life the hyaloplasm shows streaming, carrying cell organoids, inclusions and vacuoles about the cell body. Such streaming is particularly evident during pseudopodial formation, which of course also involves the plasma membrane. Particles within the hyaloplasm show Brownian movement, giving the whole a shimmering appearance. The plasma membrane demonstrates activity during phagocytosis and pinocytosis (Fig. 1.11g–j), as well as in the general changes of cell shape. Blunt or sharp pointed pseudopodia may be advanced into the environment and withdrawn, or put out to make a more permanent contact with the substratum or adjacent cells. Associated structures, such as cilia and flagella, have a rhythmic motion with waves of beating.

In all these cellular actions and interactions, in the movements of parts or the whole cell, either separately or in relation to other cellular parts, to other cells, or the environment, the cell demonstrates a persistence of structure which allows it to be positively identified as an animal cell. Impermanence, inconstancy and flow at every level of organization results, nevertheless, in a recognizable morphological entity.

Further Reading List

1. de Robertis, E. D. P., Nowinski, W. W. and Salz, F. A., *Cell Biology*, 4th Edit., Saunders, London, 1965.
2. Mercer, E. H., *Cells and Cell Structure*, Hutchinson, London, 1961.
3. Downes, H. R., *The Chemistry of Living Cells*, Longmans, London, 1955.
4. Bourne, G. H., *Division of Labour in Cells*, Academic Press, London, 1964.
5. Loewy, A. G. and Siekevitz, P., *Cell Structure and Function*, Holt, Rinehart & Winston, London, 1963.
6. Giese, A. C., *Cell Physiology*, Saunders, Philadelphia, 1962.
7. Barry, J. M. *Genes and the Chemical Control of Living Cells*, Prentice-Hall, London, 1964.
8. Haggis, G. H., Mitchi, D., Muir, A. R., Roberts, K. B. and Walker, P. M. B., *Introduction to Molecular Biology*, Longmans, London, 1964.

CHAPTER 2

THE ULTRASTRUCTURE OF THE NUCLEUS

IN THE previous chapter the nucleus was shown to consist of a nuclear membrane enclosing the nucleoplasm in which were embedded the nucleolus and the chromosomes in their interkinetic state. The ultrastructure of these nuclear constituents is best considered as it is observed in the vesicular type of nucleus. Subsequently, any additional significant features of nuclear structure shown by chromidial and massive nuclear types will be described.

Nuclear Membrane

The nuclear membrane has a basic ultrastructure common to all cells, but this is modified in particular cells by minor variations in the size and disposition of some of the components, and by the addition of new elements. The nuclear membrane is a tripartite structure, being composed of two adielectronic layers separated by a dielectronic space (Fig. 2.1). The adielectronic layer next to the nucleoplasm is called the inner nuclear membrane, the dielectronic space, the intermembranous space, and the adielectronic layer in contact with the cytoplasm is the outer nuclear membrane (Fig. 2.1). Typically, the nuclear membrane is 350 Å thick, the inner and outer nuclear membranes each being 100 Å wide, and the intermembranous space 150 Å. The nuclear membrane is pierced by pores wherever the two adielectronic layers unite and these round openings, which allow free passage between cytoplasm and nucleoplasm, are about 500 Å in diameter (Figs. 2.1 and 2.2).

The inner and outer nuclear membranes may vary from 50 to 100 Å in thickness and the intermembranous space from 100 to 300 Å. By some authors the outer nuclear membrane is claimed to be about twice as thick as the inner nuclear membrane. The outer nuclear membrane also differs from the inner membrane in having a "rough" outline, due to the presence of attached RNA particles which form patterns, e.g. spirals, parallel lines and crescents (Fig. 2.2). The thinner, inner membrane is smooth, and on the basis of earlier studies on isolated whole membranes was claimed to be continuous and without pores; this is unlikely in view of more recent studies using sectioned material.

At high resolution, both the inner and outer membranes are revealed as tripartite structures with an inner and outer adielectronic component separated by a dielectronic component. It has been postulated that the

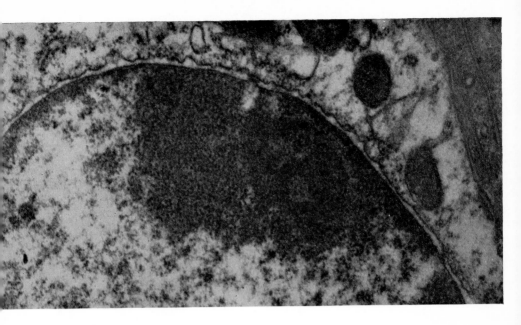

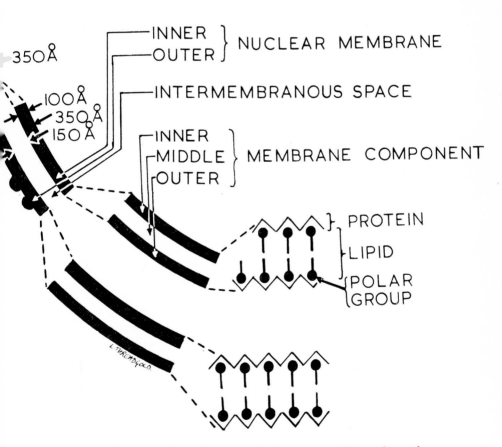

FIG. 2.1. Typical appearance, dimensions, and molecular structure of the nucleus and nuclear membrane. Photo of nucleus of avian brown fat cell. (Courtesy J. C. Lewis. × 22,000. Original.)

middle membrane component represents a bimolecular layer of lipid with its polar group outwards, and that the inner and outer membrane components represent proteins overlying the lipid layer (Fig. 2.1).

The nuclear membrane, therefore, consists of an inner and outer nuclear membrane with an intermembranous space; each nuclear membrane is itself

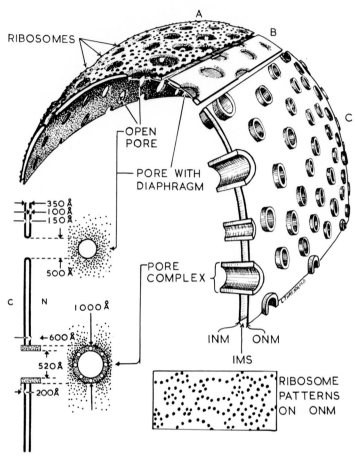

FIG. 2.2. Three-dimensional representation of the nuclear membrane. Region A, open pores; region B, pores with diaphragm; region C, pore complexes. (Original.)

tripartite, with an inner and outer membrane component separated by a middle membrane component (Fig. 2.1).

Nuclear pores vary from 400 to 1000Å in diameter, and have a maximum centre-to-centre spacing of about 1500 Å, although they may occur clumped into circular areas. Neurones are estimated to have about 10,000 pores per nucleus, and for other cells it has been calculated that if the pore diameter is 500 Å, then 10 per cent of the nuclear surface is exposed directly to the cytoplasm, the remainder of the nucleoplasm having only indirect contact through the nuclear membrane. In the acidophils of the mouse pituitary, the number of pores per nucleus has been estimated at 800, and this equals 3 per cent of the surface area. The number of pores and their disposition over the surface of the nucleus differs with the age of the cell and its degree of differentiation. Pores are apparently absent on some secretory cells and are not patent in embryonic cells such as those of the chick epiblast (Fig. 2.3d). Immature frog oocytes have areas of 4–10 pores in the ortho-gonally arranged square packing and the number of pores per μ^2 is 35, while in mature oocytes the pores are hexagonally arranged and the number of pores is 25 per μ^2 (Fig. 2.3a, b). Between the immature and mature stages of these oocytes the total number of pores per nucleus increases by a factor of 10 and the interpore area by a factor of 13. The interkinetic age of a nucleus may also affect its number of pores, for a recently constructed membrane may be expected to have numerous points of incomplete union, such points lessening progressively as the nucleus ages.

In embryonic cells the pore may be closed by a delicate membrane (a diaphragm), but this disappears in the adult. Observations reporting the presence of diaphragms in adult nuclei are usually due to the oblique plane of the section; the nucleoplasm and cytoplasm are continuous through the pore (Fig. 2.3c).† Although diaphragms may not be present crossing nuclear pores, the material within the pore is firmly attached to the pore margin. In preparations of whole nuclear membranes stripped off immature frog oocytes the pores are filled with a material whose density is considerable but varies between pores. Often pores have an adielectronic granule in their centre. In older oocytes the material filling the pores is more uniform in density from pore to pore and the central granule is absent (Fig. 2.3b). Occa-sionally granules 140 Å in diameter are seen on the pores of other animals.

Pores in amphibian and echinoderm oocytes, in rat pancreas and liver, in *Amoeba* and some somatic cells, show structures additional to an open pore. The pore plus the additional structures is called a pore complex or annulus. The pore complex is 850–1400 Å in diameter, the larger pores and pore complexes occurring in oocytes. The pore is surrounded by a collar extending out from both the inner and outer nuclear membranes (Fig. 2.3e, f). On the cytoplasmic side the collar projects out about 200 Å and on the nucleoplasmic side is about 600 Å long and 240 Å thick. The collar is composed of up to 8 smaller cylinders (subannuli) each about 150 Å in diameter, between and around which is a material of greater electron density than the subannuli themselves (Fig. 2.3e, f). The collar on the nucleoplasmic side may not be conspicuous if chromatin masses are opposed to the inner nuclear membrane. In such circumstances a low density channel starting a short distance into the cytoplasm can be observed to pass through the collar on the cytoplasmic side of the membrane, through the

---

† Recent researches suggest that diaphragms occur in the nuclei of some adult animals. Such diaphragms not only fill the pore but project a short distance into the intermembranous space (Fig. 2.1, avian brown fat cell).

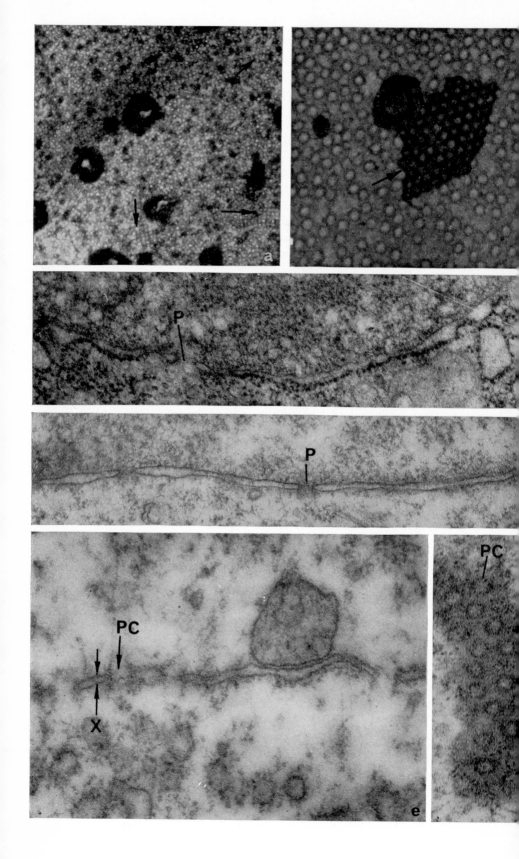

pore and up to $1.0 \, \mu$ into the nucleus, where the channel becomes diffuse. In the pancreas and liver of the rat, channels are 1000–1500 Å wide near the pore and they are filled with chains or filaments 50–150 Å in diameter. Such channels demonstrate clearly a nucleocytoplasmic continuity. Although pores are present in most nuclear membranes, and pore complexes in some, both structures are absent in others. The nuclei of the apocrine sweat gland of man have pores 1000 Å in diameter, and these are thought to be equivalent to the pore complexes in cells such as oocytes.

The Nucleolus

Nucleoli can be classified on the basis of their fine structure as either homogeneous or heterogeneous. The homogeneous type of nucleolus is composed of a tightly packed mass of granules (ribosomes) about 150 Å in diameter. The outline of this mass may be spherical and smooth, or somewhat irregular, with a small number of internal areas of lower density (Fig. 2.4a).

The heterogeneous type of nucleolus may be divided into two sub-types. The first sub-type has a slightly irregular outline, and consists of a mass of granules of medium electron density, measuring 150 Å in diameter, within which is a network of strands 1000–2000 Å thick composed of 150 Å granules which are very adielectronic. The whole nucleolus is therefore granular and more electron-dense than the nucleoplasm, the dense areas being considered as homologous with the nucleolonema and the less dense with the pars amorpha (Fig. 2.4b). In the second sub-type, the nucleolar outline is very irregular and is composed of a dense net, the interstices of which are dielectronic. These areas of low density are in reality enclosed nucleoplasm which also penetrates into the nucleolus at its periphery. The pars amorpha is, therefore, only apparent, being in reality nucleoplasm in and around the tangled mass of the nucleolonema (Fig. 2.5a).

At high resolution the 150 Å granules of the nucleolonema are arranged obliquely or transversely to the long axis of the 1000–2000 Å strands, so giving it a striated appearance. These parallel rows of beads have been called the primary nucleolonema, and combine into spirally twisted bundles, the secondary nucleolonema, which is the nucleolonema of the light microscope. It has been suggested that the granules are in reality

---

Fig. 2.3. (a) Part of the nuclear membrane stripped from the young oocyte of a frog. Square packing of the pores is evident at the arrows. (Courtesy Dr. K. W. Merriam. × 16,000.) (b) Part of a nuclear membrane stripped from an old oocyte of a frog. Hexagonal packing of the pores is evident at the arrows. (Courtesy Dr. K. W. Merriam. × 20,500.) (c) Open nuclear pore (P) in the nucleus of a murine plasma cell neoplasm. Ribosomes lining the outer nuclear membrane are conspicuous. (Courtesy Dr. R. F. Zeigel. × 62,000.) (d) Nuclear membrane of chicken epiblast, showing a pore with diaphragm (P). (Courtesy Dr. A. Jurand. × 73,000.) (e) and (f) Nuclear membrane of the salivary gland cell of *Bradysia mycorum* showing pore complexes (PC) composed of a subannuli (SA) and the tripartite nature of each nuclear membrane at X. (Courtesy Dr. A. Jurand. (e) × 80,000. (f) × 43,000.)

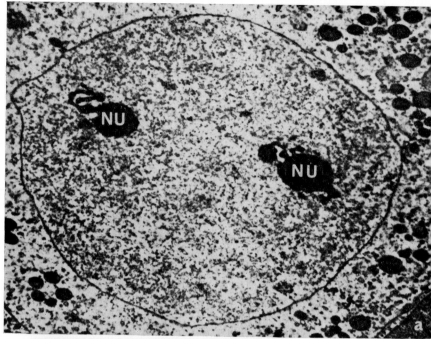

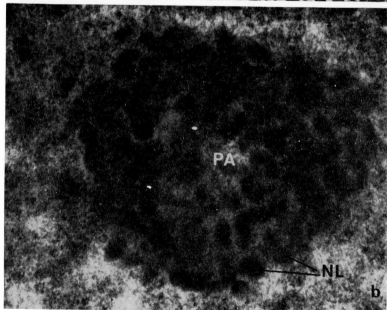

Fig. 2.4. (a) Nucleolus of the dense, homogeneous type (NU). Rabbit oocyte. (Courtesy Dr. E. J. Blanchette. × 7600.) (b) Nucleolus, heterogeneous type, with pars amorpha (PA) and nucleolonema (NL). Rat liver. (Courtesy Dr. J. M. G. Davis. × 80,000.)

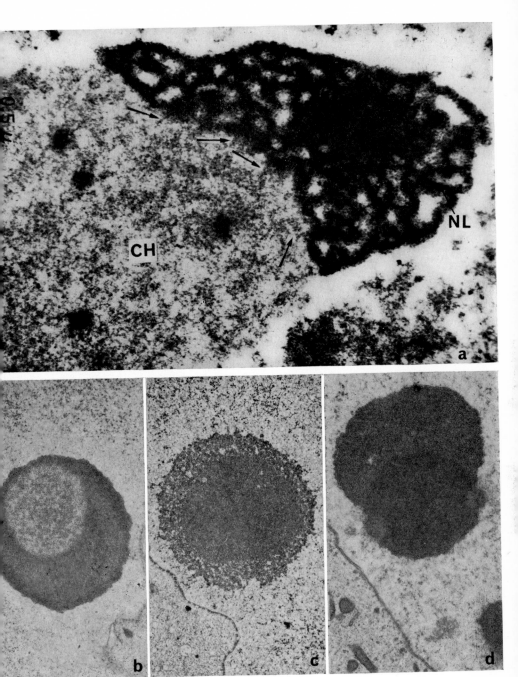

FIG. 2.5. (a) Nucleolus, heterogeneous type composed of nucleolonema (NL) only. CH, chromosome. Secondary spermatocyte of mouse. (Courtesy Dr. G. Yasuzumi. × 80,000.) (b) Nucleolus of a young oocyte of *Triturus viridescens* showing a light, granular medulla and a dense, granular cortex. (× 13,500.) (c) Nucleolus of a mature oocyte of *Triturus viridescens*, with a dense medullar and a less dense, granular cortex; compare with (b). (× 7000.) (d) Nucleolus of a young oocyte of *Rana clamitans*, showing a dense, homogeneous medulla and a less dense, granular cortex. (× 13,500. (b–d) courtesy Dr. O. L. Miller.)

gyres of a helically coiled filament 50 Å thick. This conclusion is supported by studies of suspensions of whole ribosome granules and stereoscopic electron micrographs of thick sections of thymus nuclei which show no evidence of granules; instead only fibrous material is found in these preparations. The coiled filament is considered to run longitudinally down the nucleolonema. The secondary nucleolonema has been claimed by some researchers to be made up of fibres 60–80 Å thick, although no coiling was observed.

The nucleolus, therefore, may appear as pars amorpha only, as pars amorpha and nucleolonema, or as nucleolonema only. It appears very possible that these three types of nucleoli are only different stages in the condensation, dispersion and arrangement of electron-dense 150 Å granules or of filaments 50 Å thick coiled helically or paranemically twisted to form thicker strands. The characteristics which the nucleolus displays at any particular time in any particular tissue are very probably related to its functional state. For example, in amphibian oocytes during their early development, the nucleolus is composed of either only a dense fibrous part, or of an internal mass of associated granules and fibres surrounded by an adielectronic mass of fibres. In older oocytes the dense fibrous part is internal and is surrounded by a less compact ring of granules and fibres; the dense fibrous part of such nucleoli decreases with age (Figs. 2.5c–e). The interkinetic age of the cell may also play a part. Dense amorphous nucleoli, presumably concentrated amorphous and nucleolonemal granules, occur in nuclei which will undergo no more divisions, e.g. late spermatid nuclei of mouse and bull. The composite type nucleolus with pars amorpha and nucleolonema appears in cells which are actively synthesizing or are dividing. Nevertheless, whatever its shape, the nucleolus is never enclosed in a membrane, thereby being in continuous contact with the nucleoplasm. In some cases it may be in contact with the chromosomes, in others with the nuclear membrane or the nucleolar associated body.

The Chromosomes

The ultrastructure of the interphase chromosomes can be studied by the use of either whole chromosomes or sections. Whole chromosomes are obtained by isolating and disrupting nuclei in a variety of media, such as saline–versene, and observing the result directly in the electron-microscope. The elements so isolated are believed to be chromatids and can be resolved into eight microfibrils called chromonema, each 200–500 Å in diameter. Each chromonema can in turn be resolved into two fibrils 100–150 Å in diameter, called sub-chromonema (Fig. 2.6a), each of which is in turn made up to two fibrils, or protochromonema 20–50 Å in diameter (Fig. 2.6b).

The chromonemata and chromocentres, which are such conspicuous features of the vesicular type of nucleus when observed by the light

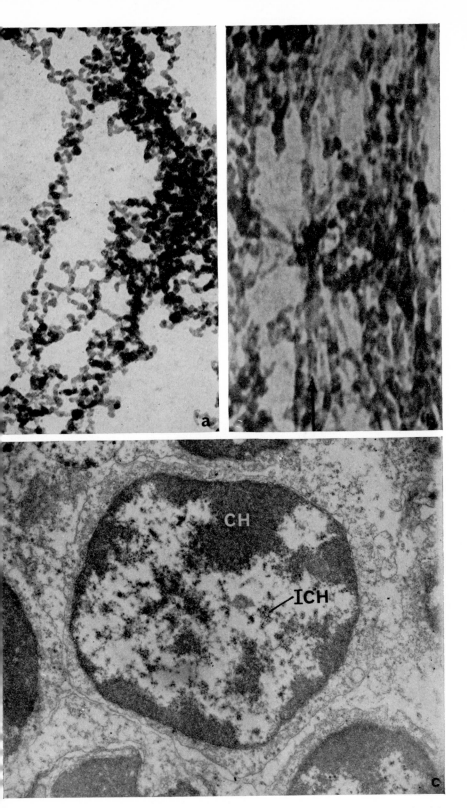

F<small>IG</small>. 2.6. (a) 100 Å chromosomal fibres, subchromonema, from calf thymus nuclei; isolated in saline–versene. (Courtesy Dr. H. Ris. × 90,000.) (b) Paired 50 Å subfibres (at arrow), protochromonema, making up a single subchromonemal fibre. Calf thymus nuclei; isolated in saline–versene after treatment with 0·01 N HCl. (Courtesy Dr. H. Ris. × 225,000.) (c) Section of calf thymus nucleus showing chromatin and interchromatin areas (CH and ICH respectively). (Courtesy Dr. H. Ris. × 30,000.)

microscope, show a variety of morphological features when viewed in sections within the electron microscope (Fig. 2.6c). The nucleus may have a homogeneous granular appearance, or the chromatin may appear as granular masses having an electron density which varies from moderately adielectronic to extremely adielectronic. In both, the granules are 100–200 Å in diameter. The homogeneous nuclei are considered to be of mid-interkinetic age, when the helices of the chromonemata are completely loosened. The more obvious adielectronic masses distributed randomly through the nucleoplasm, or against the nuclear membrane, occur in cells just entering upon, or about to leave, the interkinetic state. In such circumstances, the chromonemata are not perfectly loosened, and their electron density is due to the concentration of their constituents and is not a fixation artefact.

In thin sections of cells observed at high magnification and resolution, both the homogeneous granular nuclei and the chromocentres are composed of fibres. It is now agreed that the basic structure of chromatin is fibrous. The masses of aggregated fibres have been observed in many nuclei and measure 2000–5000 Å in diameter. They are presumed to be the chromosomes in their interkinetic state and are therefore called prochromosomes. The prochromosome can sometimes be observed as a bipartite structure, being composed of two coiled fibres about 600 Å in diameter; these are thought to be the chromatids.

The fibres of the prochromosomes are of three orders of magnitude and all are helically coiled. The smallest fibres, protochromonema, measure 20–50 Å in diameter and are considered to be either DNA molecules (strands) or nucleoproteins (DNA plus histone or protamine). Isolated sodium deoxyribonucleate has been shown to have a spiral form and measures 24 Å in diameter (Fig. 2.7a), while nucleohistones, each composed of a single DNA double helix with attached protein, are fibres about 4000 Å long and 35 Å in thickness. It is postulated that in the nucleohistones, the histones or protamines lie in the grooves of the DNA double helix. The fibres of intermediate magnitude, the subchromonema, measure 100–150 Å in diameter and are composed of 2 × 40 Å nucleoprotein fibres surrounded and bound together by histones (Fig. 2.7c, d). These approximately 100 Å fibres subchromonema appear to be the basic element in all chromosomes, in the sense that they are the most commonly observed fibrillar component of the chromatin. The largest fibre, the chromonema, measures 200–300 Å in diameter and consists of subchromonema associated in pairs. Thirty-two protochromonema, therefore, combine in pairs to give sixteen subchromonema. In turn these sixteen subchromonema combine in pairs to form eight chromonema, which make up one chromatid. In human sweat gland and plasma cells the chromonema have been reported to be hollow cylinders, but such observations do not seem to be universal.

Between the fibrous masses of chromatin of the vesicular nuclei are interchromatin areas composed of coarse fibres 200–300 Å thick and these

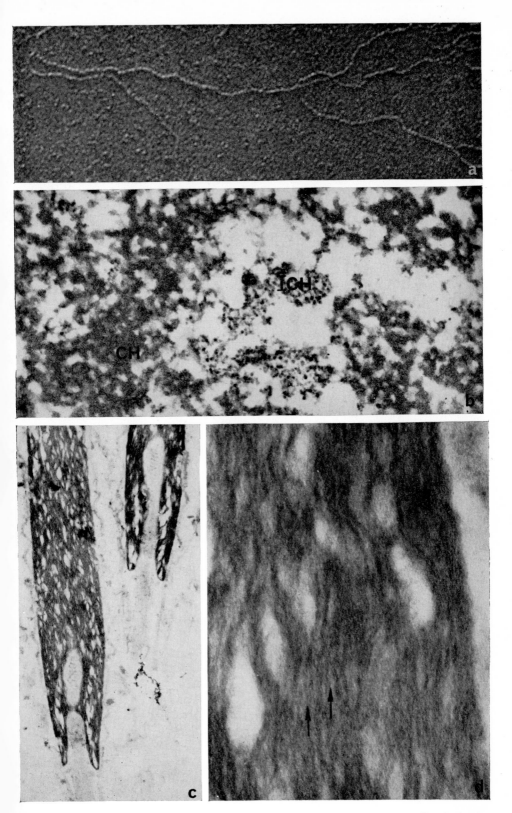

FIG. 2.7. (a) Isolated DNA molecules from salmon sperm. (Courtesy Drs. C. E. Hall and M. Litt. × 154,000. Shadow cast.) (b) Nucleus from the calf thymus showing the union of chromatin (CH) and interchromatin (ICH) areas. (Courtesy Dr. H. Ris. × 35,000.) (c) Subchromonemal fibres (100 Å) in octopus spermatid nuclei. (Courtesy Dr. H. Ris. × 15,000.) (d) High magnification of an area similar to that shown in (c). Two protochromonemal fibres (40 Å) are visible within each subchromonemal fibre (arrows). (Courtesy Dr. H. Ris. × 100,000.)

appear in places to be continuous with the 100 Å subchromonemal fibres (Fig. 2.7b). After treatment with a salt solution, the subchromonema dissolve to leave only a few ragged threads, but the interchromatin fibres remain and therefore represent the non-histone residual protein and RNA, which must be intercalated between the nucleoprotein molecules.

The measurements of the various orders of fibres from a great variety of animals have a quite narrow range, differences being doubtless due to differences in preparative techniques, intensity of fibre coiling, etc., as well as species variation. As might be expected, measurements from isolated chromosomes are not identical with those made on thin sections, and although the former are somewhat larger than the latter, there is a fair correlation between results from these two techniques.

The spatial arrangement and interrelationships of the various fibrous elements when combined into a chromosome is not clear, for a three-dimensional reconstruction from thin sections is difficult. Many theories based on electron microscope evidence have been proposed but are subject to serious objections, mainly on the following grounds: difficulty in replicating DNA in parts of the whole chromosome; the presence of sufficient DNA for genetic requirements without excessive length to the chromosome; the problem of unwinding replicated chromatids and other coils which are possibly relational; the necessity of having DNA as a structural part of the chromosome.

The most acceptable model on the present electron-microscope evidence is a multi-stranded chromosome. The strands are divided into two sets (chromatids) of 8 chromonema, each of which is formed by the union of two pairs of nucleoprotein fibres with associated histone and residual proteins. The nucleoproteins would not be continuous down the length of the chromosome strands, but lengths of DNA plus histone would be joined together by residual protein; chromosome continuity would reside, therefore, in alternating sections of DNA and protein.

Such a multi-stranded model is itself open to objections, for it imposes difficulties with respect to chromosome reduplication, separation and crossing over. The 8 chromonema must act as a unit, each DNA double helix in the 32 protochromonema must replicate synchronously and the coiled strands must separate out at the same time in such a way that all the "old" DNA remains with the parent chromatid and all the "new" DNA goes to the replicated chromatid. Furthermore, in crossing over all the 16 subchromonema must break and reunite in unison and at the same locus. Clearly at the present stage of our knowledge it is impossible to construct a three-dimensional model of a chromosome which will satisfy all the stringent demands of stereochemistry, ultrastructural cytology and genetics.

Associated with the chromosomes, at or near their surface, are bodies called perichromatin granules. These are 300 Å in diameter and are separated from the chromatin by a space 250 Å wide (Fig. 2.8a). The granule and space, therefore, measure about 750 Å and the electron density of the

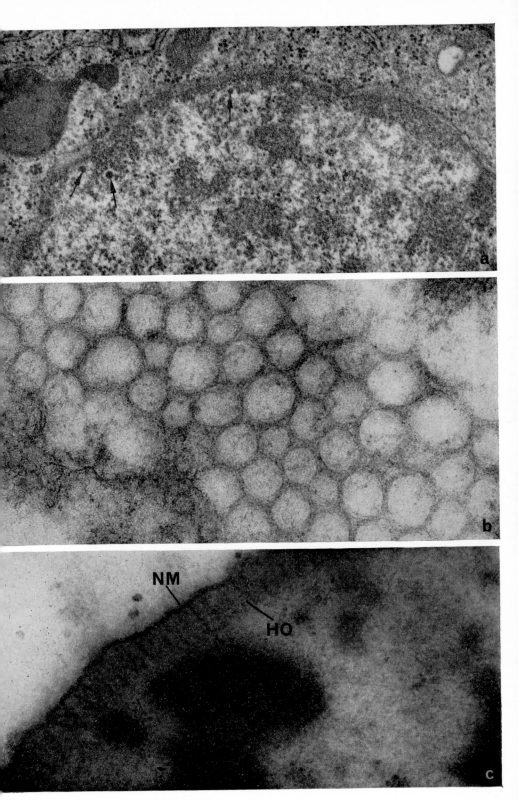

Fig. 2.8. (a) Perichromatin granules (arrows) in the nucleus of an epithelial cell from a foetal rat intestine. (Courtesy Dr. O. Behnke. × 40,000.) (b) Nuclear membrane of *Amoeba* cut obliquely through the honeycomb layer. (Courtesy Dr. L. Roth. × 65,000.) (c) Transverse section through the nucleus of *Amoeba* to show the typical nuclear membrane (NM) with the attached, inner honeycomb layer (HO). (Courtesy Dr. L. Roth. × 27,000.)

granule is slightly greater than that of the chromatin. The number of peri-chromatin granules per nucleus is estimated at 500–2000 for rat liver cells, and these may occur anywhere within the nucleoplasm. The granules are easily identified only in cells which have clumped chromatin (chromo-centres) and have not been observed in the cells of some amphibians. The granules apparently contain nucleic acids but their function is at present obscure.

The nucleoplasm of the interphase cell shows little structure. Generally it is dielectronic and made up of small, randomly distributed granular areas between the chromatin. It may contain dense granules, 150–200 Å in diameter, or clumps of such granules which are presumed to be derived from either the nucleolus or chromatin, probably the former. Inter-chromatin areas of adielectronic granules and moderately adielectronic amorphous material, which is presumed to be the non-histone protein and residual protein connected to the chromosomes has already been noted. The structure and development of massive nuclei is considered in detail in Chapter 6 under spermatogenesis and will not, therefore, be dealt with here.

Protozoan Nuclei

Protozoan micro- and macro-nuclei do not differ greatly from vesicular nuclei. The total thickness of the nuclear membrane ranges between about 200–400 Å, the outer and inner nuclear membranes being about 70 Å and intermembranous space from 70–250 Å wide. Pores and pore complexes occur, the former 400–700 Å in diameter and the latter 700–750 Å, with rims 140 Å thick containing 10–12 granules 100 Å in diameter. A further structural feature present in the nuclear membrane of some gregarines, amoeba and protomonadines is a honeycomb-like layer associated with the inner nuclear membrane (Fig. 2.8b, c). It is up to 900 Å deep, projecting into the nucleoplasm and being moderately adielectronic.

The chromatin of protozoan nuclei contains granules and filaments in three ranges of measurement; 40–50 Å protochromonema; 120–150 Å, subchromonema; and 300–500 Å, chromonema. Within the nucleus of *Amoeba proteus* and *Chaos chaos*, helices are present during interkinesis, but not at other times. The helices are arranged like bristle round a central axis, the longest being 3000 Å with 8–10 complete turns (a periodicity of about 300–375 Å) (Fig. 2.9a, b). In transverse section the helices have a doughnut or torus profile, 300–350 Å in diameter. The filament making up the helix is 120–150 Å thick, being composed of two smaller filaments 70 Å thick paranemically coiled. These helices are not chromosomes or parts of chromosomes in their interkinetic state, for they disappear as the chromo-somes make their appearance in prophase. They are either not DNA at all or they are DNA in a specialized interphase form.

Chromatid bodies in certain protozoa such as *Tokophyra* appear as dense

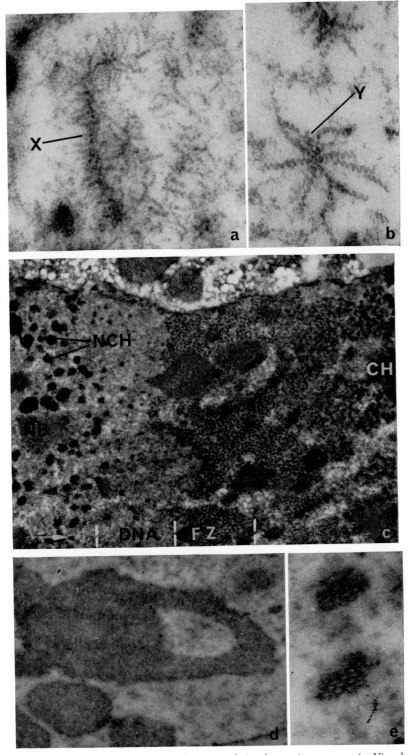

FIG. 2.9. (a) and (b) Helices in the nucleoplasm of *Amoeba* seen in transverse (at Y) and longitudinal (at X) section. (Courtesy Dr. L. Roth. × 53,000.) (c) The reorganization band in the macronucleus of *Euplotes patella*. The arrow shows the direction of band movement. NB, nuclear bodies; CH, chromatin; FZ, zone of twisted fibres; DNA, zone of DNA synthesis; NCH, new chromatin. (Courtesy Dr. B. C. Kluss. × 11,000.) (d) and (e) Chromatin bodies in *Tokophyra* showing the banding and honeycomb characteristics. (Courtesy Dr. M. A. Rudzinska. (d) × 27,000. (e) × 70,000.)

spongeworks, homogeneous throughout. In old organisms, however, some chromatin exists as a honeycomb which appears in cross section as 350 Å wide, with a dielectronic centre 220 Å across and in longitudinal section as a series of parallel lines 120 Å thick and 230 Å apart (Fig. 2.9d–e). These bodies are Feulgen positive and therefore contain DNA.

A feature of other protozoan nuclei is the reorganization bands, in which DNA is synthesized during interphase. Two bands appear, one at each extremity of the macronucleus, and these transverse their particular half of the nucleus, to meet in the middle and disappear. The chromatin is greatly altered during this process. These macronuclei have bodies of two types, the more adielectronic chromatin being composed of 50–150 Å granules, and the less adielectronic, but larger, bodies of loosely packed granules believed to be nucleoli. The nucleoli pass through the reorganization band little altered, except for some reduction in size and number. The chromatin bodies, however, are destroyed and reconstructed. As the reorganization band approaches the chromatin, it breaks up into small particles which then form a network of twisted filaments 110 Å thick. These filaments finally disappear to form an amorphous zone (Fig. 2.9c). In these early zones RNA, DNA and protein synthesis ceases. The amorphous zone is followed by the appearance of fine, less clearly resolved filaments which eventually aggregate to form larger chromatin bodies. In these latter zones, and only in these zones, DNA is synthesized, and subsequently RNA synthesis also takes place. There is therefore firstly RNA synthesis, followed by DNA synthesis, and finally a return to RNA synthesis.

Chromidial nuclei or chromatoid bodies consist of 200 Å granules arranged in a crystalline fashion. The granules are resolved into subunits which form rings 70 Å in diameter with electron-transparent centres 30 Å across (Fig. 2.10a). With formalin fixation fibrils take the place of the granules, and these contain RNA and unspecified proteins.

Functional Activity of the Nucleus

Claims that nuclear and nucleolar material pass from the nucleus into the cytoplasm have been made frequently in the light microscope studies, but although such claims have been supported by physiological studies, they have had to be accepted with reservation because of lack of resolution. Electron microscopy has now revealed further details of some of the mechanisms by which these migrating nuclear materials reach the cytoplasm, and has added additional support to the idea that such nuclear extrusions are the initiators of secretory and other cytoplasmic activities.

The salivary gland of the third instar larvae of *Drosophila melanogaster* is the classical subject for cytogenetical studies, because of the giant chromosomes their nuclei contain. Electron microscope studies have shown these cells to be of interest also from the viewpoint of nuclear extrusion. The nuclear membrane of salivary gland cells has the typical bilamellar structure, is 250 Å wide, and has pores 500–600 Å in diameter, spaced 1000 Å apart, centre to centre, in hexagonal array. During the third instar stage the membrane evaginates locally, a process called blebbing (Fig. 2.10b, c).

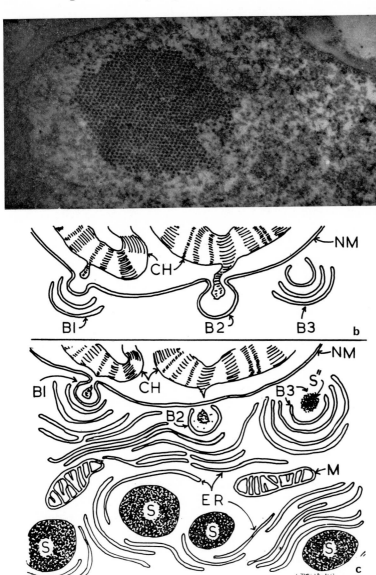

Fig. 2.10. (a) Chromatoid body in *Entamoeba* showing the subunits of 70 Å in crystalline array. (Courtesy Dr. D. Barker. × 20,000.) (b) and (c) Diagrams illustrating nuclear activity in the salivary gland of the third instar larva of *Drosophila melanogaster*. CH, chromosome; ER, endoplasmic reticulum; B1, B2, etc., successive stages of nuclear bleb formation; S, secretion. (Original after Dr. H. Gay.)

Adjacent to the blebs is chromosomal material more adielectronic than elsewhere, and frequently such chromatin contains granules or vesicles. Sometimes a connection exists between the chromosome and bleb in the intercalary region of the chromosome, or even occasionally at its terminal part (Fig. 2.10b). The blebs are eventually pinched off and contain moderately adielectronic granules or homogeneous material which includes nucleic acids. It is suggested that these detached blebs become flattened into endoplasmic cisternae (Fig. 2.10c). In the first and second instars, the salivary gland produces saliva, but in the third instar the gland changes over to the production of a mucoprotein which may serve to anchor the puparium to the substrate. It appears as though specific chromosomal regions (genes), by way of the blebs, induce the cytoplasm to secrete the new material.

Blebbing similar to that occurring in *Drosophila* has been observed also in crayfish spermatocytes, the water newt, and pancreatic acinar cells of the rat. In the latter animal the blebbing is of a very exaggerated type, and a typical bleb is approximately circular in outline, limited by a double membrane which has pores and is continuous with the bilamellar nuclear membrane (Fig. 2.11a, b). The inner nuclear membrane sometimes forms a narrow neck at the point of origin of the bleb, so that a large space appears between the inner and outer bleb membranes at this point. The content of the bleb is directly continuous with the nucleoplasm and is usually made up of a dielectronic matrix containing small granules and filaments. It is assumed that the blebs of the acinar cells are detached from the nucleus, for structures, with features identical with undetached blebs, are present throughout the cytoplasm, although they are somewhat smaller in diameter. The blebs may contain both DNA and RNA, and by the transfer of their substance to the cytoplasm, initiate a functional cycle by the cell.

The postulated passage of nuclear material through the pores of the nuclear membrane has been substantiated by a number of observations on the oocytes of insects and amphibians. The ovary of *Rhodnius* consists of several lobes, each with anterior nurse cells and posterior developing oocytes. The nurse cell has a spherical nucleolus which is located centrally within the nucleoplasm, and is made up of 200 Å granules forming a reticulum. Masses of similar granules are found between the nucleolus and the nuclear membrane, and of these masses some, very adielectronic, lie as local masses against the inner aspect of the nuclear membrane (Fig. 2.11c). In the cytoplasm immediately outside the nuclear membrane at points opposite to the nucleolar masses are dense aggregates of diffuse material and small adielectronic bodies composed of many 200 Å granules (Fig. 2.11c). In favourable sections, the intranuclear adielectronic material can be observed to be continuous with the cytoplasmic dense material by way of the nuclear pores. Clearly, nuclear material is being transferred directly to the cytoplasm via the nuclear pores.

A type of nuclear extrusion similar to that just described occurs in the developing oocytes of *Rana esculenta*, *R. clamitans* and *Triturus viridescens*.

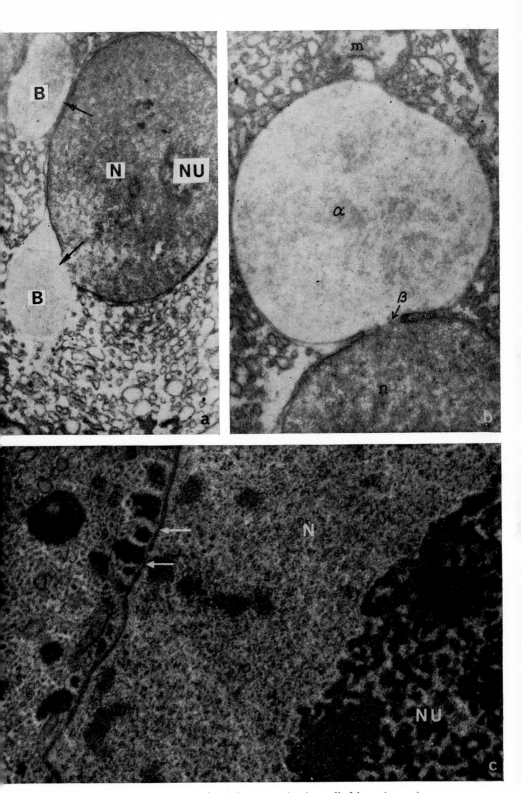

FIG. 2.11. (a) and (b) Nuclear blebs (B and α) in the pancreatic acinar cell of the rat (arrows). (Courtesy Dr. S. L. Clark. (a) × 12,000; (b) × 17,000.) (c) Nucleolar extrusion through the pores in the nuclear membrane of *Rhodnius* nurse cells (arrows). (Courtesy Dr. E. Anderson. × 30,000.)

Soon after the pachytene stage of meiosis, the number of nucleoli increases greatly to near a thousand. These nucleoli lie peripherally near the nuclear membrane and are not structurally related to the chromosomes. They are made up of two components, an adielectronic fibrous core surrounded by a less compact group of small granules and fibres. This configuration of adielectronic core and dielectronic periphery is reversed in the young oocytes of *Triturus* (Fig. 2.5a). Between nucleoli and nuclear membrane, and lying close against the latter, are small groups of adielectronic granules. Finely granular or fibrous material passes through the nuclear pores and in *Rana* condenses some 200–400 Å from the nuclear membrane as a cylinder whose diameter is identical with that of the pore (Fig. 6.24a). These extrusions coalesce to form relatively large masses with which mitochondria eventually associate (Fig. 6.24a). Soon afterwards the number of mitochondria increases greatly. It is suggested that some substance necessary for the mitochondria comes from the nucleolus, perhaps NAD.

Experiments with the giant amoeba, *Chaos chaos* have shown the reverse passage of substances from the cytoplasm through the nuclear pores into the nucleoplasm. If colloidal gold coated with polyvinyl-pyrrolidone (PVP) is injected into the amoeba, gold particles can be observed confined exclusively to the cytoplasm two minutes later, but individual particles are also found within the centre of the nuclear annuli or immediately within the nucleoplasm (Fig. 2.12a–c). Ten minutes after injection, as many particles are present in the nucleus as in the cytoplasm, and after 24 hr the highest concentration of particles is in the nucleoplasm. Passage through the pores clearly occurs and is limited to the centre of the annulus. If the passage of the particles were by free diffusion, gold particles would occur in any part of the annulus or against its walls. As particles are never observed in such positions, it is suggested that they are absorbed on to material occupying the centre of the annulus. Whether they are moved into the nucleoplasm by the inward flow of the annular material, or by successive steps of absorption and desorption from binding sites, could not be solved.

Another mode of transference of nuclear material and information to the cytoplasm is by the replication of the nuclear membrane, to give structures which have been named annulate lamellae. These annulate lamellae have been observed in the ovaries and spermatocytes of a wide variety of invertebrate and vertebrate animals. In insect spermatocytes stacks of annulate lamellae are found throughout the cytoplasm and are probably derived from the nuclear membrane in the following manner. Nucleolar material comes to lie against the inner surface of the nuclear membrane. At this point the space between inner and outer nuclear membranes widens considerably, and the outer membrane is very adielectronic because of its associated ribosomes. It is suggested that a bleb attached by a narrow pedicle is developed in this thickened region of the nuclear membrane (Fig. 2.12d). Successive stacks, joined together by narrow interconnecting bridges, are continuously given off. Because the pedicles and bridges are rarely in the

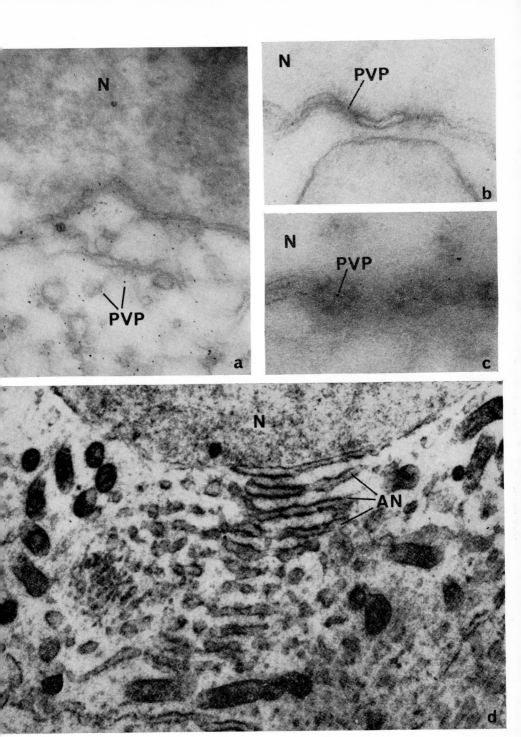

FIG. 2.12. (a)–(c) These three photos demonstrate the passage of colloidal gold PVP from the cytoplasm to the nucleoplasm, through the nuclear pores, in *Chaos chaos*. Time, 2 min after injection. (Courtesy Dr. C. M. Feldherr. × 115,000.) (d) The formation of annulate lamellae (AN) in an insect spermatocyte. (Courtesy Dr. R. Barer. × 15,000.)

plane of the section, however, a stack of flattened sacs unconnected to each other or to the nuclear membrane are frequently observed. The stacks migrate into the cytoplasm and in some cases fragment, such fragments fusing with the endoplasmic reticulum. The annular nature of the stacks is more apparent in some lamellae than others, e.g. in *Otala* oocytes the lamellae have many pores, but in the secondary spermatocytes of *Locusta* the pores may be absent, although in the same testis the primary spermatocytes have lamellae of typical annulate form.

In the eggs of the sand dollar, *Dendraster excentricus,* annulate lamellae are derived in a different manner than in insects. Associated with many areas of the nuclear membrane are intranuclear vesicles with a diffuse dense material. The nuclear membrane in these regions may be diffuse in appearance and disorganized. In the cytoplasm adjacent to the intranuclear vesicles and disorganized nuclear membrane are either groups of small vesicles, 200–500 Å in diameter, or stacks of annulate lamellae. In some cells paired membranes are associated with the intranuclear vesicles and lie closely applied to the inside of the nuclear membrane. Such membrane pairs are without the annulate character of the cytoplasmic annulate lamellae. It has been postulated that a portion of the old outer nuclear membrane is shed and the underlying new membrane is used to fill the gap but it is equally possible that the outer nuclear membrane fragments into the small vesicles and the intranuclear vesicles, and adjacent old membranes fuse to restore continuity.

In many cells the stacks of neighbouring lamellae are lined up in register and are packed hexagonally. In the developing oocytes of *Necturus* these stacks arise as follows. The nuclear membrane forms numerous blebs (Fig. 2.13a) which are released into the ooplasm at about the same time (Fig. 2.13b). The result is successive chains of vesicles lined up in series and lying parallel to the nuclear membrane. Eventually the chains of vesicles fuse to form typical annulate lamellae (Fig. 2.13c). In other cases, masses of tightly packed granules (heavy bodies) become associated with the lamellae shortly after their appearance in the cytoplasm; the heavy bodies are basophil, of a size similar to the ribosomes, and are probably RNA. Some annulate lamellae fragment into vesicles, and vesicles and lamellae appear to be interchangeable.

The function of annulate lamellae is not clear, but they are presumably involved in the transfer of information between the nucleus and cytoplasm. As lamellae are conspicuous elements in rapidly growing cells, they may be involved in cytoplasmic differentiation in embryos.

The annulate lamellae of some animals are considered to fragment and join on to the endoplasmic reticulum, so that the nuclear membrane contributes indirectly to the granular reticulum. Many observations have been made, however, on the cells of adult animals showing a definite continuation between the nuclear membrane and the granular endoplasmic reticulum. The outer nuclear membrane with its attendant ribosomes becomes

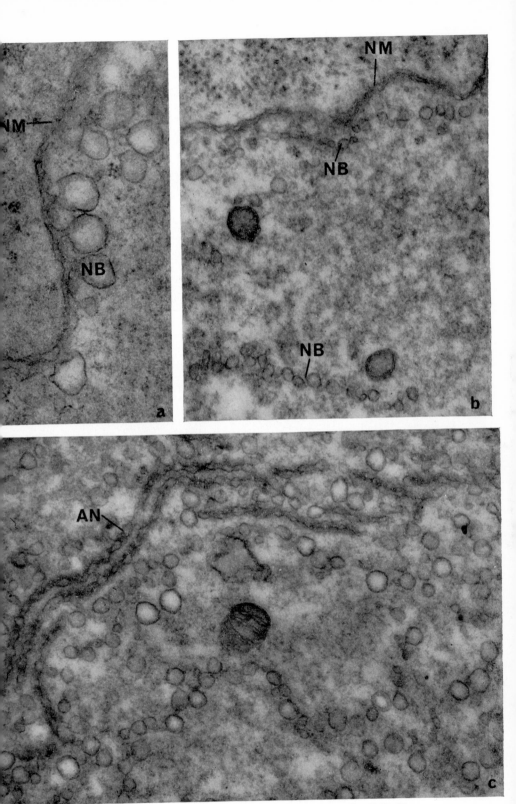

Fig. 2.13. (a)–(c) Successive stages in the formation of annulate lamellae (AN) (Fig. 2.13c) by the fusion of rows of nuclear blebs (NB); NM, nuclear membrane (Fig. 2.13a, b). Developing oocytes of *Necturus*. (Courtesy Dr. R. G. Kessel. (a) ×52,000. (b) ×31,600. (c) ×31,600.)

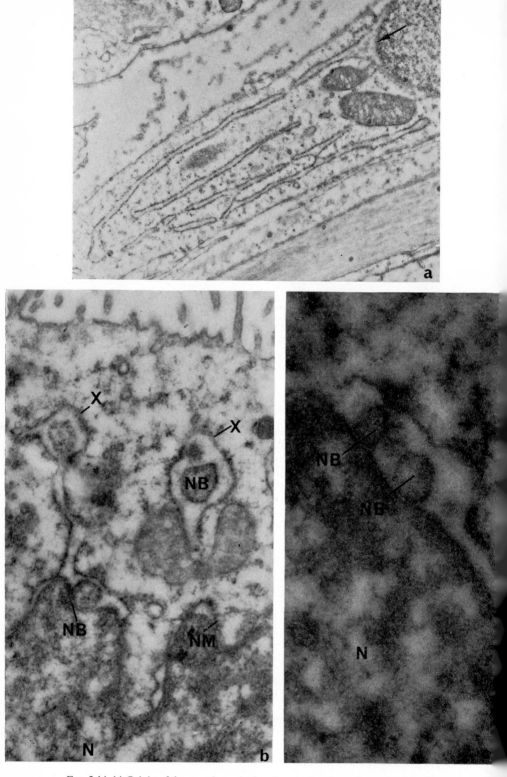

Fig. 2.14. (a) Origin of the granular endoplasmic reticulum from the nuclear membrane
(arrow); amphibian notochordal cell. (Courtesy Drs. C. H. Waddington and M. M.
Perry.) (b) and (c) Intracisternal granules derived from the nucleoplasmic blebs (NB)
and freed into endoplasmic cisternae of nuclear membrane origin (at X); N, nucleus.
(Courtesy Drs. R. Hadek and H. Swift. (b) × 29,000. (c) × 43,000.)

the membrane of the cisternae, and the cisternal lumen is continuous with the intermembranous space of the nuclear membrane. The nuclear membrane, therefore, contributes directly to the formation of granular endoplasmic reticulum. In cells in which a direct connection between nuclear membrane and reticulum is observed, the rows of cisternae parallel each other and the nuclear surface, suggesting the continuous production of endoplasmic reticulum by the nuclear membrane and the subsequent pushing out into the peripheral cytoplasm of the cisternae so formed. Such formations of endoplasmic reticulum are especially evident in embryolic cells, for example, in the formation of the notochord in amphibians (Fig. 2.14a) and birds, and the pancreas during its cytogenesis in the chick. The increase in the reticulum during the development of tissues and organs is undoubtedly under the influence of the nuclear membrane and, presumably in the preliminary stage, the genes.

The formation of the granular endoplasmic reticulum with intracisternal granules has been observed in the rabbit blastocyst, haemocytoblasts of rabbit embryos and the stratum germinativum of the hamster epidermis. The process starts with a local increase in the width of the intermembranous space of the nuclear membrane, and the evagination of the outer membrane, possibly by osmotic shock. The inner nuclear membrane subsequently gives rise to a small bleb of nucleoplasm from the dielectronic intrachromosomal area (Fig. 2.14b–c). The bleb is pinched off and the resulting membrane bound body passes into the intermembranous space.† The outer nuclear membrane projects progressively further into the cytoplasm and gives rise to endoplasmic cisternae, the lumen of which is naturally confluent with the intermembranous space of the nuclear membrane (Fig. 2.14c). The extruded blebs are free to move from the intermembranous space into the endoplasmic cisternal cavities and are, therefore, found within cisternae which lie relatively far from the nucleus. The function of these intracisternal granules is at present unknown.

Further Reading List

1. MIRSKY, A. E. and OSAWA, S., The Interphase Nucleus, *The Cell,* Vol. II, edit. BRACHET, J. and MIRSKY, A. E., Academic Press, London, 1961.
2. RIS, H., Interpretation of Ultrastructure of the Cell Nucleus, *The Interpretation of Ultrastructure,* edit. HARRIS, R. J. C., Academic Press, London, 1962.
3. BRACHET, J., Nucleocytoplasmic Interactions in the Unicellular Organism, *The Cell,* Vol. II, edit. BRACHET, J. and MIRSKY, A. E., Academic Press, London, 1961.
4. MOSES, M. J., The Nucleus and Chromosomes, *Cytology and Cell Physiology,* 3rd ed., edit. G. H. BOURNE, Academic Press, London, 1964.

† The interpretation of the origin of the intracisternal granules given here is that of this author, being derived from a study of the electron micrographs of R. Hadek and H. Swift, in their paper "Nuclear extrusions and intracisternal inclusions in rabbit blastocytes", *J. Cell Biol.* **13**, 445–51 (1962). Hadek and Swift postulate the origin of these bodies by the passage of intrachromosomal material through the pores in the inner nuclear membrane, but admit this mode of origin does not account for the enclosing membrane. The mode of origin given here does account for this membrane.

CHAPTER 3

THE ULTRASTRUCTURE OF THE CYTOSOME

I. The Plasma Membrane and Associated Structures

The Plasma Membrane

The plasma membrane, which in classical microscopy remained a structural enigma, has been revealed by recent electron microscopy in all its expected complexity. Furthermore, it has been observed that modifications of this structure give rise to structures previously thought to be unrelated to the plasma membrane as such.

The plasma membrane is observed in electron-micrographs to possess a morphology which depends to a large extent on the particular chemical fixative, embedding medium and stain used, and the resolution. With osmic acid fixation, methacrylate or epoxy resin embedding and low resolution, the plasma membrane is generally a single adielectronic layer less than 100 Å thick (mostly measuring between 40–80 Å). With permanganate fixation and epoxy resin embedding, the plasma membrane is resolved as a tripartite structure of two adielectronic layers enclosing a dielectronic central layer (Fig. 3.1a, b). The three layers have been measured variously as either 25, 25, 25 Å or 20, 35, 20Å, the middle measurement referring to the middle dielectronic layer. The total thickness of the membrane in either case is 75 Å, and the whole has been termed a unit membrane. Subsequently such tripartite membranes were discovered as a structural component of the mitochondrion, the Golgi complex, the endoplasmic reticulum and the nuclear membrane, and unit membranes were considered to be a universal cell constituent. This view of the universality and basic character of the unit membrane as a component of cell organoids partly or wholly composed of membranes, is an over-simplification and can no longer be accepted in view of recent discoveries (see subsequent chapters). The term "unit membrane", however, is convenient and should continue to be used, provided that its use is confined to the designation of a tripartite membrane of no specific diameter, either as a whole or in its parts. The term is so used throughout this text.

The 75 Å tripartite plasma membrane is generally considered to be equal to the previously demonstrated 40–80 Å single adielectronic layer. Its molecular structure is thought to be as follows: the 25–35 Å middle layer is a bimolecular layer of lipids, with its non-polar hydrophobic groups facing inwards and its polar groups facing outwards. These outward facing groups

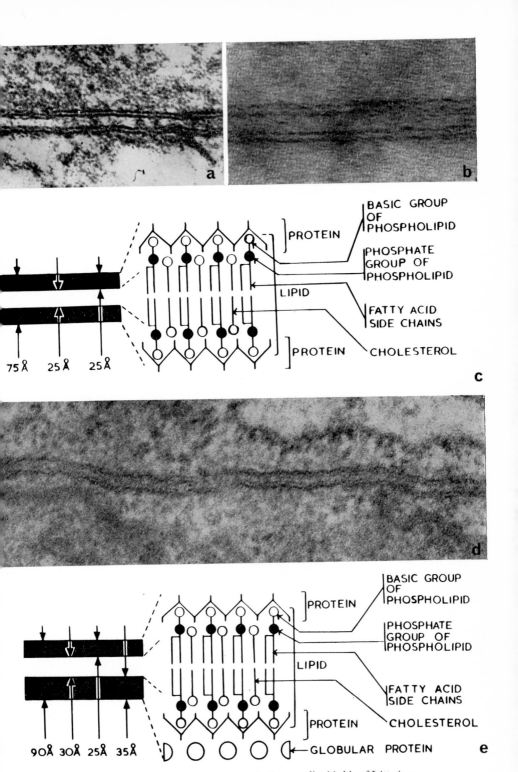

FIG. 3.1. (a) and (b) Opposed plasma membranes of adjacent cells; (a) skin of *Littorina* sp.; (b) smooth muscle of mouse intestine. The tripartite nature of each plasma membrane is evident. ((a) Courtesy Dr. G. Owen. ×206,000. (b) Dr. J. D. Robertson. ×540,000.) (c) Proposed molecular structure of the plasma membrane after KMnO₄ fixation. The membrane is symmetrical. (Original.) (d) Opposed plasma membranes of adjacent exocrine cells of the cat pancreas. The asymmetrical nature of the membranes is evident. OsO₄ fixation and uranyl acetate staining. (Courtesy Dr. F. Sjostrand. ×160,000.) (e) Proposed molecular structure of the asymmetrical plasma membrane. (Original.)

are thought to be covered by a protein layer 20–25 Å thick, the protein chains lying at right angles to the lipids, but it has also been suggested that the 20–25 Å layer facing the external environment is carbohydrate in nature, because of its less marked adielectronicity (Fig. 3.1b).

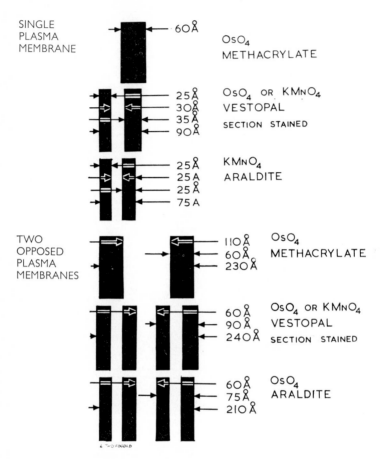

FIG. 3.2. A comparison by diagrammatic representation of the dimensions and relation-ships of the plasma membrane as it appears after different fixatives, embedding, and staining procedures. (Original, after Dr. F. Sjostrand.)

The more recent use of potassium permanganate or osmic acid fixation, combined with Vestopal embedding and uranyl acetate or lead staining, has revealed the plasma membrane as asymmetrical (Fig. 3.1d). It is a tripartite structure having a thick adielectronic inner (cytoplasmic) component, 35–40 Å, a narrow adielectronic outer (external) component 25 Å thick, and a central dielectronic component 30 Å wide (Fig. 3.1d). This gives a plasma membrane with a total thickness of 90–95 Å. It has been shown further that the former tripartite membrane of 75 Å is not equivalent to the 40–80 Å single dense line described from the earliest electron-microscope studies. Only the 20–25 Å inner (cytoplasmic) component of the 75 Å tripartite membrane is equal to the 40–80 Å single layer and to the 35–40 Å inner component of the 90–95 Å unit membrane of potassium permanganate or osmium–Vestopal-stained tissues (Fig. 3.2). The molecular structure of this asymmetrical unit membrane is thought to be the same as that for the 75 Å unit membrane, but with the addition of a layer of globular proteins to the adielectronic inner cytoplasmic component (Fig. 3.1e). It has been pointed out, however, that globular proteins are metabolically (enzymatically) active, whereas expanded (structural) proteins are not, so that an inner layer with both globular and stretched proteins is precluded. Furthermore, a comparison of the osmic and permanganate fixed materials suggests that although the thick inner component is certainly proteinaceous, the thin outer component, which shows up poorly with osmic fixation, is probably carbohydrate in nature. The lipoproteins of the membranes must lie in a matrix, and organized water structures, of ice-like or crystalline hydrate type, must permeate the lipoprotein component and form an integral part of the membrane. Such a hydrate continuum would have important implications for charge transfer, energy storage, selective permeability, localized reversible phase changes and other membrane functions in all unit membranes.

The asymmetrical plasma membrane results in the reduction of the intercellular space of adjacent cells from an average of 150 Å to one of about 60 Å (Fig. 3.2). This feature will be dealt with more fully later in the chapter. The other unit membranes in cell organoids, such as endoplasmic reticulum, Golgi complex and mitochondria, appear to be symmetrical and in other ways different from the plasma membrane (see Chapters 4, 5 and 9).

Many cells, if not all, have layers superficial to the unit membrane at their surface. The extraneous coats appear as coarse amorphous projections from the free surface of the plasma membrane, e.g. as at the luminal surface of a tubular organ (Fig. 3.3a). This extraneous coat is presumably the same as the so-called "cement" occurring between adjacent cells laterally, and between the cells' basal membrane and the basement membrane. This material is a mucopolysaccharide and appears to be poorly preserved, or partly or wholly lost from the cell surface during preparative techniques. Its function, however, seems to be to bind and concentrate large molecules, leading eventually to the formation of pinocytotic invaginations which pinch off to form vesicles within the cytoplasm. Ions or water are apparently not hindered by this additional barrier external to the true plasma membrane.

The extraneous coat is very conspicuous on the surface of amoebae. Immediately outside the plasma membrane (80 Å thick) is an amorphous layer 200 Å thick, with hair-like extensions 50–80 Å in diameter and 1000–2000 Å long, projecting from it. These filaments bind large particles, and the whole structure has a polysaccharide composition (Fig. 3.3b, c).

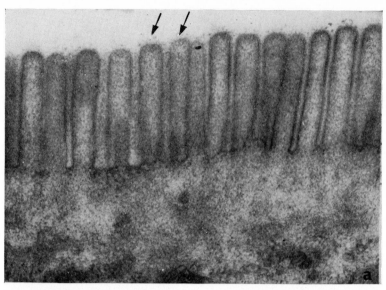

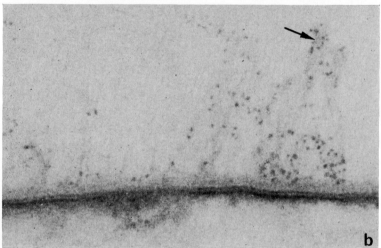

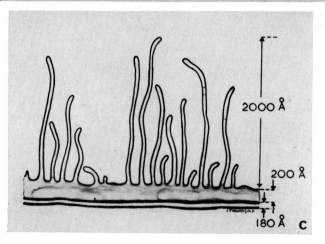

FIG. 3.3. (a) Microvillous border from the bullfrog small intestine showing the extraneous surface coat to the plasma membrane (arrows). (Courtesy Dr. M. Bonneville. × 50,000.) (b) The extraneous coat on the plasma membrane of *Amoeba*, with attached dense particles (arrow). (Courtesy Drs. P. Brandt and G. Pappas. × 19,000.) (c) Diagram and dimensions of the extraneous coat to the plasma membrane of *Amoeba*. (Original.)

The molecular interpretation of the plasma membrane given above is not the only interpretation possible on the basis of both physiological and electron-microscopical studies. It has been postulated that the plasma membrane has two diverse equilibrium states, the "open" and the "closed"

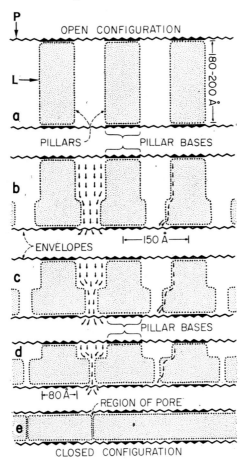

FIG. 3.4. A series of diagrams illustrating the sequence of changes between the open, intermediate, and closed configurations of the plasma membrane. (Courtesy Dr. J. L. Kavanau.) L, lipid; P, protein.

configurations, with every possible variation in between these extremes (Fig. 3.4). In the open configuration the lipid component is considered to be a series of pillars (lipid micelles) 80 Å in diameter and 180–200 Å long (Fig. 3.4). The pillars are arranged hexagonally with a centre-to-centre spacing of about 150 Å; the pillars are therefore about 70 Å apart, and the space between them is filled with a mainly water matrix. The ends of the pillars are bound to the 10–15 Å thick protein components by stable polar interactions (ion–ion, ion–dipole, dipole–dipole and hydrogen bonding) or by non-polar interactions (penetration of non-polar amino acid side chains between the lipid head groups into lipophilic regions, where unstable dipole-induced dipole interactions occur).

The closed configuration is similar to that generally accepted as the molecular structure of the plasma membrane. The pillars, reduced to bimolecular discs 50–60 Å in height and appropriately wider in diameter than in the open state, are juxtaposed or fused to give a more or less continuous layer, with or without "pores" (Fig. 3.4). At the protein–pillar junction the interactions are essentially unchanged, but in the expanded regions lateral to the 80 Å diameter pillars of the open state the lipid–protein binding is less stable and mainly polar.

It is postulated that a particular membrane is usually in either the open or closed configuration, in which it is stable or metastable. The change from open to closed state occurs by the forcing out of the matrix between the expanding pillars and through the protein layer. The transformation starts at one point on the membrane (due to cationic displacement accompanying specific functions) and is propagated longitudinally to other regions. The reverse change is assumed to be the simple reversal of the open to closed transformation. In addition, different membranes would likely have different protein and lipid compositions, resulting in variations in pore size, shape, structure and total pore area per membrane, thereby conferring selective permeability on the membranes.

The preponderance of the closed configuration of the plasma membrane in electron micrographs is presumed to be due to the preparative techniques employed, especially the dehydration of the tissues and the use of multi-valent heavy metal cations. Nevertheless, some electron-microscope studies appear to show the open configuration not only in the plasma membrane but also in the closely opposed external membranes and cristae of mitochondria. Oblique sections of the plasma membrane of mouse kidney cells show adielectronic circular areas 50 Å across, surrounded by less dense rings approximately 125 Å in diameter. The plasma membrane of synaptic discs fixed in permanganate and cut transversely show a beaded pattern with a periodicity of 85–95 Å, and if cut obliquely reveal a series of darkly stained regions surrounded by lighter areas (Fig. 3.5a). In the double membrane discs of the outer segment of the retinal rod cells electron-dense components are associated with the unit membranes. The granules are particularly conspicuous in dark-adapted eyes and appear to be related to photopigment complexes (Fig. 3.5b).

Although it must be supported by a greater weight of evidence before it can be unreservedly supported, the above theory is attractive on two counts. Firstly, it emphasizes the dynamic and highly labile nature of the plasma membrane, which would alter its structural state with function. There is no reason to suppose that the plasma membrane is any more stable at the molecular level than any other cell structure. Secondly, the theory provides a common molecular explanation of such diverse activities as protoplasmic

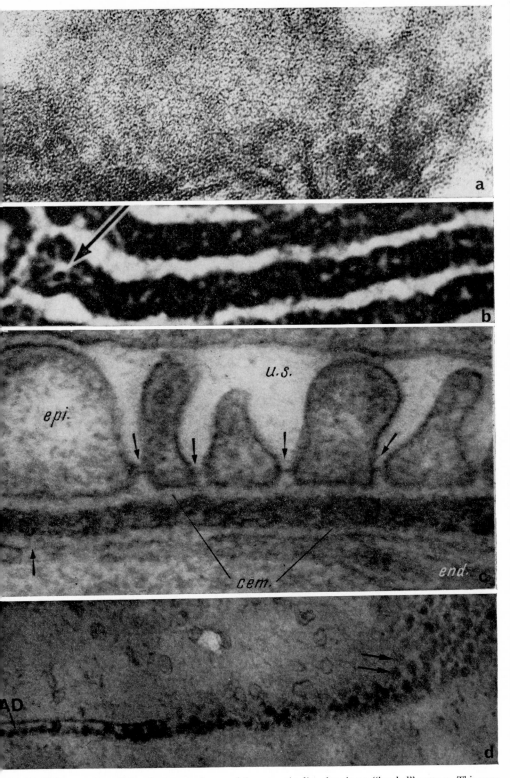

. 3.5. (a) Oblique section of the plasma membrane of the synaptic disc showing a "beaded" pattern. This may esent the open configuration of the membrane, the dense "beads" being cross-sections of the lipid pillars. ırtesy Dr. J. D. Robertson. × 200,000.) (b) Dense granules (arrow), associated with the membrane discs of ıal rod cells. The membrane discs are derived from the plasma membrane. (Courtesy Dr. H. Fernandez-Moran. 00,000.) (c) Basement membrane between an endothelial cell (END), and podocytes of the glomerular epithelium). U.S., urinary space; CEM, cement. (Courtesy Dr. D. G. Pease. × 80,000.) (d) Adepidermal granules (arrows) ı the adepidermal space (AD) at the base of epithelial cells of frog skin. (Courtesy Dr. P. A. Pillai. × 54,000.)

streaming, membrane contraction, expansion and growth, impulse conduction, active transport and diffusion.

The plasma membrane shows a variety of modifications, some quite extreme, and associated with these specializations are other structures which are generally inseparable from the membrane itself. The membrane specializations and associations are most logically described by reference to the various tissues, of which connective tissues appear to have the least number of plasma membrane modifications and epithelial tissues the most.

Epithelial Tissues

Epithelial cells often show polarity and therefore have the following surfaces at which modifications of the plasma membrane may occur: (a) the basal cell surface and the basement membrane; (b) the lateral cell surfaces with desmosomes and terminal bars; (c) the apical cell surface and cilia. Those epithelial cells which do not have polarity, or lack particularly the apical surface abutting on a lumen, naturally have specializations which are equal to one basal surface and 3 lateral or to 4 lateral surfaces. Such cells do not show features additional to the polarized cell.

The Basal Cell Surface

The Basement Membrane

The basement membrane is a zone ranging from 150–400 Å thick (exocrine pancreas and thyroid, respectively), which is generally considered to be secreted by the overlying cells and not by the adjacent fibroblasts (Fig. 3.5c). It is probably a gel in life and appears as an amorphous zone in electron micrographs, although some authors claim it has a fibrous nature.

The basement membrane is not in direct contact with the overlying cells but is separated from them by a 150 Å (range 150–300 Å) amorphous cement substance, which is continuous with the cement between the lateral boundaries of adjacent cells (Fig. 3.5c). In amphibian larval skin, dense granules form a single row in the cement layer (adepidermal layer) between basal plasma membrane and basement membrane (Fig. 3.5d). The basement membrane may be flanked on both sides by cement substance and cell layer or layers, or may be split into two basement membranes whenever a central connective tissue layer intervenes. The membrane which is probably a polysaccharide, provides a mechanical base upon which cells can develop complexities, and is an essential precursor for specializations of cell bases. In addition, the membrane acts as an efficient, but not perfect, filter for large molecules, though the adjacent plasma membranes are probably more effective and selective barriers. Diffusion through the basement membrane must be easy, so that the active principle of selection can be carried out by the cell itself. In renal glomeruli, electron-opaque tracers pass through the endothelium by means of 600 Å diameter pinocytotic vesicles, but pile up against the luminal side of the basement membrane. The glomerular epithelium is a monitoring filter for whatever material does traverse the basement membrane, and the third deep cell type removes excess filtrate by vesicles 600–2000 Å in diameter.

The Basal Plasma Membrane

In the majority of cells the basal plasma membrane is smooth, following the contours of the basement membrane, but other cells show modifications, apparently in response to functional activities. A major type of modification is an inward turning of the plasma membrane at intervals to form narrow folds. The folds appear as two adielectronic parallel layers joined at their inner ends and separated by a dielectronic zone, 150–200 Å wide. This latter middle zone, which is continuous with the cement substance between cell base and basement membrane, varies in width with function. The folds penetrate the cell for distances of up to about one third of the cell depth (3–5 μ) in Malpighian tubules of *Rhodnius* and almost to the cell apex in the salt gland of marine birds (Fig. 3.6b).

Serial sections and three-dimensional reconstructions show that the folds are septa and not tubules (Fig. 3.6c). The septa branch and anastomose to divide the basal cytoplasm into compartments which are open above to the perinuclear cytoplasm. The compartments frequently contain mitochondria aligned parallel to the septal surface. The degree to which this septal system is developed depends upon the epithelial type, and its presence seems to be correlated with the function of transporting water and water-soluble substances from the cell to the blood stream or extracellular fluid. In some cells this basal infolding is limited, e.g. frog nephron, choroid plexus, ciliary body, and insect Malpighian tubules, so that some compartments are too small to contain mitochondria (Fig. 3.6b). In cells such as the distal convoluted tubule of the mammalian kidney, the striated ducts of the salivary glands and sweat glands, the infoldings are deep and mitochondria almost always fill the compartments (Fig. 3.6c). The infoldings greatly increase the surface area of the cell at its base, and the mitochondria presumably furnish the energy required to transport ions across the plasma membrane.

In some cases the septa form loops, so that an area of cytoplasm is enclosed by a continuous pair of membranes commencing at the cell base and returning to it. These loops may enclose smaller loops or straight septa. Such forms are evidently due to the insertion of processes of the same cell or neighbouring cells between the cell and its basement membrane (Fig. 3.6a; 3.7a–c). An interlocking labyrinthine system of intracellular compartments and extracellular clefts is thereby formed. The membrane pairs within any one cell may represent, therefore, the boundaries of two different cells or the infolding of the plasma membrane of the same cell.

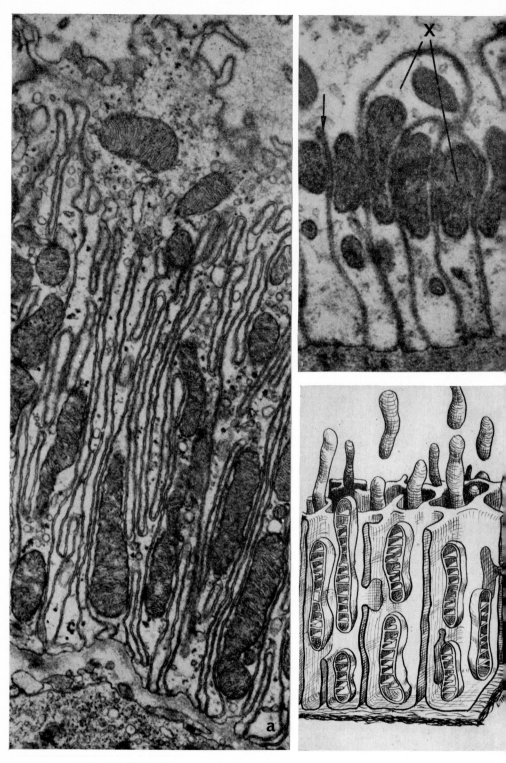

Fig. 3.6. (a) Distal convoluted tubule cell from the frog, showing deeply penetrating infoldings of the basal plasma membrane due to interdigitations of adjacent cells. (Courtesy Dr. M. Karnovsky. × 24,000.) (b) Malpighian tubules of *Rhodnius prolixus* with short infoldings of the basal plasma membrane (arrow), and interdigitations from adjacent cells, at X. (Courtesy Sir V. B. Wigglesworth and Dr. M. M. Perry. × 20,000.) (c) A three-dimensional diagram of infoldings of the basal plasma membrane to form septa, and the associated mitochondria. (Original.)

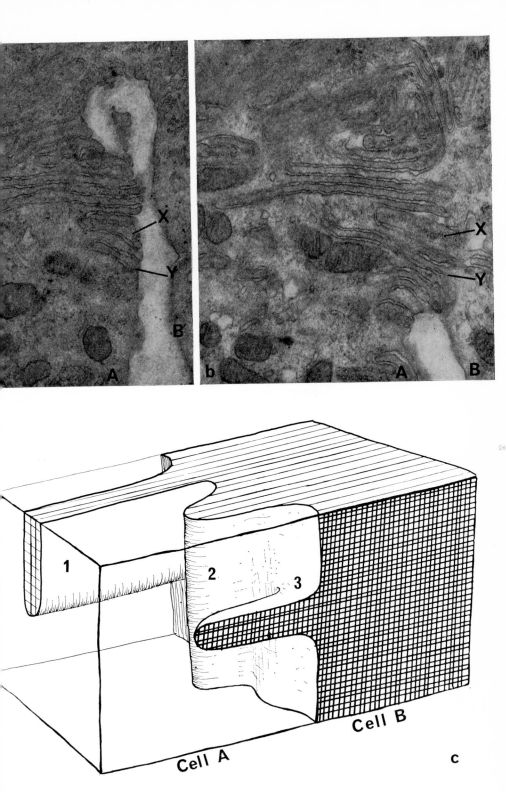

Fig. 3.7. (a) and (b) Serial sections of ciliary epithelium, showing that many infoldings of the basal plasma membrane are due to interdigitations of adjacent cells, A and B. Note especially points X and Y. (Courtesy Dr. J. McD. Tormey. ×28,000.) (c) Three-dimensional drawing showing types of interdigitations between adjacent cells. (Original.)

Associated with some septa are small vesicles, usually aligned in rows, which continue in line with the septa. A row of vesicles may commence at the cell base, be continuous with a septum, or appear as curved rows between, or uniting, two or more septa. It has been suggested that the presence of these vesicles indicates a functioning of the septa from which they are pinched off. This may be so in some instances, but experiments designed to stimulate uptake of water and solutes have failed to increase the number of vesicles, e.g. ciliary epithelium by diamox injection. Furthermore, recent experiments have shown that some preparative techniques can "vesiculate", so that a previously continuous sheet is broken up into a row of vesicles.

Little is known of the origin of the septa, but the most simple and direct method of formation would be by an inward growth of the plasma membrane. It has been claimed, however, that vesicles arise in the cytoplasm and fuse into flattened sacs, which, in turn, contact the plasma membrane and so open out to the exterior.

The visceral epithelium covering the glomerular capillary loops of the renal glomerulus has a modification of its basal region which is peculiar to these cells. Between the endothelium of the capillaries and the glomerular epithelium is a central basement membrane flanked on both sides by a narrow cement layer. Whereas, however, the endothelial cell provides a more or less continuous, if sometimes tenuous, cytoplasmic layer over its cement, the glomerular epithelium does not. The visceral cells have pseudopodium-like processes, podocytes, which in turn give rise to numerous finer processes, feet or pedicels. These pedicels terminate on the cement layer where they are somewhat expanded, though always separated from each other by a space about 70 Å wide. Elsewhere the pedicels are separated by considerable spaces, and as pedicels from adjacent cells interdigitate, narrow slit-like spaces result. These spaces are continuous with the urinary space of the Bowmans capsule (Fig. 3.8a).

A completely different basal specialization is found in the capillary endothelium of rat choroid, mouse thyroid, adrenal cortex, and kidney, and also between the pedicels of the visceral epithelium of the glomerulus. This structure will probably be found in other tissues eventually. This modification is the diaphragm which appears as fenestrations (very dielectronic circular areas) 700 Å in diameter, with slightly denser rims and a 100 Å diameter central knob (Fig. 3.8b). The fenestrations are in rows with a centre-to-centre spacing of 1300 Å, and occupy about 35 per cent of each micron of surface, that is, average about 30 per μ^2. The fenestrations are not openings or pores in the endothelium, as has been claimed in the past, but are closed by a diaphragm 60 Å thick, not 120 Å as would be expected from the union of two 60 Å endothelial plasma membranes (Figs. 3.8c, d; 6.9a, b). The diaphragms must be an effective barrier to large molecules, and as the endothelium is actively engaged in passing certain substances back and forth, it must determine the final size of the particles passed.

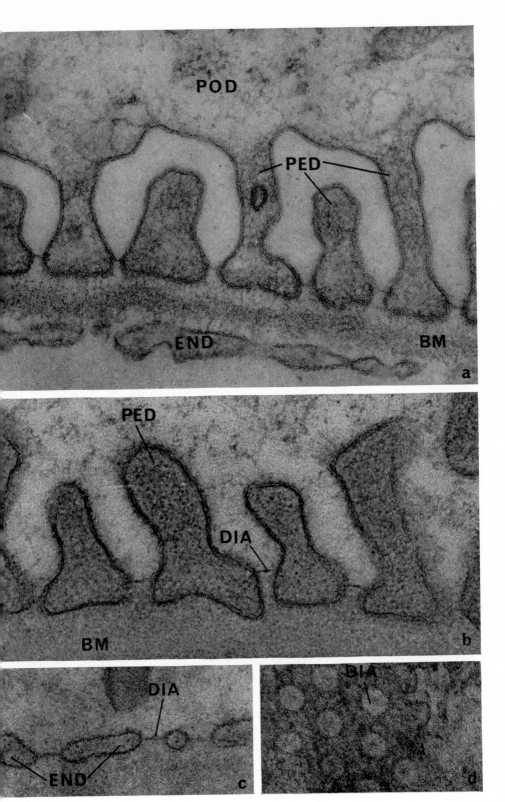

FIG. 3.8. (a) Podocytes (POD), and pedicels (PED), of the glomerular epithelium of the rat kidney. BM, basement membrane; END endothelial cell. (Courtesy Dr. M. G. Farquhar. ×92,000.) (b) Diaphragms (DIA) with central knob, in the region between pedicels of the glomerular epithelium. (Courtesy Dr. J. A. Rhodin. ×100,000.) (c) and (d) Diaphragm (DIA) across fenestrations in the capillary endothelium (END). (c) transverse section; (d) oblique section. (Courtesy Dr. J. A. Rhodin. ×100,000.)

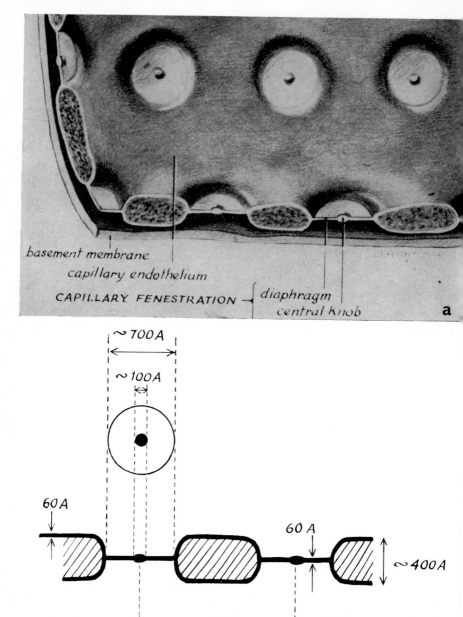

basement membrane
capillary endothelium
CAPILLARY FENESTRATION ─ { diaphragm
                            central knob

a

∼700A

∼100A

60A

60A

∼400A

∼1300A

b

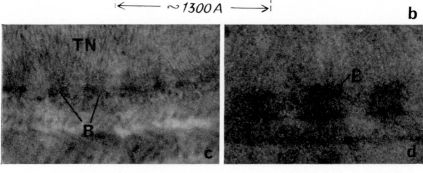

TN

B

B

c

d

FIG. 3.9. (a) Three-dimensional drawing of the capillary fenestrations. (Courtesy Dr. J. A. Rhodin.) (b) Dimensions of the capillary fenestrations of endothelial cells. (Courtesy Dr. J. A. Rhodin.) (c) and (d) Bobbins (B) (half desmosomes) and tonofibrils (TN) of the basal plasma membrane of amphibian larval skin. (Courtesy Dr. P. Weiss. (c) × 37,000. (d) × 55,000.)

Associated structures of the basal plasma membrane are the half desmosomes and the bobbin-shaped bodies so prominent in the epidermis of certain species. In amphibians the bobbins are about 1100 Å high and 1800 Å wide at base and apex, with a narrow waist. The base and apex are adielectronic and the waist less so. The base rests directly on the basal plasma membrane, and from the flat apex a bundle of fine fibrils radiates deep into the cytoplasm of the epithelial cells to form a feltwork with fibres from other bobbins (Fig. 3.9c, d). The bobbins appear, therefore, as half desmosomes; full desmosomes occur at the lateral margins of adjacent cells and will be described in the appropriate section.

The Lateral Plasma Membrane

The plasma membranes of neighbouring cells are not in intimate contact, and early in electron microscopy the two 75 Å plasma membranes were shown to be separated by a dielectronic zone measuring between 110–200 Å. By newer techniques, which reveal the plasma membrane as 90–95 Å thick, the intercellular zone is only 60 Å (Fig. 3.2). The zone varies in width with different tissues, being wider in respiratory epithelium and the dermis than in glandular epithelium, and it may widen greatly to give a definite intercellular space in bile capillaries, between the basal cells of the bladder epithelium, in amphibian embryonic epidermis and in the convoluted tubules of the kidney (Fig. 3.10a, b). The intercellular zone is filled with a material which is presumably a cementing substance(mucopolysaccharide), although cells probably adhere by selective cohesion, such as occurs in the antigen–antibody reaction.

Selective cohesion is, however, not the only adhesive mechanism between cells. The adjacent membranes may be folded in a simple or complex manner. The simple folds are S- or Z-shaped, but may appear as long zones of interleaved plasma membranes (Fig. 3.10c, d). Hooked projections which turn to run parallel to the lateral cell surface, or press-stud interlockings, are other simple forms (Fig. 3.10e). A more involved type of the simple fold is a large undulation with a multitude of small finger-like projections. The foldings may interdigitate so extensively as to radiate tridimensionally, resulting in sections showing the cytoplasm of one cell as isolated areas within the cytoplasm of its neighbour (Fig. 3.10c, d).

A characteristic adhesive complex occurs at the apical ends of adjacent cells in the epithelia of many glands and cavitary organs. This complex consists of three parts in an apical–basal direction, a tight zone (zonula occludens), an intermediate junction (zonula adhaerens) and a desmosome (macula adhaerens) (Fig. 3.11a). The zonulae occludens and adhaerens probably correspond to the terminal bar of light microscopy, the major part of the bar being occupied by the zonula adhaerens. Desmosomes can, of course, occur elsewhere along the lateral cell surface quite unconnected

4

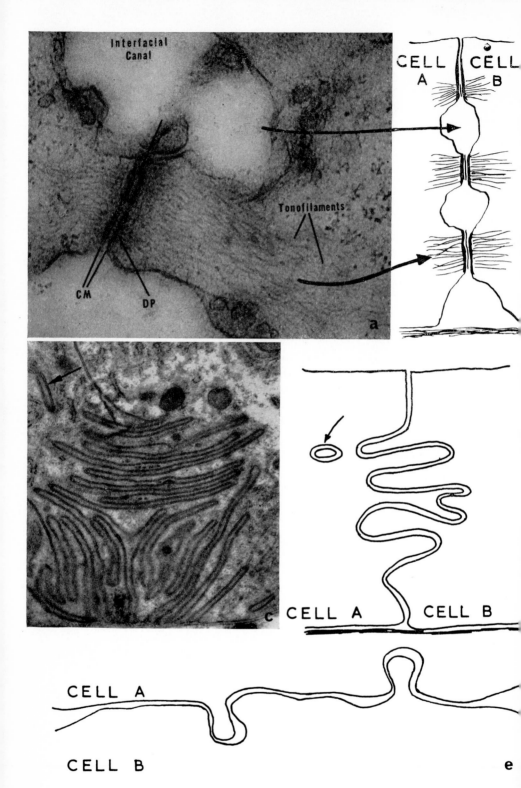

FIG. 3.10. (a) and (b) Intracellular (interfacial) canals between the lateral surfaces of adjacent cells in larval amphibian skin. (Courtesy Dr. E. Hay. × 50,000.) (c) and (d) Lateral interdigitations between opposed ciliary epithelial cells. Arrows on photo and drawing point to apparently isolated areas of cytoplasm. (Courtesy Dr. J. McD. Tormey. × 20,000. Original drawing.) (e) Diagram of button interlockings of adjacent liver cells. (Original.)

with this complex, but they always have an identical structure, whatever their position.

The zonula occludens commences at the junction of apical and lateral cell borders and is 2000–5000 Å long, with a straight or wavy course. The zonula appears to form a continuous belt-like attachment which runs completely around the cell, unlike the desmosome. The zonula occludens is characterized by the fusion of the adjacent plasma membranes, resulting in the obliteration of the intercellular zone (Fig. 3.11b). Within the zonula the outer adielectronic components of the adjacent tripartite plasma membranes fuse into a single layer, so that the junction appears as quintuple layered (a central dense layer flanked on each side by a light and dense layer, respectively). This quintuple layer measures approximately 150 Å across, and is to be compared with a width of 250–300 Å in other parts of the lateral cell margins of neighbouring cells, where each plasma membrane is completely tripartite (75 or 95 Å) and the intercellular zone is present (150 or 60 Å). A diffuse band of dense cytoplasm is generally associated with the zonula occludens, but its development varies between epithelia. Other minor variations in the structure are one or several localized splittings of the fusion layer, followed by their refusion, to give a series of beaded intercellular regions. In some places the central fusion layer is absent and the distance between the outer adielectronic components of adjacent plasma membranes is reduced to less than 90 Å. In such cases a molecular rearrangement of the fused membranes must be involved. The zonula occludens is impervious to concentrated protein solutions and appears to act as both a barrier to diffusion and a seal.

The zonula adhaerens arises as a continuation of the tight junction and extends over 3000–5000 Å, with a straight or slightly wavy course (Fig. 3.11a). The apposed plasma membranes, which run strictly parallel to each other, appear to form a belt around each cell in most cases. The membranes have a distinct tripartite structure, although the inner (cytoplasmic) adielectronic component is more pronounced than the outer one, giving an asymmetrical appearance. The immediate cytoplasm has a conspicuous densification and is composed of tightly matted fibrils, most of which are parallel to the cell surface. Sometimes the density forms a plate separated from the plasma membrane by a dielectronic line, and the whole structure is obviously a cell web derivative. The opposed membranes are always separated by a true intercellular zone, approximately 200 Å wide, which is amorphous, but may have a central band of greater electron density.

The desmosome, or macula adhaerens, follows the zonula adhaerens and is usually located at a distance of 200 Å or more from the basal end of the latter (Fig. 3.11c). The desmosome is a circumscribed oval or circular area 2000–3000 Å in length and is strictly opposed by a desmosome which lies parallel to it in the adjacent cell. The neighbouring tripartite

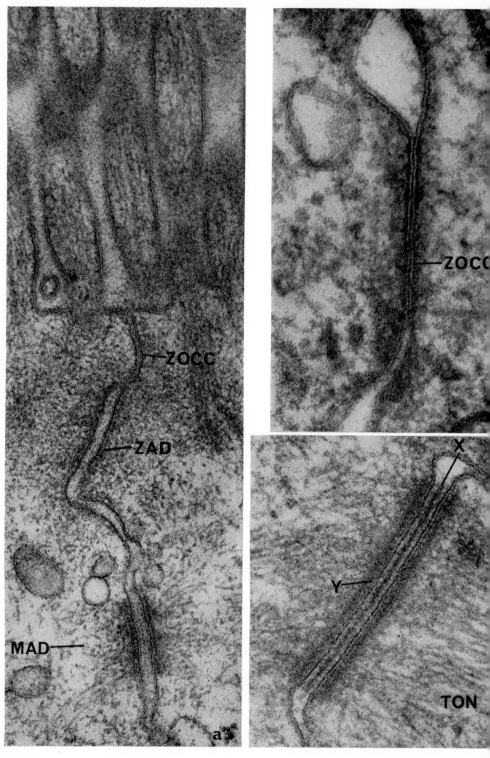

FIG. 3.11. (a) Junctional complex between adjacent cells of the rat intestine. Zonula occludens (ZOCC), zonula adhaerens (ZAD), and macula adhaerens (MAD), or desmosome. (× 96,000.) (b) Zonula occludens of rat kidney. (× 150,000.) (c) Desmosome or macula adhaerens in frog skin; the dense intermembraneous line is at X, and the lateral dense layer at Y. TON, tonofibrils. (× 144,000. (a–c) courtesy Dr. M. G. Farquhar.)

plasma membranes can be followed clearly through the desmosomes, the inner adielectronic component showing some densification in the desmosome itself (Fig. 3.11c). The intercellular zone is about 240 Å wide and has a central dense line. The cytoplasm immediately adjacent to the desmosome is modified and consists of an inner and outer part. The inner part is very adielectronic and about 300–800 Å wide. It is separated from the plasma membrane by the dielectronic zone and is called the attachment plaque. The outer part, of less density, grades into the cytoplasm and consists of tonofibrils each about 75 Å in diameter (these are not visible in potassium permanganate fixed tissues). Possibly the attachment plaque is merely very compacted tonofibrils. An additional feature of some desmosomes is the attachment to each outer part of a single mitochondrion, which gives the structure a wing-like appearance. This type of desmosome occurs in the epithelia of the interlobular bile ducts of rabbit, and liver and gastric glands of rat.

A variation of the typical vertebrate desmosome occurs in *Hydra*, *Rhodnius*, and certain other invertebrates. It has been called a septate desmosome. In typical desmosomes there is no direct connection between opposed desmosomes through the intervening intercellular material. In septate desmosomes dense transverse bars give a ladder-like appearance to this material. The dense bars are spaced 300–400 Å apart and number 50–150 per desmosome. Each bar is made up of two adielectronic lines 50 Å in diameter, 50 Å apart, and these lines appear continuous at both ends with the outer dense component of the opposed plasma membranes. There are no tonofibrils in the adjacent cytoplasm (Fig. 3.12a, b).

Recent research on the growing stolon of *Cordylophora* reveals septate desmosomes which differ somewhat from those described above. In this case the intercellular septa consist of two adielectronic bodies lying close together. They are positioned midway in the 150–300 Å region between cells, but are separated from the latter by a dielectronic space. The plasma membranes consist of alternating light and dense zones 70 Å long, with their light zones opposite to the dense bodies of the septa (Fig. 3.12c). When the plasma membranes are cut obliquely, the septa appear as a bar, which suggests that further observations on *Hydra* and other invertebrates with septate desmosomes may reveal that they also are bipartite structures not in contact with the plasma membranes.

The Apical Plasma Membrane

The apical cell surface shows a great variety of forms, the majority of which are impermanent and reflect the very active state of what is so often the luminal surface of the cell. Nevertheless, there are a number of structural modifications which are permanent, in the sense that although they are basically functional modifications, they do not alter their main

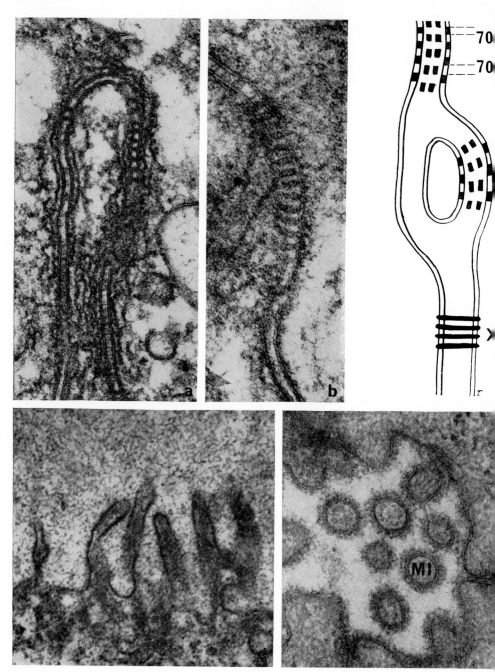

FIG. 3.12. (a) and (b) Septate demosomes in *Littorina* sp. (a) Transverse section. (× 97,000. (b) Oblique section. (× 173,000. Courtesy Dr. G. Owen.) (c) Drawing and dimensions of septa desmosomes in *Cordylophora*. Appearance of septa in oblique section is shown at X. (After Dr. J. Overton.) (d) Microvilli, of irregular form and disposition, on the apical surface of avian thyroid epithelium. (Courtesy J. C. Lewis. × 53,000.) (e) Short, irregularly disposed microvilli (MI) on the surface of cat pancreatic cells. A fuzzy extraneous coat is also evident on the microvillous surface. (Courtesy Dr. L. G. Elfvin. × 90,000.)

morphological characteristics during individual cell activity. The structures commonly associated with this region of the cell are cilia, which also show some extreme form modifications.

Most cells have a by no means level apical surface; it is usually thrown into minor or major undulations. A fixed type of this undulation is a finger-like process, a microvillus (Fig. 3.12d, e). A cell may have very few micro-villi, e.g. thyroid, other gland cells, and bladder epithelium, or a great many packed in parallel array, e.g. 225–1717 per cell in jejunal epithelium, 3000 in intestinal mucosa and 128 per μ^2 in nephron brush border. Generally where few microvilli are present, they are irregular in length, diameter and shape (Fig. 3.12d, e), whereas whenever great numbers occur, the microvilli have a more constant length, diameter, direction and shape over relatively large areas (Fig. 3.13a).

Microvilli are projections which usually have parallel sides and rounded ends. The villi vary in length from a few hundred angstroms to 10 μ and in diameter from 800 to 1400 Å. The gap between microvilli may be as little as 100 Å in striated and brush borders (Fig. 3.13a, b), 1000 Å apart in insect Malpighian tubules (Fig. 3.13c), and some microns in cells which have few microvilli (Fig. 3.12d). The plasma membrane between micro-villi may run transversely, but in the striated border it is sometimes invag-inated in small vesicles, while in the brush border it is often invaginated in this way (Fig. 3.13b).

The microvilli are covered by a unit membrane with a structure common to the plasma membrane elsewhere, except that it is thicker, 100–125 Å, compared to the normal 75 or 95 Å. Furthermore, 20 Å diameter pore-like interruptions in the lateral membrane of the villus have been demonstrated which, on present evidence, do not appear to be artefacts, as the "pores" are widened to 50 Å when microvilli are pretreated with 0·3 N saline for half an hour (Fig. 3.14a–c).

Microvilli are frequently covered with an extraneous granular layer. This is often unevenly distributed over small irregular microvilli, more regu-larly between and over the surface of the intestinal striated border (Fig. 3.13a) and forms an amorphous matrix of considerable electron density between the microvilli of the brush border (Fig. 3.13b). The extraneous coat is thought to be a mucopolysaccharide which is extracted to various degrees during preparative techniques. A more ordered extraneous layer to micro-villi has been observed in mucous cells of the bat, and the intestinal epi-thelium of parasitic nematodes. In the former the microvilli have a nap-like coating of exceedingly fine filaments, although the microvilli of adjacent parietal cells are without such a layer (Fig. 3.15a). In nematodes the micro-villi are covered by fine filaments which originate at the cell surface and lie parallel to the villi (Fig. 3.14f). The filaments are arranged in rows 4–8 deep, aligned together and radiating from a centre which is the microvillus. The filaments are beaded, the adielectronic regions being 130 Å apart. The luminal surface of the intestine is positive for histochemical tests for

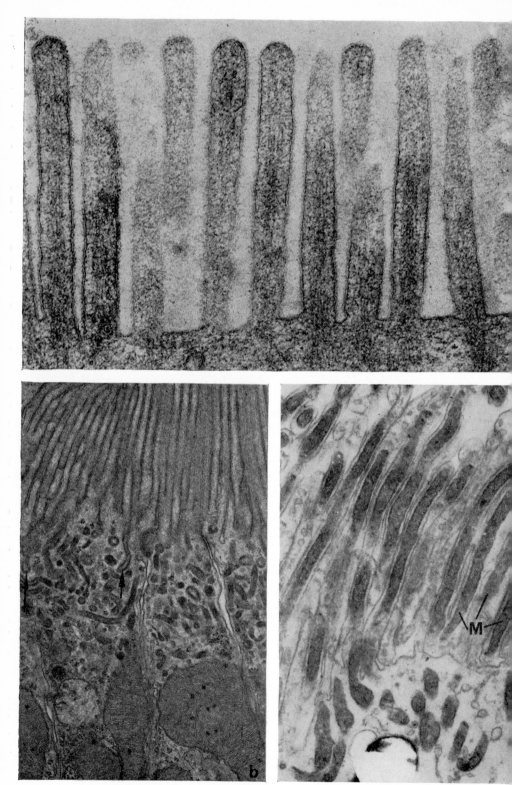

FIG. 3.13. (a) Long, regularly spaced microvilli in the epithelial cells of the mouse intestine. (Courtesy Dr. F. Sjostrand. × 88,000.) (b) Microvillous (brush) border of the epithelial cells of the proximal convoluted tubules of the mouse kidney. Deep invaginations of the plasma membrane arrows) between the microvilli are characteristic. (Courtesy Dr. K. Porter. × 17,000.) (c) Microvilli containing mitochondria (M) from the Malpighian tubule cells of *Rhodnius*. (Courtesy Sir Vincent Wigglesworth. × 20,000.)

mucopolysaccharides, and the filaments are considered to be responsible for the response.

The material in the centre of the microvilli has the same electron density as the cytoplasm and the two are continuous. Its immediate centre, however, has a core of dense tubules, or paired fibres, which project into the apical cytoplasm and join the transverse fibres of the cell web (Fig. 3.14a). At the lateral margins of the cell, the cell web fibres join into the adielectronic material of the zonula adhaerens. The core fibres are also connected to the lateral membranes of the microvillus by fine adielectronic strands (Fig. 3.14b).

In the microvilli of the Malpighian tubules of insects, in which microvilli average 2500 Å in diameter and are 3–10 μ long (*Rhodnius*), their centre is occupied by mitochondria which may almost reach the apex (Fig. 3.13c). There is generally one long mitochondrion per microvillus, but one mitochondrion may have an end in different villi. In addition, profiles of agranular endoplasmic reticulum may run up into the microvilli and are especially prominent when mitochondria are absent.

In addition to the fact that the overall function of the cell determines the abundance or scarcity of microvillus processes, it is thought that the size, shape and perhaps number of microvilli change with cell function. The microvilli obviously increase the area of the apical cell surface and are therefore interpreted as being specialized for absorption or resorption. Nevertheless, the great frequency of microvilli in a variety of cell types suggests that other functions may be involved. Certain observations suggest that microvilli may have contractile properties, e.g. the protoplasmic collar of the sponge choanocyte consists of 30 microvilli which are free at their apices but are fused at their bases into a circlet; the cilia of the mussel gill epithelium and of the ciliated band of sea-urchin larvae are surrounded by 8–11 microvilli; the microvilli of the dividing sea-urchin egg are prominent, densely packed and have their distal ends embedded in a mucopolysaccharide layer. The contractile property of microvilli may reside in the core fibres, and the contraction of these fibres could account for the withdrawal and extension of the choanocyte collar and the movements of the cell surface during cleavage.

The surface of the tegument (cuticle) of cestodes is evaginated into microtriches, which appear to be a type of microvillus (Fig. 3.15b). The microtriches are slender projections of variable length lying approximately parallel to each other. Their distal ends are adielectronic, taper to a point and may show striations, whereas the proximal part is dielectronic. The whole structure is covered by a reflection of the plasma membrane, the inner component of which appears thickened. The centre of the microthrix is filled with an amorphous or finely granular material of variable density and amount. Occasionally, fine fibres run longitudinally down the central core. The base of some microtriches penetrates into the cytoplasm of the tegument, giving the impression of a basal body, though it is doubted that microtriches are ciliary derivatives.

4*

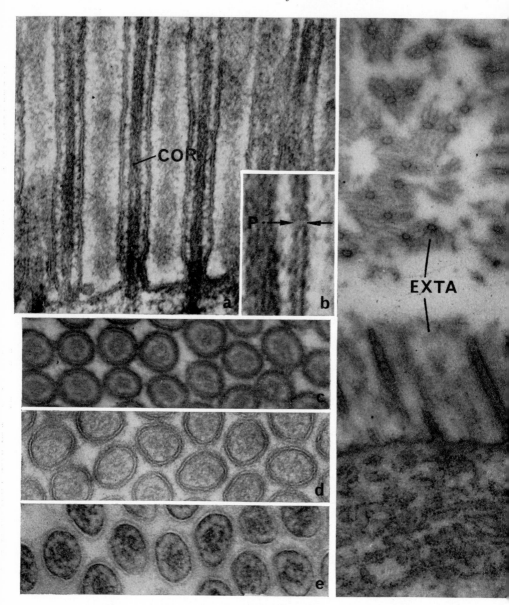

FIG. 3.14. (a) Microvilli from rat intestinal epithelium to show the core (COR) of filaments and the cross-bridges between core and the 102 Å plasma membrane. (× 90,000.)
(b) A 50 Å pore (P) in the plasma membrane of a rat intestinal cell microvillus.
(× 300,000.) (c)–(e) Three photos showing the effect of staining on the appearance of rat intestinal microvilli in cross-section; (c), phosphotungstic acid ; (d) lead monoxide; (e) aqueous uranyl acetate. (All photos × 200,000.) (a–e) Courtesy Dr. P. F. Millington.)
(f) Microvilli of the intestine of the nematode, *Capillaris hepatica.* showing the unusual arrangement of the extraneous material (EXTA). Microvilli are cut longitudinally in the lower part of the photo and transversely in the upper part. (Courtesy Dr. K. Wright. × 45,000.)

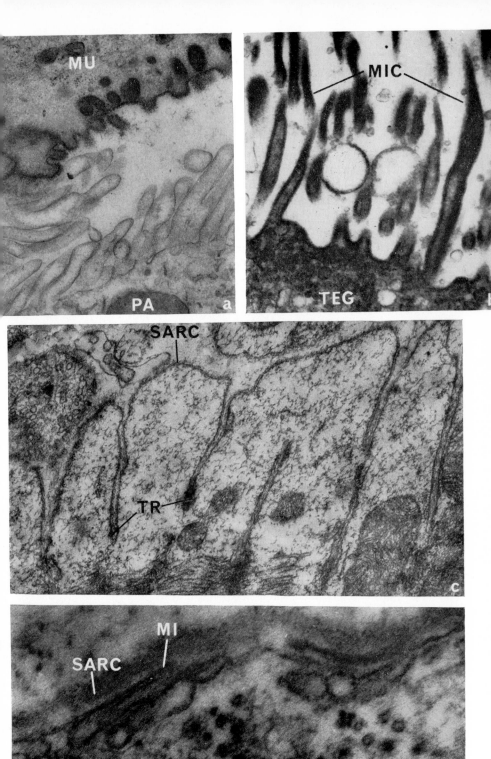

FIG. 3.15. (a) Gastric gland of the bat showing the extraneous coat on the microvilli of the mucous cell (MU) and its absence on the adjacent parietal cell (PA). (Courtesy Dr. S. Ito. ×23,000.) (b) Microtriches (MIC) projecting from the surface of the tegument (TEG) of *Proteocephalus pollanicoli*. (Original. ×23,000.) (c) Surface of rabbit myocardial cell showing sarcolemma (SARC), and transverse process (TR). (Courtesy Drs. D. A. Nelson and E. S. Benson. ×32,000.) (d) The sarcolemma of leech muscle and the microvilli (MI). (Courtesy Dr. I. Pucci. ×106,000.)

Muscle Tissue

As might be expected, muscle cells do not show the range of plasma membrane modifications so characteristic of epithelia. Muscle fibres are often separated by considerable areas of connective tissue, and even when lying close together have reticular fibres between them, although cytoplasmic bridges between smooth muscle cells have been reported. Most authors consider the sarcolemma of light microscopy to be composed of the combined basement membrane, intervening material, and muscle cell plasma membrane; these measure, respectively, 75–200 Å, 150 Å and 75 Å in rabbit and human myocardial cells (Fig. 3.15c), and make a total sarcolemmal thickness of between 300–425 Å. The sarcolemma is thicker in invertebrates, e.g. 570 Å in leech muscle (Fig. 3.15d), than in vertebrates, 100–200 Å in mouse. The closest lateral apposition of two muscle fibres would therefore be about 1000 Å in leech but only 200–400 Å in mouse; in practice it is somewhat less, and such a separation would presumably be equal to the interstitial material between smooth muscle fibres. An additional feature in leech muscle, which is of the helical type (the classification of which as smooth or striated muscle is in dispute), is the presence of microvilli 200–300 Å thick and 1000–3000 Å long. These villi lie parallel to the surface of the muscle cell and do not extend very far from it (Fig. 3.15d).

The sarcolemma is modified in the myocardial and other muscle cells of some vertebrates and invertebrates, and in the flight muscles of some insects. The modification consists of an invagination of the sarcolemma at the level of the Z line of the myofibrils and these penetrate as deep as the nucleus, although they do not contact it. The invaginations are called the transverse system, to distinguish them from the longitudinal system which is the endoplasmic reticulum (sarcoplasmic reticulum) of the muscle fibre (Fig. 3.16a). In cross-section the tubules of the transverse system have a structure like the sarcolemma. In human and rabbit myocardium the system is composed of an inner 75 Å layer, which is the muscle fibre plasma membrane, followed by a dielectronic line 150 Å wide, and an outer zone 75–100 Å wide, similar in appearance to the basement membrane (Fig. 3.15c). Invaginations at adjacent Z lines may be joined together by a tubular connection which runs over the surface of the myofibrils in a longitudinal direction (Fig. 3.16a).

In the asynchronous (fibrillar) flight muscles of some insects the sarcoplasmic reticulum (longitudinal element) is greatly reduced. It is replaced by an extensive tubular system derived from the transverse system which arises, as usual, from invaginations of the sarcolemma (Fig. 3.16b). In some insect species the tubules are abundant, but not orientated with respect to striations of the muscle, whereas in others they lie opposite the M line. In cyclops, the transverse and longitudinal systems are apparently united into one. The system has longitudinal elements between myofilaments and

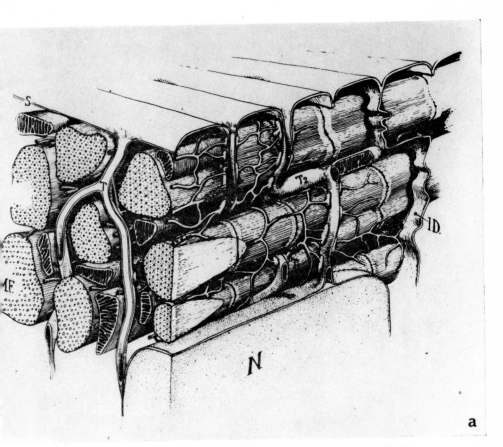

FIG. 3.16. (a) Three-dimensional drawing of a portion of a rabbit myocardial cell. T, transverse process; T_2, longitudinal element joining adjacent transverse processes. (Courtesy Drs. D. A. Nelson and E. S. Benson.) (b) Fibrillar flight muscle of a wasp (*Polistes*) showing the absence of a longitudinal element (sarcoplasmic reticulum). The transverse system (TR) is extensive. (Courtesy Dr. D. Smith. × 14,000.)

myofibrils, and these are connected by transverse tubes at each side of the
Z line (Fig. 3.17). The whole system in cyclops could be interpreted as an
extension of the transverse system, as in the other insects cited above; the
point is still controversial.

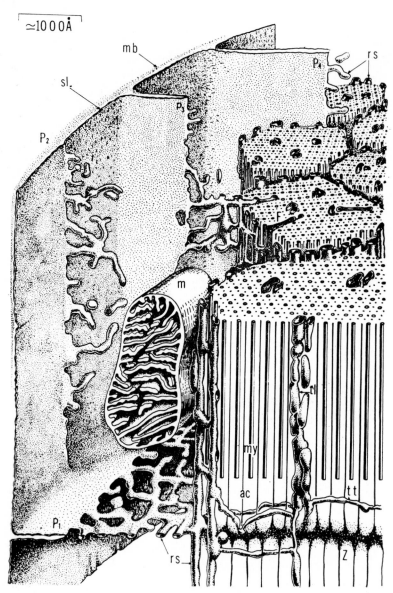

Fig. 3.17. Three-dimensional reconstruction of the muscle of *Cyclops* sp. *ac*, actin
filament; *m*, mitochondrion; *my*, myosin filament; *rs*, sarcoplasmic reticulum; *mb* basement membrane; *sl*, sarcoplasmic membrane; *tl*, longitudinal sarcoplasmic reticulum;
tt, transverse sarcoplasmic reticulum; *P*, transverse processes. (Courtesy Dr. Y.
Bouligand.)

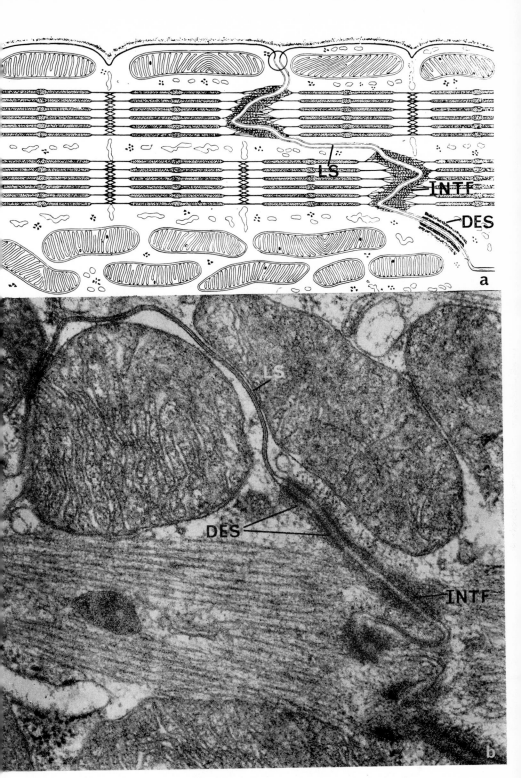

Fig. 3.18. (a) Diagram of the intercalated disc of the guinea-pig cardiac muscle, showing the desmosomes (DES) in the intersarcoplasmic region, the interfibrillar region (INTF), and the longitudinal connecting surfaces (LS). (Courtesy Dr. F. Sjostrand.) (b) Intercalated disc of guinea-pig cardiac muscle. Labels as above. (Courtesy Dr. F. Sjostrand. × 90,000.)

In consequence of this transverse system, the plasma membrane and extracellular fluid penetrate all depths of the myocardial fibre (Fig. 3.16a). On physiological evidence, such as the time relationship between excitation and activation of muscle contraction, and the rate of diffusion of substances into fibres during the latter process, it has been postulated that these transverse processes are concerned with the conduction of action potential and its spread at each Z line. These invaginations at the Z line are related to the sarcoplasmic reticulum, which terminates as bulbous sacs, on each side of the transverse tubule (Fig. 4.5b). This combination of a central sac flanked by two thin-walled sacs is called a triad. The distribution of the sarcoplasmic reticulum will be described under the general heading of endoplasmic reticulum.

Heart muscle has two types of attachment bodies at the intercalated disc, the latter being in reality the opposed apical and basement membranes of two individual muscle fibres. The intercalated disc can be divided into three regions, the interfibrillar region where the longitudinal myofilaments reach the cell surface, the intersarcoplasmic regions which extend over the sarcoplasm which is without myofilaments and contains mitochondria, and the longitudinally connecting surfaces which extend between two steps of an intercalated disc (Fig. 3.18a, b). In the interfibrillar region the cytoplasm contains a regular network of fine filaments extending inwards from the plasma membrane for about 1000 Å. At this point the I band myofilaments fuse with the network, so that the latter appears to be equivalent to a Z line elsewhere (Fig. 3.18a, b). In the intersarcoplasmic regions are desmosomes with the characteristic alternating adielectronic and dielectronic zones, while the longitudinally connecting surfaces have no specializations (Fig. 3.18a, b). In toad myocardium the Z line is intimately related to the dense component of the desmosomes of the intercalated discs. The Z line widens as it approaches the plasma membrane and often terminates beneath it as a characteristic discoidal plate. Because of the relationship of the Z line and the desmosome, it has been suggested that the latter plays a role in both impulse conduction and the splitting and growth of new sarcomeres.

Nervous Tissue

Nervous tissues, because of their very function, make contact with many types of cells and consequently show a variety of plasma membrane specializations. The modifications which have attracted most attention are the synapse, the Schwann cell and myelin, the polyploid border, and the rod cells of the retina; the latter are modified cilia and will be considered under the section on that structure.

The neurilemma is in many ways analogous to the sarcolemma, if it is thought of as the combined Schwann cell plasma membrane and basement membrane, but usually the neurilemma is considered to be the Schwann cell cytoplasm which lies outside the myelin sheath.

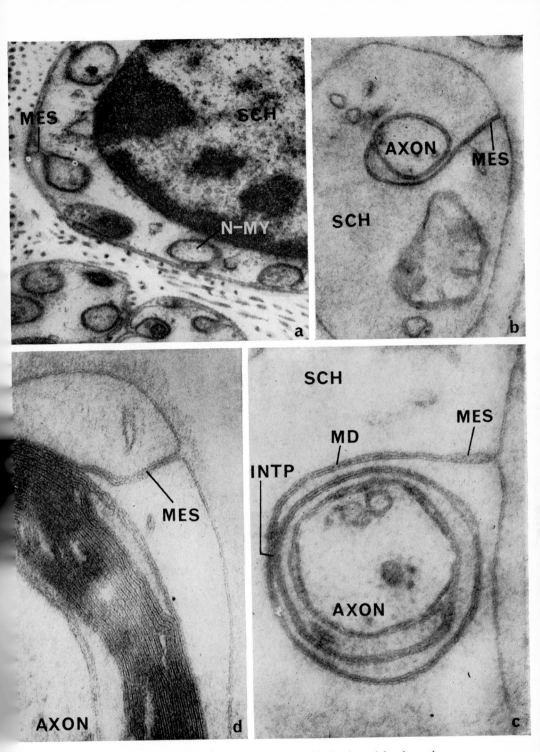

FIG. 3.19. (a) Non-myelinated nerve fibres (N-MY) embedded in the peripheral cytoplasm of a Schwann cell (SCH). MES, mesaxon. (Courtesy the late Dr. H. S. Gasser. ×20.000.) (b)–(d) Development of the myelin sheath during embryogenesis; (b) and (c), mouse sciatic nerve; (d) adult frog sciatic nerve. The major dense line (MD) develops wherever the outer components of the Schwann cell plasma membrane come in contact, and the interperiodic line (INTP) wherever the inner, cytoplasmic components of the Schwann cell plasma membrane come in contact. MES, mesaxon; (b) ×60,000, (c) and (d) ×120,000. (Courtesy Dr. J. D. Robertson.)

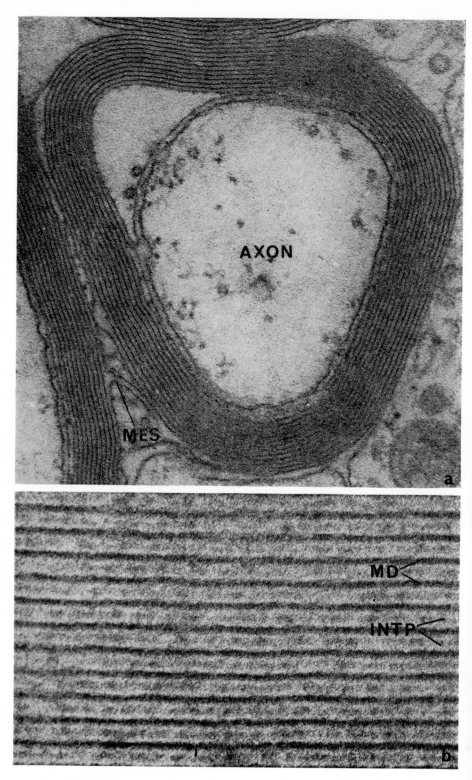

Fig. 3.20. (a) Section of myelin sheath showing its periodicity and mesaxon. (Courtesy Dr. J. Metuzals. × 135,000.) (b) Enlarged part of a myelin sheath showing clearly the major dense line (MD), and the interperiodic line (INTP). (Courtesy Dr. J. D. Robertson. × 480,000.)

Electron-microscope observations show clearly that the neurilemma and myelin sheath are all parts and specializations of the Schwann cell and its plasma membrane.

Both unmyelinated and myelinated nerve fibres are embedded in the Schwann cell (Fig. 3.19a–d). In the unmyelinated fibres the Schwann cell membrane is indented to a greater or lesser extent by the axon and nearly, but never in fact, meets around the nerve (Fig. 3.19a). The almost closed lips formed by the Schwann cell plasma membrane are called the mesaxon. The axon, therefore, is open to the exterior by a narrow channel and is always separated from the Schwann cell by an intercellular zone of a width normal between adjacent cells, approximately 150 Å

In myelinated fibres the relationship of the axon and Schwann cell plasma membrane is very different and more complex, and is most easily understood by a study of the embryological origin of myelin. Initially, the relationship of axon and Schwann cell in young mice is much like that of an unmyelinated fibre (Fig. 3.19b). The axon is surrounded by the Schwann cell, the enclosing arms of which come into close apposition but do not meet. As the axon sinks further into the Schwann cell, the opposed membranes of the latter, which are separated by cement substance, form two parallel lines, so that the whole structure resembles a longitudinal section of a long-necked flask. Subsequently, the neck, or mesaxon, grows and begins to wind around the axon until a number of concentric bilamella rings are formed (Fig. 3.19c, d). The final result is a thick electron-dense ring made up of alternating adielectronic and dielectronic layers (Fig. 3.20a, b). The adielectronic layers, called the periodic line, are 30 Å wide with a repeat period of 110–140 Å.† In the intervening dielectronic layer, which is 80–110 Å thick, there is a thin discontinuous layer with osmium fixation, and a continuous dense layer with formalin–dichromate fixation. This line, which bisects the dielectronic layer is the interperiodic line. The myelin sheath therefore consists of a series of successively thick and thin adielectronic layers, alternating with which are dielectronic layers of only one thickness (Fig. 3.20a).

This characteristic structure of the sheath can be explained with reference to the tripartite structure of the plasma membrane. In the mesaxon the Schwann cell plasma membrane is doubled, due to its invagination, and wherever the outer components of the tripartite membrane meet and fuse, the interperiodic layer is formed, while wherever the inner components of the tripartite plasma membranes meet and fuse, the period layer results (Fig. 3.19b–d). Each side of the periodic line is the dielectronic layer which is the middle lipid layer of the two plasma membranes. It is therefore, the doubling of the Schwann cell plasma membrane by its invagination, and the fusion of inner–inner and outer–outer components of these plasma

† In low angle X-ray diffraction on unfixed myelin, the repeat period is 170 Å on amphibian peripheral nerves, and 180–185 Å on mammalian peripheral nerves. Fresh optic nerves of amphibia have a repeat period of 160 Å.

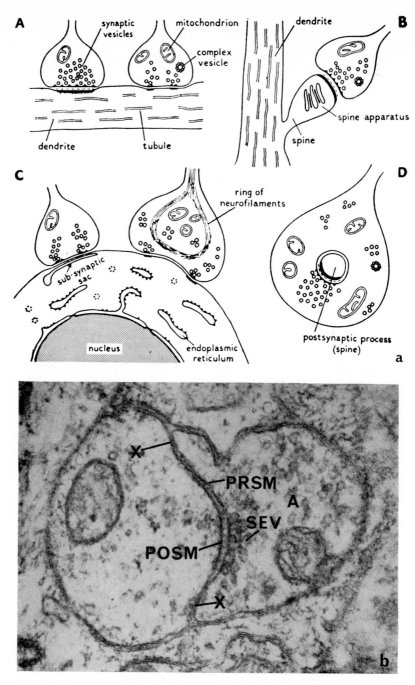

FIG. 3.21. (a) Drawing of various types of synapses. A, left, Type 1 axodendritic synapse; right, Type 2 axodendritic synapse. B, synapse with dendritic spine (see Fig. 3.22b). C, left, axosomatic synapse with narrow sac in the sub-synaptic cytoplasm; D, axosomatic synapse with post-synaptic spine invaginating the pre-synaptic process. (Courtesy Dr. E. G. Gray.) (b) A pentapartite junction in the synapse between a pre-ganglionic fibre (A), and a cell process (at X); SEV, synaptic vesicles; PRSM, presynaptic membrane; POSM, postsynaptic membrane. (Courtesy Dr. L. G. Elfvin. × 82,000.)

membranes whenever they meet, that produce the adielectronic layers of two different thicknesses, alternating with a dielectronic layer of only one thickness.

Another prominent modification of the plasma membrane of nervous tissues is the synapse, which includes such structures as the boutons terminaux, the neuromuscular junction, and the axo-axinal junction of invertebrates. All these synapses have features in common and consist of two parts, the effector presynaptic component and the receptor postsynaptic component (Fig. 3.21). The glial and Schwann cells do not cover the actual synapse where the plasma membranes of the pre- and postsynaptic compononents are closely opposed. The presynaptic component contains either numerous (mossy fibres of cerebellum), few (ventral acoustic ganglia), or no (retinal rod–bipolar cell synapse) mitochondria, some endoplasmic reticulum, some or no, neuroprotofibrils, and always the synaptic vesicles. The vesicles are round or oval, 200–650 Å in diameter, and are enclosed in a limiting membrane 40–50 Å thick (Fig. 3.21). These bodies are confined almost exclusively to the presynaptic side of the synapse, but may be observed apparently fused with the presynaptic plasma membrane, or discharging their contents into the intersynaptic cleft between the presynaptic plasma membrane (PRSM) and the postsynaptic plasma membrane (POSM). Some few synaptic vesicles may occur in the cleft or as ghosts in the cytoplasm of the postsynaptic component, having presumably migrated through the PRSM and the cleft. The number of vesicles alters with nerve stimulation, and within the presynaptic component the vesicles may be either homogeneously distributed or be localized at the extreme distal part of the termination. The vesicles are presumed to contain acetylcholine and possibly other chemical substances, but this is not proven. In addition to synaptic vesicles, so-called complex vesicles occur in mossy fibres and cat spinal cord boutons and are composed of a central sphere within a shell of smaller particles; the nature of such complex vesicles is unknown (Fig. 3.22c).

Both the pre- and postsynaptic membranes are about 60 Å wide and are separated by a cleft which is 120–200 Å wide, although in the neuromuscular junction it is 500 Å. With recent techniques the PRSM and POSM are 70–75 Å thick and asymmetrical, and the cleft is 60–70 Å, although in places the two membranes are fused, forming a pentapartite layered unit about 140–150 Å thick (Fig. 3.21b). The PRSM and POSM appear thicker and more adielectronic throughout the length of the apposition than elsewhere, due to a zone of associated dense material 100–400 Å wide on the inner side of the plasma membranes (Fig. 3.21). In addition, localized adielectronic regions 1500–2000 Å long occur where synaptic vesicles lie very close to the PRSM. In the internal hair cells of the cochlea there is, internal to the PRSM, a synaptic ribbon of electron-dense granular material covered by a single layer of synaptic vesicles (Fig. 3.22a). Generally, the cytoplasm of the postsynaptic component has no specializations other than those already mentioned.

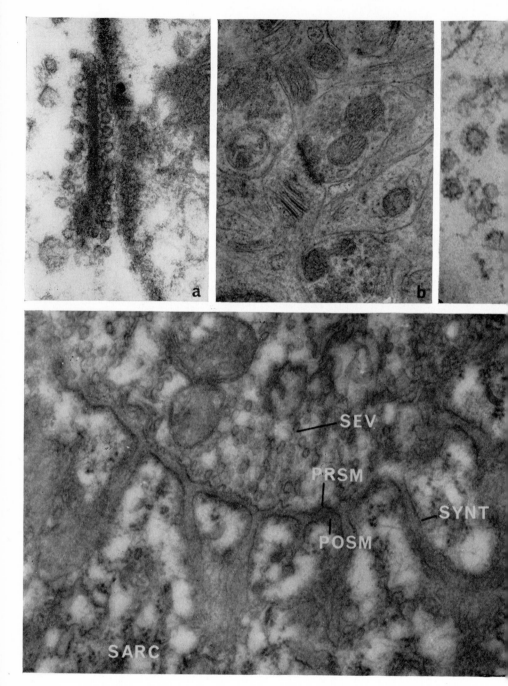

Fig. 3.22. (a) Synaptic ribbon in a cochlea hair cell synapse. (Courtesy Dr. G. A. Smith. × 96,000.) (b) Dendritic spine synapse. (Courtesy Dr. E. G. Gray. × 60,000.) (c) Complex synaptic vesicles. (Courtesy Dr. E. G. Gray. × 60,000.) (d) Cross-section of neuro-muscular junction showing synaptic troughs formed by invaginations of the postsynaptic membrane into the sarcoplasm. SEV, synaptic vesicles; PRSM, presynaptic membrane; POSM, postsynaptic membrane; SYNT, synaptic trough; SARC, sarcoplasm. (Courtesy Dr. G. M. Lehrer. × 70,000.)

In the bouton and axo-axon types of synapse the opposed plasma membranes are virtually straight. In other synapses, however, considerable modifications occur. In the neuromuscular junction the postsynaptic membrane is invaginated into finger-like projections, 800 Å in diameter and 7000 Å long, which form channels running transversely across the elongated axon (Fig. 3.22d). In the bipolar cell synapses of rods and cones, the dendrites of the bipolar cells penetrate deeply into indentations of the presynaptic membrane. In addition, the presynaptic membrane has small microvillus-like invaginations at the tip of the major indentations, and around the former great numbers of synaptic vesicles accumulate. In invertebrates, where neutrophiles are formed (great numbers of synaptic contacts per unit volume), because of the scant glial elements and blood vessels, the presynaptic membrane of the axo-axonic synapse may be indented in a broad region by the postsynaptic membrane.

Some axodendritic and axosomatic synapses do not have thickened postsynaptic membranes. In the spinal cord axosomatic synapses no thickening of the pre- or postsynaptic membranes occurs; instead a flattened sac lies just below the postsynaptic membrane (Fig. 3.21a). In the central nervous system dendritic spinous processes are about $3\cdot0\ \mu$ long and are in reality synapses. In the mammalian cerebral cortex, but in no other site in vertebrates, the spinous process contains a spine apparatus consisting of a series of flattened sacs with a dense plate between each pair (Fig. 3.22b).

The origin of the synaptic vesicles seems to reside in the cell body of the neurone. The vesicles appear to arise in the Golgi region of the neurone, and as the axoplasm flows along the axon, it carries the synaptic vesicles with it. The vesicles eventually accumulate in the synapse and are used as required. It is not known by what mechanism new vesicles are caused to be produced upon the exhaustion of the vesicles in the synapse itself. Perhaps a steady rate of production is maintained, and steady axoplasmic flow ensures a constant supply in the synaptic termination.

Another modification which appears in nervous tissue is the polyploid border of the epithelial cells of the choroid plexus. In many ways it resembles a microvillus border, but the evaginations are less packed and do not have long parallel sides. The polyploid processes are flask-shaped, with expanded ends, some balloon-like, and give the appearance of a random arrangement. The material within the processes is generally homogeneous, of low electron density, and without a core structure (Fig. 3.23a).

Connective Tissue

The cells of this tissue have very few permanent modifications of their plasma membrane, and those they do possess have been described already under the headings for other tissues. Connective tissues are characterized as much by the matrix in which the cells lie, as by the morphology of the cells themselves. The cells are usually relatively widely separated by matrix,

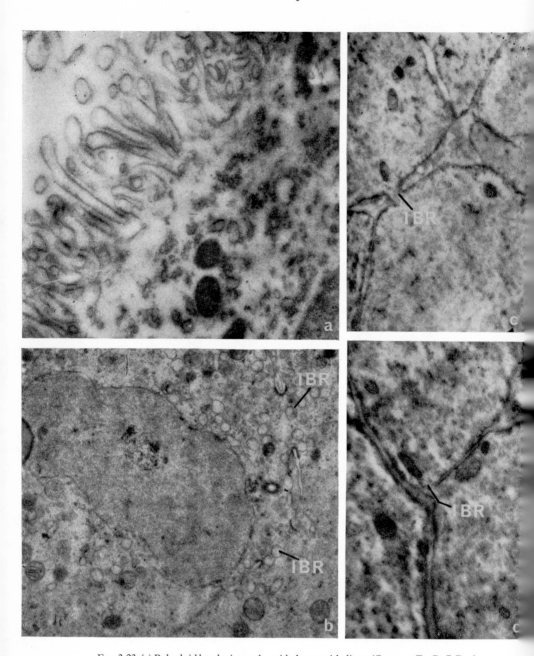

FIG. 3.23. (a) Polyploid border in rat choroid plexus epithelium. (Courtesy Dr. R. C. Buck. × 30,000.) (b) Intercellular bridges (IBR) between spermatids of the domestic chicken. (Courtesy Dr. T. Nagano. × 12,000.) (c) and (d) Intercellular bridges (IBR) between smooth muscle cells; (c) × 10,000. (d) × 20,000. (Courtesy Dr. J. C. Thamert.)

and plasma membrane features, which the close attachment of adjacent cells necessitates, are consequently rare. Small microvilli are common in the fluid or semi-fluid matrices, and some areas of the plasma membrane are poorly defined in relation to that matrix; this is to be expected from the known relationship between cell and matrix, the latter being a product of the former.

Intercellular Bridges

In addition to the plasma membrane attachment zones already detailed under epithelial tissues, true intercellular bridges occur in some cells, with protoplasmic continuity between neighbouring cells. The smooth muscle cells of the gastro-intestinal tract of rats are connected by tubular bridges, 400–500 Å long and 1000–7000 Å in diameter (Fig. 3.23c–d). They are transitional structures, for reforming plasma membranes can be observed between some muscle cells. The bridges do not contain any cytoplasmic inclusions. A similar situation is seen in the smooth muscle of the rat uterus. Protoplasmic bridges which contain endoplasmic reticulum, and mitochondria are present between developing male germ cells of many vertebrates (Fig. 3.23b), of *Drosophila,* and the cnidoblasts of *Hydra.* There is one bridge for each pair of cells, and these have a C-shape in longitudinal section. The bridges exist from the first spermatocyte until the spermatid stage, when they break. The intercellular bridges of smooth muscle are thought to be an adaptation to facilitate conduction of action potentials, while in germ cells they would ensure synchronized development of all spermatozoa derived from a single primary spermatocyte.

Structures Associated with the Plasma Membrane

Two structures associated with the plasma membrane, and which appear in a wide variety of animal species and tissues are the cilium and the flagellum. Cilia and flagella, excluding the flagella of some vertebrate spermatozoa, are essentially similar in structure, and therefore the term cilia only will be used in the text to include both cilia and flagella. The additional morphological features of mammalian and other vertebrate sperm flagella will be discussed in a later chapter.

The cilium consists of a shaft projecting above the surface of the plasma membrane and a basal body which is intracellular and is the kinetic centre and origin of the free portion. The shaft is covered by a membrane 90 Å thick, which is continuous with the plasma membrane elsewhere. Internally is a matrix of medium adielectronicity containing the axial filament complex which is a set of 11 longitudinal fibres running straight down the shaft without coiling (Fig. 3.24a). Exceptions to this number of 11 in the axial complex do occur, e.g. ctenophore swimming plates have a complex of 12 fibres, 2 central tubular fibres and an associated compact fibre, the

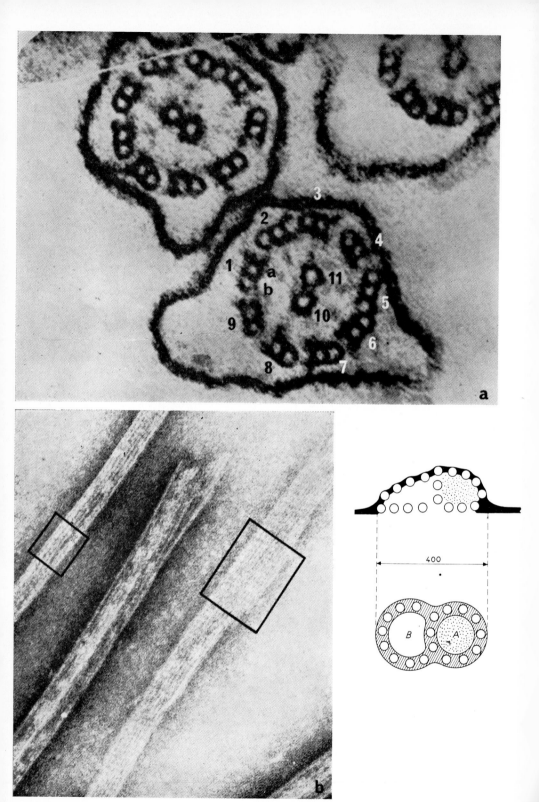

FIG. 3.24. (a) Cross-section of sperm flagellum from *Psammechinus*. The peripheral axial filaments are numbered 1–9, and the central axial filaments 10 and 11. The two subfibres of which each peripheral axial filament is composed are labelled a and b. (Courtesy Dr. B. Afzelius. ×225,000.) (b) Axial filaments from ruptured human spermatozoa. 10 or 11 protofibrils making up each axial filament can be seen in the marked areas. Negative staining. (Courtesy Dr. J. Andre. ×200,000.) (c) Drawing of the arrangement of the protofibrils within the A and B subfibres of a peripheral axial filament. *Above,* after negative staining; *below,* after OsO₄ fixation and sectioning. (Courtesy Dr. J. Andre.)

midfilament (Fig. 3.26a). Where 11 fibres are present, they are divided into two groups; first a pair of central fibres each 200 Å in diameter, which always lie so that the line passing through their centres is at right angles to the direction of the ciliary beat (Fig. 3.24a). The central fibres are circular in cross-section and have a tubular appearance due to the adielectronicity of their walls, 50–70 Å thick, and their dielectronic centre. Second are the 9 peripheral fibres encircling the central pair. These doublet fibres, with a figure of 8 configuration, lie with their long axis at a 5–10° angle to a line drawn tangential to the ciliary surface at a point opposite to the doublet fibre. The long axis of the doublets is 300–500 Å, and the short axis 180–220 Å. Each doublet is about 500 Å from its neighbours and is composed of two fused subfibres, designated *a* and *b* (Fig. 3.24a). The *a* subfibre lies nearer the centre of the cilium than the subfibre *b*, has a smaller diameter and is characterized by 2 projecting arms which face clockwise.† In longitudinal section the arms are small rectangles 150 Å long and 50 Å wide, separated from each other by a space 130 Å long. The *b* subfibres are larger and less electron dense than the *a* and lie closer to the ciliary membrane.

The central and peripheral axial components are themselves composite, consisting of 35 Å solid protofibrils, 18 to each peripheral fibre and 10 to each central one. There is some evidence that the protofibrils have an oblique periodicity (Fig. 3.24b, c).

Some additional structural features are revealed by high resolution microscopy; first a curved adielectronic line from one central fibre to the other, giving an oval profile. In longitudinal section these connecting fibres are slanted and therefore must be a fine filament coiled around the central fibres. The second feature is spokes apparently joining peripheral to central fibres. In some instances, however, the spokes are replaced by a ring of 9 small solid fibres between the outer 9 doublets and the inner central fibres; these are considered to be secondary fibres by some researchers (Fig. 3.25). Finally, in ctenophore swimming plates the 3rd and 8th peripheral fibres are connected to the ciliary membrane by compartmentalizing lamellae which divide the cross-section of the cilium into two unequal parts (Fig. 3.26a).

There is differentiation within the length of the cilium with regard to the fibrils. Towards the ciliary tip the peripheral fibres end at different levels, while the central fibres stop a short distance beyond the peripheral. At the base, the axial filment complex shows differences with the animal group. In molluscs and amphibia all fibres end in a distinct transverse basal plate, which is separated from the basal body by a narrow dielectronic zone (Fig. 3.26b). In mammals and protozoa the peripheral fibres pass through

---

† A method of indexing the peripheral fibres has been devised. A line is drawn through the centres of the two central fibres and a second line is drawn at right angles to the first, running between the two central fibres. This second line will run through an unpaired fibre, called No. 1, and between fibres numbered 5 and 6. This indexing may fail if the 2 central fibres are distorted over 20° in relation to the peripheral fibres (Fig. 3.24a).

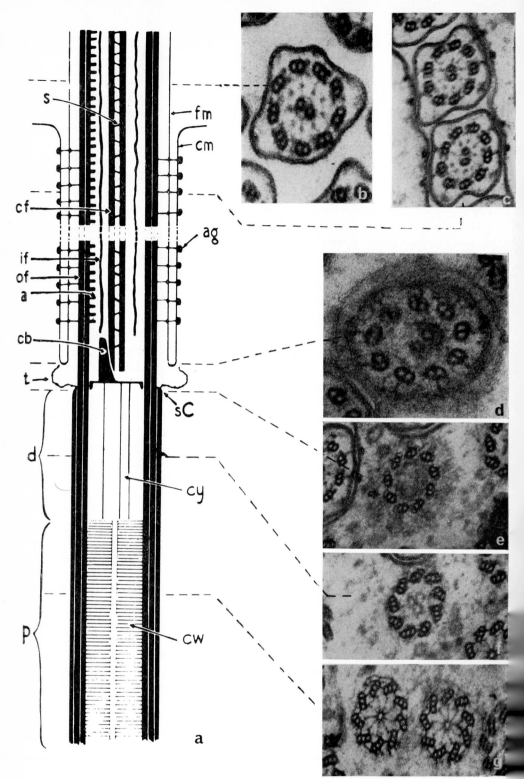

Fig. 3.25. Cilium of *Pseudotrichonympha*. (a) Drawing of a longitudinal section of the cilium. (b)–(g) Electron micrographs of appropriate cross-sections. (Courtesy Dr. I. R. Gibbons. All photos × 95,000, except (d) which is × 140,000.) *a*, arms; *ag* anchor granule; *bp*, basal plate; *cf*, central fibre; *cb*, crescentic body; *cm*, cell membrane; *cw*, cartwheel structure; *d*, distal region of basal body; *fm*, flagellar membrane; *if*, inner fibre; *of*, outer fibre; *p*, proximal region of basal body; *s*, central sheath; *sC*, distal end of subfibre C; *sf*, secondary fibre; *t*, transitional fibre.

the basal plate and join the basal body, so the basal plate and basal body are in contact (Fig. 3.26b). The central fibres may either (a) stop at, or a short distance before, the basal plate, (b) pass through the basal plate and form either a deep loop in the central cavity of the basal body, or join on to an 800 Å diameter axial granule situated in the upper part of the basal body (*Opalina* and some other ciliates). In *Trichonympha* and *Pseudotrichonympha* one central filament ends 250 Å from the basal plate and the other joins on to a crescentric body situated off centre, and which projects a short distance from the basal plate (Fig. 3.25).

The basal bodies are embedded in the cytoplasm immediately below the basal plate and the cell surface (Fig. 3.26b). They are in straight parallel rows when numerous and exhibit variations in form. The simplest form of basal body is about 3000–5000 Å long and 1200–1500 Å in diameter, with a cylindrical shape. In mollusca and amphibia one end of the cylinder is closed either by the basal plate or another plate separated from the basal plate; the other end is open (Fig. 3.26b). The cylinder walls are composed of 9 triplet fibres with a tube-like appearance. At the basal plate end, the triplets almost delimit the circumference of a circle, but towards the other end the triplets rotate 30–50° to form a pinwheel (Fig. 3.25). The two outer fibres of the triplet are continuous, or in line with, the *a* and *b* subfibres of the cilium, and the additional fibre is outside the *b* subfibre and is designated the *c* subfibre. The *a* subfibre of each triplet is joined to the *c* subfibre of the next triplet by a 45 Å thick adielectronic line (Fig. 3.25).

Modifications of this simple system are as follows:

(a) The lower end of the basal body is closed and forms a curved structure in which the triplets intermingle and are irregular in direction—mammalian cilia (Fig. 3.26b).

(b) Fibrous rootlets attached to the closed curved inner end of the basal body. One, two or more rootlets may occur, 600–1600 Å in diameter, and striated, with a periodicity of between 550–700 Å (Fig. 3.27a). The dark bands are 200–450 Å wide and the light about the same, but bisected by a narrow adielectronic line. Mitochondria lie very close to the rootlets in ascidians and rotifers, the cristae of the mitochondria being lined up with the adielectronic parts of the fibres, suggesting the latter may have other functions besides that of anchorage (Fig. 3.27b). Rootlets are not well developed in vertebrates, *Rana* excepted, but do appear commonly in invertebrates.

(c) The interior of the basal body contains structures of a variety of types. In *Pseudotrichonympha* the region immediately below the basal plate has a large central triplet of triangular form, while further down this triplet is replaced by a single small fibre to which the *a* subfibre of each peripheral triplet is joined by an electron-dense line, to give a complex cartwheel (Fig. 3.25). In other organisms either small adielectronic bodies, intrabasal granules, occur centrally, or the cavity is packed with 200–300 Å granules,

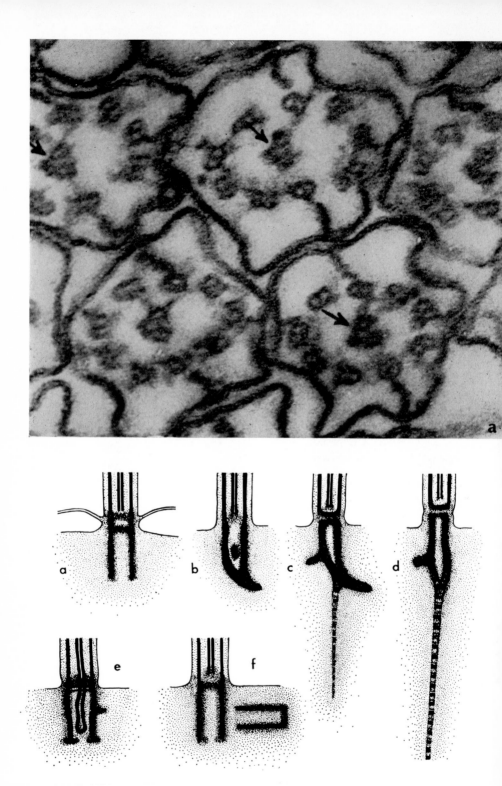

Fig. 3.26. (a) Cilia from a ctenophore swimming plate showing a triplet of central filaments (arrows) and the union of peripheral filaments 3 and 8, with the plasma membrane. (Courtesy Dr. B. Afzelius. ×270,000.) (b) Various types of basal bodies. *a, Paramecium* simple cylinder open below; *b,* Mammalian cilium simple cylinder with closed base; *c, Rana* asymmetrical type with rootlet fibre (RTF); *d, Elliptio* asymmetrical type with rootlet fibre (RTF); *e, Euplotes* central axial filament continues into basal plate; *f, Hydra* gastrodermis centriole at right angles to basal body. (Courtesy Dr. D. Fawcett.)

or paired central fibres project into the basal body lumen and fuse to form a loop (Fig. 3.26b).

Basically, therefore, all motile cilia have a ciliary membrane enclosing an axial complex of two central and nine peripheral fibres, a basal plate and basal body. Other ciliary types exist, however, such as kinetodesmosomal fibres, infraciliary lattice systems, infraciliary rods, retrociliary fibres and hispid flagellae.†

There are some ciliary derivatives in which the basic pattern is modified and fibres are lost or extensively altered, with a consequent loss of motility. These differentiated cilia are often, but not always, sensory in function. Solitary cilia are commonly found in connective tissue cells, epithelial cells of the renal collecting tubules, thyroid epithelia, B cells of the pancreas, neurosecretory cells and cells of the hypophysis. In all cases the paired central fibres are absent from the shaft, an observation that adds support to the idea that the peripheral fibres are concerned with conduction and the central ones with contraction. The sensory function of such solitary cilia is doubtful.

Two extreme modifications of ciliary structure are the crown cell processes of the saccus vasculosus in the 3rd ventricle of the brain of fish and the photoreceptors (retinal rods and cones) of vertebrates. The crown cells have short club-shaped processes projecting from their free surface, the base of such processes having a typical basal body with two short cross-striated rootlets. From the basal body fibres run a short distance into the process where they appear to end blindly. The ends of the clubs contain many small vesicles, some apparently empty and others filled with a homogeneous adielectronic material. The function of these crown cells is unknown.

The photoreceptive cells of the vertebrate eye can be subdivided into four regions, commencing with the point farthest from the source of light: (a) cell body with nucleus, (b) an inner segment, (c) a connecting "neck", (d) an outer segment. The cell body and inner segment do not concern us here, but the "neck" and outer segment are ciliary derivatives. Immediately below the base of the neck is a centriole lying at right angles to the basal body, the latter being orientated normally, e.g. with its long axis parallel with the long sides of the "neck". The basal body contains no central fibres, but only the nine peripheral fibres which pass up the "neck" and into the outer segment for a short distance, where they terminate (Fig. 3.28a).

The outer segment is made up of closely packed piles of flattened sacs (double membrane discs), resembling a stack of coins separated from each other by a distance which varies with species, e.g., 150 Å in toad and 120 Å in mouse (Fig. 3.28a, b). The flattened sacs are formed by successive narrow invaginations of the plasma membrane up the length of the outer segment, on all its sides except for a narrow region into which the abortive ciliary fibres penetrate. The flattened sacs are 150 Å thick, being formed by the

† See additional reading list.

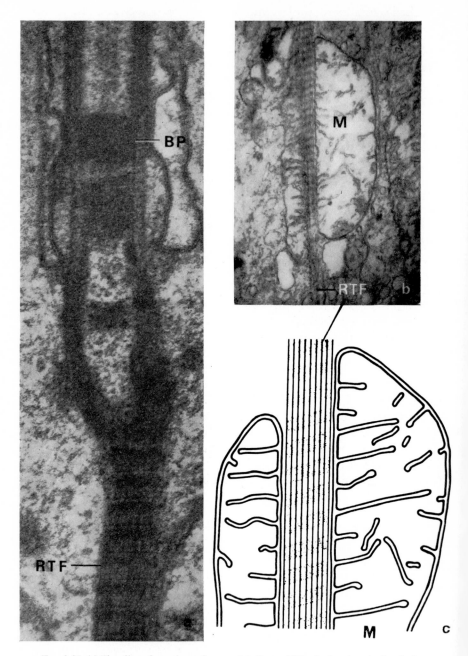

Fig. 3.27. (a) Flagellum from the style sac epithelium of *Nucula* showing the basal plate (BP), and rootlet fibres (RTF) with periodicity. (Courtesy Dr. G. Owen. × 142,000.) (b) Ciliary rootlet fibres of the endostyle of the lancet, *Amphioxus*. The cristae of the associated mitochondria are aligned with the periodicity of the fibres (RTF) as in (c). (Courtesy Dr. R. Olsson. × 25,000.)

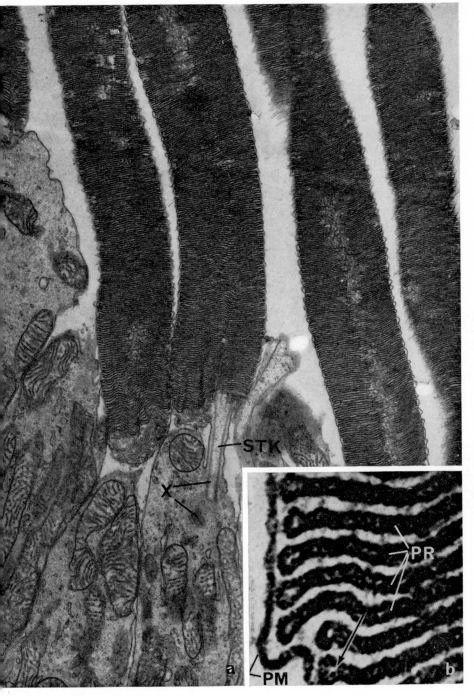

FIG. 3.28. (a) Photoreceptors of the retina of the Kangaroo rat, *Dipodomys ordi*. The outer segment of the rod cells (upper part of photo) are connected to the inner segment by a stalk (STK). The outer segment is a modified cilium, the basal plate and centriole of which can be seen at X. (Courtesy Dr. K. Porter. × 20,000.) (b) Enlarged part of an outer segment showing the stacks of paired membranes (PR) which resemble a pile of coins; PM, plasma membrane. (Courtesy Dr. H. Fernandez-Moran. × 200,000.)

5

adhesion of two unit membranes with the typical tripartite structure (Fig. 3.28b). In section, therefore, the sacs appear quintuple, a central adielectronic layer being flanked on both sides by dielectronic and adielectronic layers, respectively. The paired unit membranes are not always in contact, however, with the resulting central dielectronic gap making the sacs seven-layered instead of five. The gap is about 20 Å for cones and 30 Å for rods in the toad. The inner termination of the sacs is always rounded into a hairpin loop, and the spaces between the paired membranes are thought to contain an aqueous ionic medium.

Studies of the development of the outer segment in vertebrate rods have shown that the primitive cilium first develops by evagination from the surface of the cell and its apical end becomes swollen and contains vesicles. The next stage is a great enlargement of the apical end of the cilium by the formation of more vesicles and cisternae, due to the infolding of the plasma membrane in an asymmetrical manner on only three sides of the evagination. These vesicles flatten and become arranged in piles of sacs separated by a distance which is variable. In rod cells not all the sacs show a connection with the plasma membrane on their outer side, either because the connection between plasma membrane and sac is narrow, or the sacs are actually pinched off.

The rhabdomes of arthropods and octupuses closely resemble the outer segment of the vertebrate rods and cones. Instead of the sacs, however, the rhabdome consists of densely packed microvilli of the retinal cells. The villi lie perpendicular to the direction of light and in longitudinal section, therefore, the rhabdome consists of a series of hexagonally arranged "tubules", whose walls are tripartite unit membranes. Where adjacent "tubules" touch, the outer dense component of each tripartite unit membrane fuses into a 40 Å adielectronic line. The interior of the "tubules" has a dielectronicity similar to that of the cytoplasm. An abortive cilium runs up into the outer segment as in vertebrate rods and cones.

Functional Activity of the Plasma Membrane

As the plasma membrane is the immediate contact between the cell and its environment, the frequent observations of activity by this structure are only to be expected. The maintenance of the cellular environment requires the active ingestion of larger particles and of solutes by cell "drinking", as well as active and passive transport across the plasma membrane of ions and molecules. The active or passive passage of ions and molecules, although probably accounting for the major part of the exchanges between cell and environment, cannot be visualized by electron microscopy at present, so that only the former type of cell uptake can be illustrated here.

Although it is probable that all modes of vesicle formation by the plasma membrane have a basic cause, slight differences in the morphological events

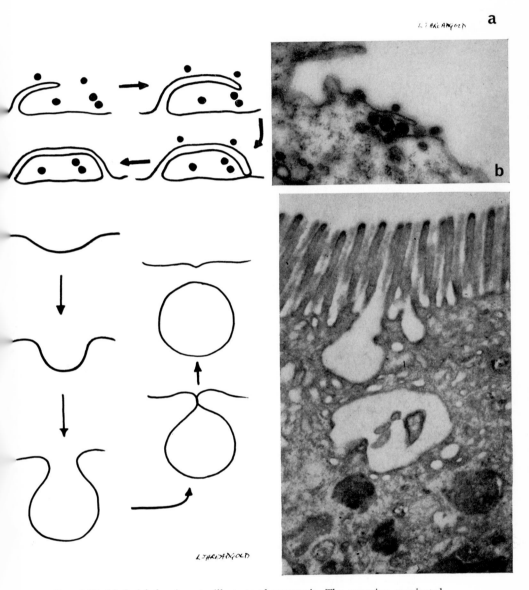

Fig. 3.29. (a) Serial drawings to illustrate phagocytosis. The opposing evaginated pseudopodia eventually fuse and trap the particle. (Original.) (b) Photo and drawing of pinocytosis. The photo shows pinocytosis of erythrocyte fragments by a macrophage. (Courtesy Dr. E. Essener. × 28,000. Original drawing.) (c) Photo and drawing to illustrate micropinocytosis. The photo shows micropinocytosis of a protein solution by the brush border epithelium of the mouse intestine. (Courtesy Dr. S. L. Clark. × 18,000.)

leading to the formation of one type of intracellular vacuole when compared to another, has led to the classification of these processes.

Phagocytosis (cell "eating") is the ingestion of large particles, i.e. bacteria, protozoa, etc., and leads to relatively large vacuoles. The attachment of the particle to the cell surface has been considered an important step in this process, but does not always occur. The particle is engulfed by the formation of pseudopodia, and the cytoplasmic membranes eventually fuse to give a membrane-limited vacuole (Fig. 3.29a). Invagination of the cell surface does not appear to play an important part in phagocytosis, as it does in some other types of vacuole formation.

Pinocytosis (cell "drinking"), as originally described, is the formation of very active membranous fringes or veils by the cell surface, and these occasionally fall back on to the cell, thus trapping a droplet and incorporating it into the cytoplasm (Fig. 3.29b). The range of pinocytotic vacuoles is wide, being $1\cdot0$–$2\cdot0$ μ in *Amoeba* and tissue culture cells, as observed by the light microscope, and $0\cdot1$–$0\cdot01$ μ as observed by electron microscopy.

Micropinocytosis and rhopheocytosis (cell aspiring) differ from the two types of vacuole formation already mentioned, because they do not involve the formation of pseudopodia or veils of cytoplasm. In both cases the plasma membrane invaginates into the cytoplasm, eventually drawing together the lateral sides of the depression until a vacuole is pinched off (Figs. 3.29c; 3.30a–c). The vacuole may be just below the cell surface or at the end of a deep narrow channel. The difference between micropinocytosis and rhopheocytosis is that the attachment of the macromolecule to the plasma membrane is an essential feature of the latter process; the inclusion of liquids along with the attached particles is incidental (Fig. 3.30a, b). In micropinocytosis, liquids and/or solids are incorporated into vacuoles without prior attachment to the plasma membrane (Fig. 3.29c). There is considerable confusion in the use of the term pinocytosis, micropinocytosis and rhopheocytosis. Pinocytosis is often used to describe the formation of any small vacuole by invagination of the cell surface, whether or not prior attachment to the plasma membrane occurs. Strictly used, the term pinocytosis requires the formation of a veil of cytoplasm. The distinction between micropinocytosis and rhopheocytosis is perhaps academic, as some form of attachment or contact with the plasma membrane, whether that attachment is visible or not, must be involved in both cases, in order to stimulate invagination. If used precisely, micropinocytosis would involve the formation of a veil at the ultrastructural level, in which case it would be only a specialized type of pinocytosis. The term rhopheocytosis could then be limited to vacuole formation by invagination. Current usage, however, suggests that pinocytosis or micropinocytosis will become the universal term for the formation of any vacuoles by the plasma membrane.

Cytopemphis, or podocytosis, is the origin of vacuoles in a manner identical to that of rhopheocytosis, but it is thought that the vacuoles so formed cross the cytoplasm intact and are discharged at another cell surface without benefiting the cytoplasm. This process is very evident in endothelial cells (Fig. 3.30c).

The vacuoles derived by any of these methods are always bounded by a single membrane, and therefore their contents must be considered to be still extracellular. Until the enclosing membrane breaks down, or the

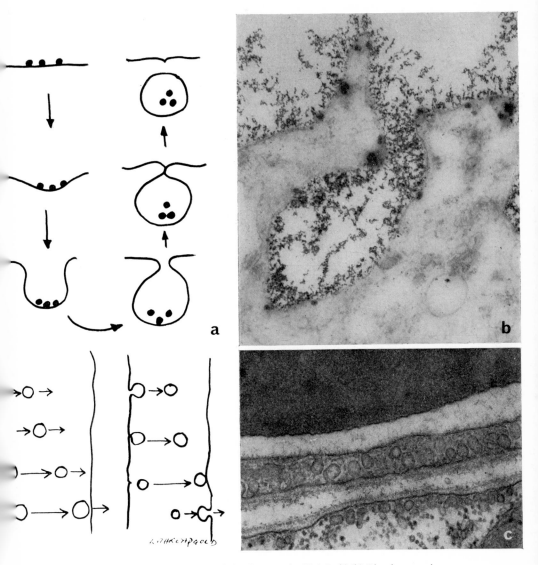

Fig. 3.30. (a) Drawing of the process of rhopheocytosis. (Original.) (b) Rhopheocytosis in *Amoeba*. Thorium dioxide particles are attached to the extraneous coat of the plasma membrane and this attachment apparently induces invagination of the plasma membrane. (Courtesy Drs. P. Brandt and G. D. Pappas. × 25,000. Original drawing.) (c) Photo and drawing illustrating cytopemphis. The photo shows cytopemphis in the endothelium of capillaries of the rat thyroid. (Courtesy Dr. S. L. Wissig. × 48,000. Original drawing.)

substance within diffuses through into the cytoplasm, the vacuolar contents cannot be metabolized. In most cases the vacuolar membrane appears to persist, and as its breakdown cannot be observed by electron microscopy, it is only inferred. It is probable that the characteristics of the membrane are changed by enzyme or other action once the vacuole is within the cell, so that the enclosed solutes can diffuse out quite readily, and more solid particles are perhaps subjected to the action of cell enzymes which have diffused into the vacuole. Doubtless, vacuoles lose water and shrink, so concentrating their contents.

An excellent example of the origin of vacuoles by the plasma membrane, and their subsequent fate, can be observed during erythrophagocytosis by macrophages, phagocytosis by macrophages in the lung, and micropino-cytosis in the developing oocytes of mosquitoes.

Phagocytosis by macrophages follows the same pattern, whether these cells are in the lung or in haemaorrhagic fluid. The substances to be phago-cytosed, either fragments of erythrocytes or inert particles, come to lie either very close to, or actually on contact with the plasma membrane. The substances may occur singly, or in small groups, but in either case the plasma membrane shows increased electron density at the point of attach-ment, indicating structural and/or physiological alteration. The proximity or attachment of the particle apparently acts as an inducer for the formation of thin irregular pseudopodia; sometimes only one pseudopodium is formed, when the process could rightly be called pinocytosis. The pseudo-podium, or veil, eventually falls back on the cell, or two pseudopodia meet to give rise to an intracellular vacuole or a string of vacuoles. The fate of these vacuoles is not known. In erythrophagocytosis, the vacuoles do not contact other cell organoids, although in lung macrophages it has been suggested that complex, crystalline, or phospholipid-like inclusions develop from the vacuoles. Rhopheocytosis also occurs to a small degree in macrophages at both sites.

The developing oocytes of mosquitoes have specialized sites on their cell surface where blood proteins are taken up by micropinocytosis and the resulting vacuoles are eventually turned into yolk platelets. The sequence of events is as follows. A pit appears on the oocyte surface and measures approximately 1300 Å in diameter. The outer layer of the plasma membrane has attached to it proteins in the form of a dense amorphous fibrous sub-stance 250–300 Å thick. On the cytoplasmic side of the plasma membrane are fibrous elements projecting radial to the surface, molecular spines, and these are 200 Å long. Two spines may be joined at their outer ends. It is suggested that the repulsion of the ends of the spines causes the infolding and pinching off of the pit to form a vacuole. A series of stages involving intracellular vesicles, small protein droplets, large proteid bodies, and yolk platelets can be observed in the oocytes. Pits with a structure similar to those appearing in mosquito oocytes have been observed in liver and Kupfer cells of the chick and rabbit, where they are considered to be specific sites for the uptake of denatured plasma proteins. Doubtless, spines associated with pits derived by micropinocytosis will be revealed by further high resolution studies of other cells.

The plasma membrane is involved in not only the uptake of solutes and solids, but also the passage of cellular products to the environment, i.e. secretion and excretion. These aspects have not received the same attention as cellular uptake, but some mechanisms have been revealed.

Most secretory granules are bounded by a membrane which, during secretion, fuses with the plasma membrane; the contents of the secretory granules thereby become extracellular. This sequence of events occurs in the secretion of zymogen granules from the pancreas, in many other exocrine glands, and in endocrine glands such as the anterior pituitary of foetal rats (Fig. 3.31a–c). This mode of release of cellular products is eccrine secretion.

A completely different secretory mechanism is found in the submandibular sweat gland of the rabbit, and is called apocrine secretion. In this gland the luminal surface of the cells bulges outwards to form secretory projections. These are large spherical bodies attached to the cell by a narrow stalk (Fig. 3.31d). A layer of condensed cytoplasm eventually forms across the stalk, and the secretion body is set free into the lumen (Fig. 3.31e).

The chloride secretory cells of fish are concerned with salt balance in the animal, and secrete electrolytes. These cells have an extensive reticular system of agranular endoplasmic reticulum extending from cell base to secretory apex. In salmon smolt the apical endoplasmic reticulum gives off small vesicles, the membrane of which fuses with the plasma membrane and releases their contents to form an extracellular excretory mass. In *Fundulus* species, it is suggested that the swollen ends of the reticulum connect with cleft-like invaginations which project inwards from the plasma membrane (Fig. 3.32a). In both salmon and *Fundulus* the amorphous excretory mass contains small vesicles, resembling those lying in the apical cytoplasm of the chloride cell, suggesting that whole vesicles may be excreted in some instances. Finally, the adielectronic amorphous material within the agranular endoplasmic reticulum and the excretory mass both have histochemical properties of acid mucopolysaccharide. Doubtless, the agranular endoplasmic reticulum of chloride cells play a significant role in transporting, concentrating and excreting electrolytes.

The changes in the plasma membrane during uptake, secretion or excretion can, to some extent, be reduced to a single theory, the theory of membrane flow. It has been suggested that if plasma membrane is synthesized at one point and destroyed at another, then there would be a flow of membrane from source to site of breakdown (Fig. 3.32b). If the source were at the cell surface and the breakdown site at the end of an invagination, then flow would be from the surface towards the cell's interior. Conversely, the opposite direction of flow would result from a source at the tip of the invagination and a breakdown site at the surface (Fig. 3.32b). The energy

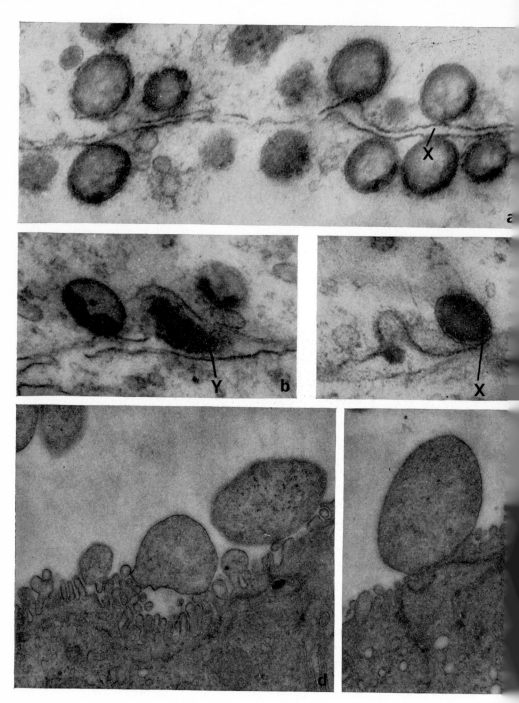

Fig. 3.31. (a)–(c) The release of secretory granules from the anterior hypophysis of the foetal rat. At X the enclosing membrane of the granule is fusing with the plasma membrane and at Y a granule is in the intercellular space. (Courtesy Dr. M. Maillard. ×70,000.) (d) and (e) Apocrine secretion in the rabbit submandibular gland. (Courtesy Dr. K. Kurosumi. ×29,100.)

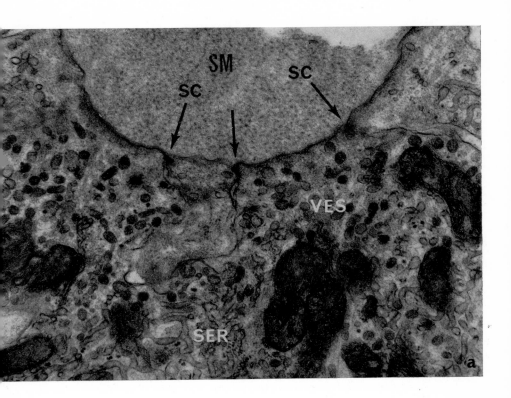

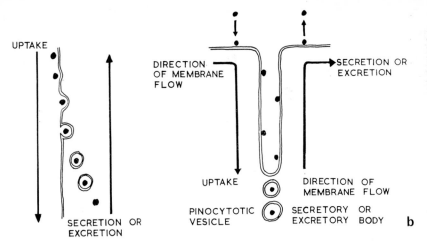

FIG. 3.32. (a) Apical region of a chloride secretory cell from the gills of *Fundulus*, showing the netlike agranular reticulum (SER), the apical vesicles (VES), and the secretory clefts (SC). The secretory mass (SM) lies in a depression (apical pit). (Courtesy Dr. C. W. Philpott. × 29,000.) (b) Drawing to illustrate the concept of membrane flow and the relationship of secretion and uptake. (Original.)

for such a system would be provided by mitochondria. If particles or other substances became bound to the membrane by ion exchange, hydrogen bonding or some other means, then they would be carried into or out of the cell by membrane flow. Particles etc., carried inwards could pass further into the cell by the pinching off of vesicles at the breakdown site within the cell. A further possibility is the binding of substances at the plasma membrane in a region which is more or less level and inactive. As the result of binding the particles, however, the plasma membrane would either stretch or be synthesized to form a small invagination which, when pinched off, would release a membrane-bound body into the cytoplasm. The breakdown of the enclosing membrane would result in the release of the enclosed substances. This process in reverse would result in secretion or excretion, e.g. ions or cellular secretions would have a membrane synthesized round them. The membrane-bound body would be moved by the cell to the cell surface, where its membrane and the plasma membrane would fuse, releasing the contents.

Further Reading List

1. FAWCETT, D., Cilia and Flagella, *The Cell*, Vol. II, edit. BRACHET, J. and MIRSKY, A. E., Academic Press, London, 1961.
2. MILLER, W. H., Visual Photoreceptor Structures, *The Cell*, Vol. IV, edit. BRACHET, J. and MIRSKY, A. E., Academic Press, London, 1961.
3. SJOSTRAND, F. S., Critical Evaluation of Ultrastructural Patterns with Respect to Fixation, *The Interpretation of Ultrastructure*, edit. HARRIS, R. J. C., Academic Press, London, 1962.
4. DE ROBERTIS, E., Submicroscopic Morphology of the Synapse, *Int. Review of Cytology*, Vol. 8, edit. BOURNE, G. H. and DANIELLI, J. F., Academic Press, London, 1958.
5. HOLTER, H., Pinocytosis, *Int. Review of Cytology*, Vol. 8, edit. BOURNE, G. H. and DANIELLI, J. F., Academic Press, London, 1958.
6. *The Plasma Membrane, Symposium*, edit. FISHMAN, A. P., *Circulation*, **26**, 1962, Grune & Stratton, New York.
7. KAVANAU, J. L., *Structure and Function in Biological Membranes*. I and II, Holden-Day, San Francisco, 1965.

CHAPTER 4

THE ULTRASTRUCTURE OF THE CYTOSOME

II. The Hyaloplasm, Endoplasmic Reticulum and Cell Inclusions

The Hyaloplasm

In an earlier chapter the cytosome was shown to be composed of a ground substance or hyaloplasm, in which were embedded a variety of formed bodies. The hyaloplasm and inclusions will be described in this chapter and the organoids in later chapters.

The hyaloplasm, which is an almost structureless region in light microscope studies, has been revealed in some of its complexity by electron microscopy. Indeed, one of the early revelations of the electron microscope concerned the structure of the hyaloplasm, namely, the discovery of the endoplasmic reticulum. The ground substance may be considered as a series of membrane-enclosed spaces, the endoplasmic reticulum and the continuous phase or hyaloplasmic matrix of granules and generally amorphous material. Under this view the hyaloplasm is a complex and polyphasic mixture. In this work the endoplasmic reticulum will be considered a cell organoid in its own right, so that the hyaloplasmic matrix and hyaloplasm are synonymous.

The hyaloplasm presents a variety of electron densities, both when comparing the matrix of different cells and when comparing one region of a cell with another. At one end of the spectrum are ill-defined areas completely without structure or with a generally dielectronic matrix, either amorphous, fibrillar, or granular to the finest degree. At the other end are matrices with considerable electron density, usually granular, and these contain many membrane-bound small vesicles, though such regions never attain an electron density equal to that of the other membrane-bound components of the cell. This polymorphism and spectrum of densities is mainly due to differences in the preparative techniques employed, but must also, to a degree which cannot be estimated, reflect underlying differences in chemical composition and physical organisation.

The indefinite vacuoles may represent either locations in which the fluid contents are high in the living cell, or where substances were leached out or otherwise removed during preparation. The small vesicles, of very varied dimensions and shapes, are undoubtedly of heterogeneous origin and function. In some cases these bodies are clearly derived from cell organoids, such as the Golgi complex, the plasma membrane, the nucleus, or the endoplasmic reticulum. The vesicles appear to be morphological representatives of intermediate stages in cell function and the production of secretory or excretory products. They are worthy of study to a much greater degree than heretofore.

The granular components are also very variable in size and shape and their functions somewhat enigmatic. Only one of these granules, the so-called particulate components of the cytoplasm, seems to occur almost universally, although, because it is often identified on morphological grounds only, it may have been mistakenly identified in some instances (Fig. 4.1a). The small particulate component is spherical in the majority of cells but may have the shape of a rod or a polygon. It averages 100–150 Å in diameter, ranging from 80 Å (an oblique section?) to 300 Å in striated muscle. Its molecular weight is calculated as 9.4×10^{-6}. The particulate component is usually very adielectronic and homogeneous, except in striated muscle where it has a peripheral dense shell, or local areas denser than the rest. Biochemical and other studies have clearly shown the particle to be rich in RNA, and the term ribosome is therefore homologous with small particulate component.

The distribution of the ribosomes ranges from a few small groups or single particles randomly scattered through the cytoplasm in cells which are undifferentiated or proliferating, to relatively large areas of packed ribosomes, especially evident in cells concerned with protein synthesis. In the differentiating epithelium of the foetal rat duodenum, and in odonto-blasts and ameloblasts in the incisors of young rats, a helical form of free ribosome has been observed (Fig. 4.1a). The angle of the helix lies between 60–70°, with the particles 250–300 Å apart. These helices are not in any way connected to membranes but lie free in the cytoplasm. It is now clear that the basophilia of the basal region of secretory cells, such as the pancreas, and of the Nissl substance of neurones, is due to the presence of free ribosomes. A general statement may be made that the degree of basophilia is directly correlated with the number of ribosomes. In neurones two types of Nissl are present, the reticular Nissl corresponding to granular endo-plasmic reticulum and the areticular Nissl composed of packed masses of particles of varying internal density. The areticular particles are 4–8 times the diameter of a single ribosome, i.e. 400–1200 Å, and appear to arise by the clustering of 150 Å single particles, with subsequent partial dispersion of the particles to unite them into one mass (Fig. 4.1b, c). Such masses may be storage deposits of RNA and associated protein synthesized by the particles themselves.

Another type of ribosome in combination is the polyribosome, or polysome, and these groups, rather than solitary granules, have been shown to be the functional units in the synthesis of proteins. Polysomes appear as 4–7 granules united by a fine filament 10–20 Å in diameter, so as to form chains, serpentine, circular, or other profiles. The filament is considered to be the morphological representative of messenger

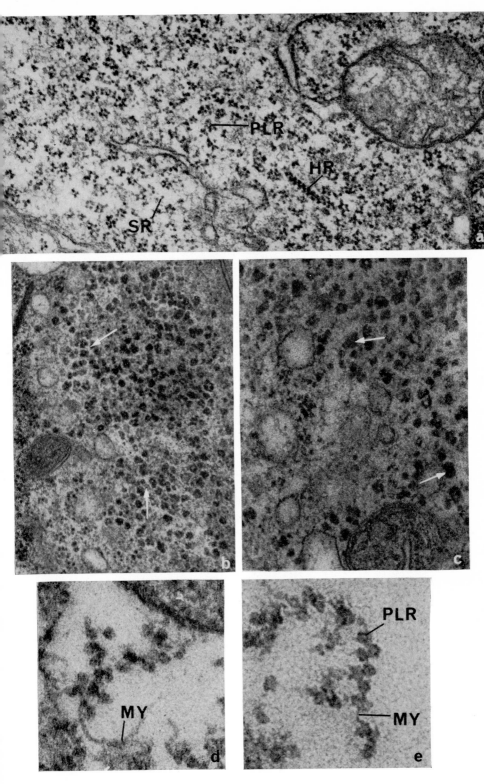

FIG. 4.1. (a) Single ribosomes (SR) and polyribosomes (PLR) lying free in the cytoplasm of an epithelial cell of an embryonic rat. A helical ribosome is at HR. (Courtesy Dr. O. Behnke. × 60,000.) (b) and (c) Areticular Nissl composed of packed ribosomes (arrows); neurone. (Courtesy Dr. S. W. Smith. (b) × 30,000. (c) × 76,000.) (d) and (e) Polyribosomes (PLR) associated with and presumably secreting muscle myofilaments (MY). Rat embryonic muscle. (Courtesy Dr. J. A. Heuson-Stiennon. × 155,000.)

RNA. In reticulocytes the polysomes synthesize haemoglobin, and during the formation of muscle in the embryonic rat, myofibrils 110 Å in diameter and 1·0–1·5 μ long arise at the ends of chains of polysomes (Fig. 4.1d, e).

The Endoplasmic Reticulum

The system of membrane-limited spaces, the endoplasmic reticulum, has already been noted as a major component within the the cytoplasm. The system has also been called the cytoplasmic vacuolar system, which is perhaps a more accurate descriptive term, but endoplasmic reticulum is more commonly used and will be retained in this text. The endoplasmic reticulum may be abundant or scarce, have a characteristic or random distribution, and be either of the granular (rough) or a granular (smooth) type, depending on the presence or absence of ribosomes over the surface of the membranes. There is, therefore, very great diversity in the form and ultrastructure of the endoplasmic reticulum, depending on the cell type, stage of growth and differentiation, and function. Furthermore, the ultrastructure of this system appears to be highly labile in living cells and is probably more affected by changes in osmotic pressure and other factors which occur during fixation and other preparative techniques than some other cellular structures. The generalized morphology and dimensions of the system will be described first and specific or special features afterwards.

The term endoplasmic reticulum is not synonymous with the classical ergastoplasm, which was defined by the following features: (a) its fibrillar nature, (b) its basophilia, (c) its functional variations. Ergastoplasm is homologous only with the granular endoplasmic reticulum with its RNA particles. Free RNA particles, agranular endoplasmic reticulum and a small amount of granular endoplasmic reticulum below the limits of resolution of the light microscope cannot be equated with ergastoplasm. It is clear, however, that the agranular and granular forms of the endoplasmic reticulum as observed in electron microscopy are related. Therefore, the term endoplasmic reticulum is used in this text to include the ergastoplasm.

In tridimensional view the endoplasmic reticulum is a lace-like net ramifying through the cytosome, although it may be less common in the peripheral part of the cytosome (the ectoplasm) (Figs. 4.2a; 4.4b, c). The system has been shown to be connected, even if only temporarily, with the Golgi complex and the plasma membrane, and to have a special relationship with the nuclear membrane. It is the consensus of opinion at present that the nuclear membrane is in reality a part of the endoplasmic reticulum, i.e. the limiting membrane of the nucleus is a cytoplasmic structure. The relationship between the endoplasmic reticulum and other cell organoids will be described in a later chapter. The reticular system appears as strings of approximately spherical, oval, or elliptical bodies or flattened sacs united

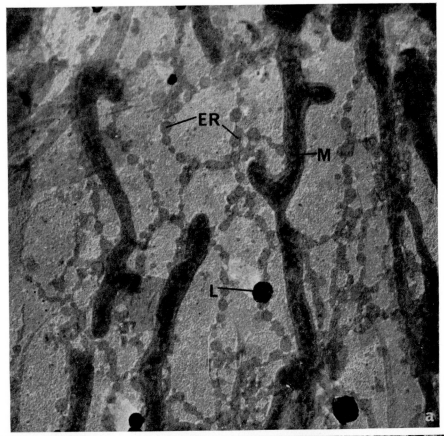

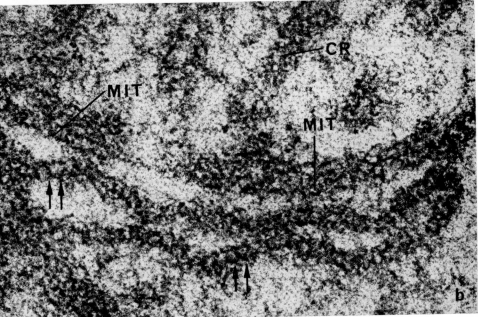

Fig. 4.2. (a) Electron micrograph of a tissue culture cell, showing the tridimensional disposition of the endoplasmic reticulum (ER). M, mitochondrion; L, lipid. (Courtesy Dr. K. R. Porter. × 10,000 approx.) (b) Endoplasmic reticulum, the membranes of which show a globular pattern of the middle lipid component (arrows). MIT, mitochondrion; CR, cristae. (Courtesy Dr. F. Sjostrand. × 600,000.)

directly or by intervening tubules. In section, these spheroidal bodies, flat sacs and tubules appear as membrane-limited units having a variety of forms. Transverse and oblique sections of tubules appear as small circular or lozenge-shaped bodies respectively; flattened sacs give long slender forms, cisternae, which usually have a narrow diameter, and spheroidal bodies give approximately circular structures. The circular profiles range from 250 to 5000 Å in diameter, and the cisternae 400–500 Å in diameter, but these figures convey little in the face of the great heteromorphism of the system.

The limiting membrane has been variously measured at 40–80 Å thick, depending on preparative treatment and staining, and the membranes are obviously of the unit type. The endoplasmic unit membranes differ from the plasma membrane, not only in width, but also in two important points. First, they are symmetrical, i.e. the inner and outer protein components are of equal width, whereas the plasma membrane is asymmetrical. Second, the central lipid component of endoplasmic membranes shows a globular pattern, due to its being crossed by adielectronic septa, the opposite ends of which are fused to the inner and outer protein components; this globular pattern has not been observed in the plasma membrane (Fig. 4.2b).

The cavity of the endoplasmic reticulum has an electron density approximately equal to, or slightly higher than, the cytoplasm when the cavity is narrow (Fig. 4.3b). If the cavity is large, however, its contents often have a lower electron density than the surrounding hyaloplasmic matrix (Fig. 4.3a). The material within the cavity is typically homogeneous and amorphous, but it may be somewhat granular or heterogeneous with regard to density (Fig. 4.3b). Furthermore, definite structures occur in the cisternae of some cells, e.g. the pancreas, in which intracisternal granules resembling small zymogen granules occur, while within the cisternae of fibroblasts and chondrocytes a dense material appears to accumulate.

The agranular reticulum is composed of only the external membrane and the internal cavity, but the granular reticulum has an additional component on the outer side of the limiting membrane. Frequently the two forms have been observed as one continuous system, so that differences are not basic enough to prevent one form altering into the other. The attached granules of the granular reticulum are rich in RNA and measure about 160 Å in diameter. These attached ribosomes give the endoplasmic membranes a castellated appearance, the projections being either circular, microvillus-like, or semi-circular, depending on the plane of section (Fig. 4.3d). Sections cut parallel to the surface of the reticular membrane and through the ribosomes show the latter to be aligned at regular intervals in rows, or in the form of circles, loops, spirals and rosettes (Fig. 4.3d). It has been suggested that the location of RNA as granules on the endoplasmic reticulum is an artefact, because cells which have a granular reticulum after chemical fixation do not show such associated ribosomes after

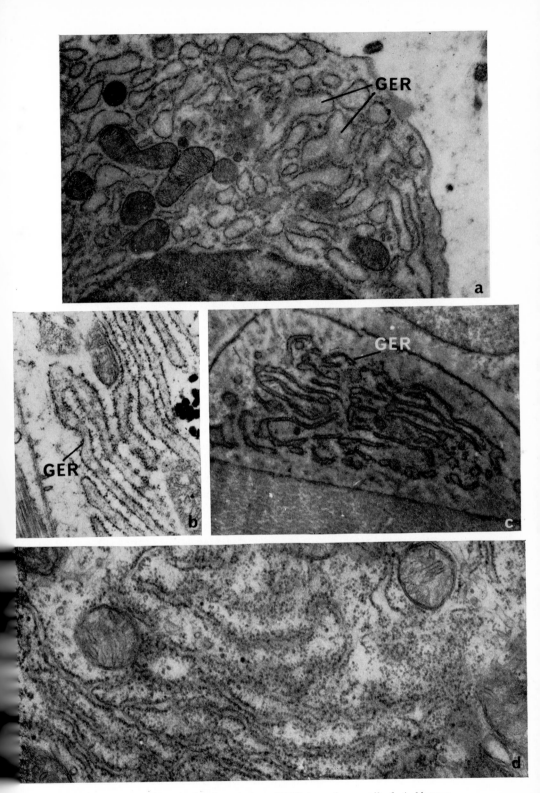

Fig. 4.3. (a) Granular endoplasmic reticulum (GER) in a plasma cell of *Amblystoma*. The contents of the large cisternae are less electron dense than the cytoplasmic matrix. (Courtesy Dr. K. R. Porter. × 17,000.) (b) and (c) Granular endoplasmic reticulum (GER) of the notochord of (b) *Triturus alpestris*, (c) *Amblystoma tigrinum*, showing the cisternal contents of greater electron density than the cytoplasm. ((b) Courtesy Dr. M. M. Perry. × 30,000. (c) Courtesy Dr. K. R. Porter. × 20,000.) (d) Ribosomes disposed as rosettes, spirals, etc., on the surface of granular endoplasmic membranes in chloride cells of *Fundulus*. (Courtesy Dr. C. W. Philpott. × 42,000.)

the same tissue is prepared by a freeze-drying technique. If sections of such freeze-dried material are stained, however, ribosomes are seen which measure 150–200 Å, while the reticular membranes measure 70 Å. The granular nature of the ribosomes on the granular endoplasmic reticulum, therefore, probably represent with some accuracy the actual disposition of RNA on the living reticular membranes. To be set against this conclusion however, is the fact that some agranular endoplasmic reticulum has a high RNA content by some methods of assay, although it has no ribosomes. It has been suggested that RNA is in life layered over the surface of the reticular membranes, and fixation causes this continuous layer to separate into isolated granules. There is not yet sufficient evidence to give unqualified support to either view.

With the above general characteristics of endoplasmic reticulum in mind, the more particular organization and disposition of this cell structure within the hyaloplasm of a variety of cells will be described.

The Agranular Reticulum

This type is characterized by a tubular form, rather than by the cisternal or circular forms. These tubules have diameters ranging from 500–1000 Å and form irregular lattices which may be quite compact (Fig. 4.4a, c). Agranular endoplasmic reticulum is most evident in cells which have a primary function concerned with steroid or lipid production, e.g. testicular and ovarian interstitial cells, adrenal and sebaceous glands; with carbohydrate metabolism, e.g. liver cells of fasted animals; with ion transport and electrolyte excretion, e.g. chloride secretory cells of fish gills; with impulse conduction, e.g. muscle cells; and with pigment production, e.g. retinal pigment cells.

In the interstitial cells of the opossum testis, the agranular endoplasmic reticulum fills the whole cytosome with a complex of tubules 300–400 Å in diameter. These tubules frequently fork, branch and anastomose to make a complex network. The agranular reticulum may also occur in the form of flattened fenestrated cisternae. Similar observations have been made on the lutein cells of the corpora lutea of rat, mink and armadillo. In such cells the tubules are 350–650 Å in diameter and form a network which is intimately associated with mitochondria.

Although the function of the chloride secretory cells of fish gills is still controversial, most evidence suggests that they are concerned with ion transport and secretion. The cells have a characteristic agranular reticulum of tubules, averaging 580 Å in diameter, which are about 3300 Å apart, and have cavities with an electron density slightly greater than that of the hyaloplasm (the guppy). The tubules branch, bend and anastomose to fill the cytosome and make contact with the plasma membrane on all cell surfaces. Within the reticulum are areas with distinct patterns, the tubules being grouped close together in parallel to form a honeycomb to which

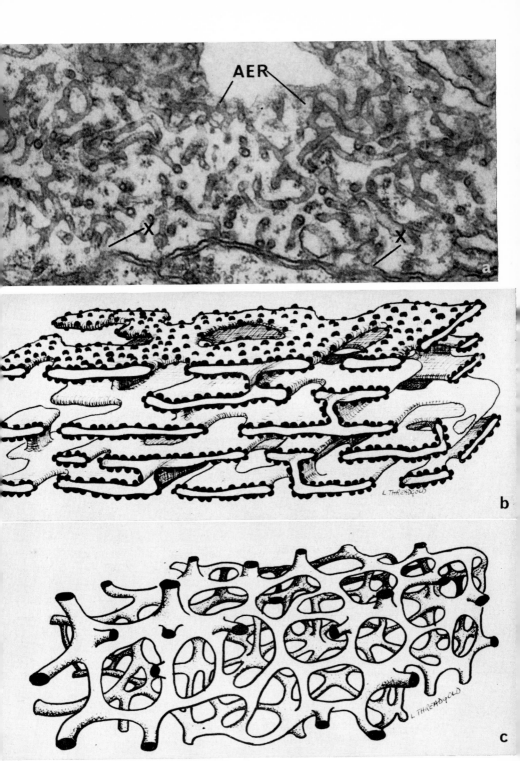

Fig. 4.4. (a) Agranular endoplasmic reticulum (AER) in a chloride cell of the sardine larva. Note connection between plasma membrane and reticulum at X. (Original. ×60,000.) (b) Tridimensional drawing of the granular endoplasmic reticulum. Ribosomes are shown only on the upper surface of the top cisternum. (Original.) (c) Tridimensional drawing of the agranular endoplasmic reticulum. (Original.)

new tubules join and from which old tubules diverge, so that the total composition of the honeycomb is inconstant. Networks of tubules resembling fenestrate membranes also occur. These chloride cells also have a small amount of granular reticulum which is in places continuous with the agranular tubules.

The agranular reticulum of muscle is called sarcoplasmic reticulum, and parts of it bear a special relationship to the muscle myofibrils. The reticulum forms a lace-like sleeve around the myofibrils (groups of myofilaments) and is, therefore, sometimes called the longitudinal element of the reticulum, in order to distinguish it from the transverse element which was previously thought also to be part of the endoplasmic reticulum, but is now known to be derived from the sarcolemma. A distinct pattern of sarcoplasmic reticulum occurs in each sarcomere and is repeated segmentally, the segments being united to form a continuous system. At the H band of the A band the sarcoplasmic reticulum is continuous round the myofibril as a collar (Fig. 4.5a). From this collar finger-shaped projections run parallel to the myofibril column along the A band to the side of the Z line, where they terminate in swollen ends, the terminal cisternae (Fig. 4.5b). At the Z line is the transverse invagination from the sarcolemma, which is flanked by terminal cisternae, so that in section the central transverse invagination and the two lateral terminal cisternae form a triad of vesicles (Fig.4.5b).

The dimensions of the sarcoplasmic reticulum naturally vary between animals and with different parts and functions of the same muscle. A general idea of dimensions can, however, be obtained from frog semitendinous and sartorious muscle. The terminal cisternae measure approximately 2400–3000 Å in a direction transverse to the length of the myofibril and 1800–2400 Å in the longitudinal direction. The opposed terminal cisternae from adjacent sarcomeres are separated by about 500 Å. The tubular part of the sarcoplasmic reticulum running parallel to the myofibrils in the A band average 300 Å in width, but expand in the I band to between 600–900 Å. The membrane limiting the cisternae measures 30–40 Å and may in places have a few associated ribosomes.

The pattern of sarcoplasmic reticulum outlined above has been observed in *Amblystoma* larva, rabbit, human and rat cardiac muscle and frog limb muscles, and appears to be typical for relatively slow acting muscles. Variations in this pattern do occur, e.g. in lizard muscle, rodent limb muscles, toadfish swimbladder and bat cricothyroid muscle the triad is located at the A–I band junction and not at the Z line, so giving two triads per sarcomere. Some of the these muscles are very fast acting, e.g. the toadfish swimbladder and bat cricothyroid muscles being used for sound production, the latter at a very high frequency. In *Calliphora* flight muscle the triad is replaced by a dyad, that is, one of the terminal cisternae is missing, leaving only the transverse process and the other cisternae (Fig. 4.5c, d). Furthermore, in this beetle the organization of the

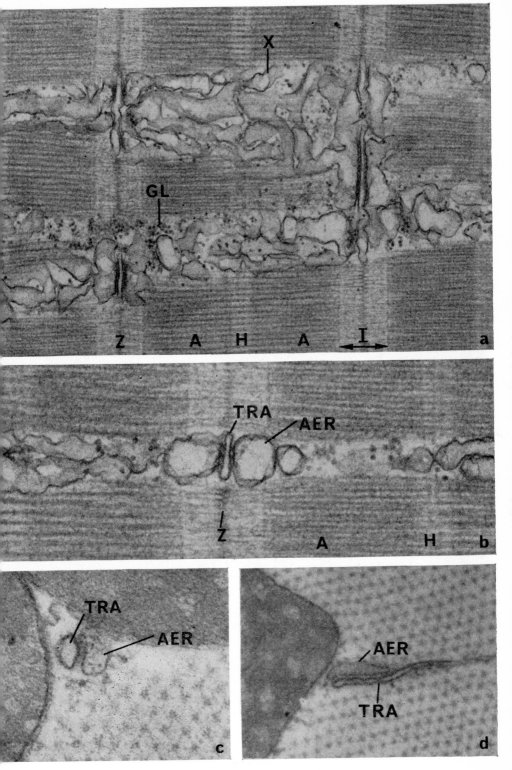

Fig. 4.5. (a) Agranular endoplasmic reticulum in striated muscle. The sleeve-like character of the reticulum round the sarcomere is evident at X. GL, glycogen. (Courtesy Dr. K. R. Porter. ×25,000.) (b) Triad at the Z line of the sarcomere. AER, terminal parts of the agranular endoplasmic reticulum; TRA, transverse process (plasma membrane invagination). (Courtesy Dr. K. E. Porter. ×50,000.) (c) and (d) Flight muscle of the insect *Calliphora*, showing only a dyad, composed of one terminal agranular reticulum, AER, and the transverse process, TRA. (Courtesy Dr. D. Smith. ×60,000.)

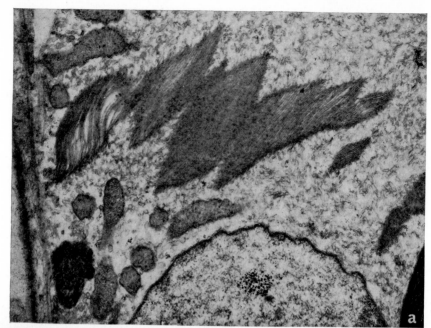

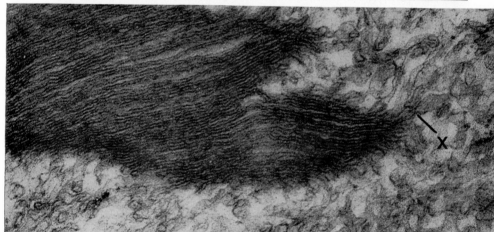

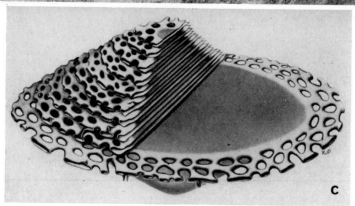

Fig. 4.6. (a)–(c) Agranular endoplasmic reticulum and myeloid bodies in the pigment cells of the frog retina. (a) ×21,000; (b) ×80,000, showing clearly the connection between the myeloid body and agranular reticulum at X; (c) tridimensional drawing of the myeloid body. (Courtesy Dr. K. R. Porter.)

sarcoplasmic reticulum at the A band is absent, and in its place occur large numbers of vesicles distributed at random without reference to the sarcomere pattern. Finally, in *Amphioxus* body muscles there is little or no sarcoplasmic reticulum, the few vesicular bodies which lie between the myofibril apparently being infoldings of the plasma membrane and therefore homologous with the transverse process.

The pigment layer of the vertebrate eye is formed of a single layer of cells lying immediately beneath the photoreceptors of the retina, and these cells send pigmented processes between the rods and cones. The agranular endoplasmic reticulum of these cells forms a compact tridimensional reticular structure occupying an estimated 50 per cent of the cytoplasm in the basal part of the cell (Fig. 4.6a–c). The reticular tubules have a mean diameter of 750 Å and vary very little from this mean. In the cell projections between the rods and cones the reticular tubules are slightly more slender, less compacted and more closely associated with the plasma membrane than in other parts of the cell. A particular modification of the reticulum in these cells is the myeloid body, considerable numbers of which are scattered through the cell body. The bodies have identical staining and physical properties, i.e. PAS positive and birefringent, as the outer segments of the rods and cones. The myeloid bodies are biconvex, 4–5 μ along the long axis, and made up of stacks of paired membranes (lamellae) slightly thicker and more dense than the agranular reticulum (Fig. 4.6a, b). The centre-to-centre spacing between the membrane pairs of a single lamella is 70 Å, and between successive lamellae sometimes slightly more and sometimes less. Any single lamella is a flat disc, its centre solid and its periphery fenestrated, the trabeculae between the fenestrations being continuous with the agranular reticulum elsewhere in the cell. From the base to the top of the myeloid body the lamellae increase in diameter progressively until the central lamella is reached, and then decrease in a like manner, giving the body a crystalline regularity (Fig. 4.6b, c). Myeloid bodies occur in groups of 5 or 6, connected by their convex faces, and may also occur attached to the nucleus and in crescentic form as an envelope around lipid bodies. The function of these myeloid bodies is unknown, but the close resemblance to other photoreceptors suggests that they may have a function related to light reception and, although not involved in pigment migration, they may stimulate the pigment cells to perform other activities important in retinal photoreception.

The Granular Endoplasmic Reticulum

Whereas the agranular reticulum is concerned with transport of both impulses and chemical substances and with non-protein metabolism, the granular reticulum is mainly concerned with the segregation of substances and the formation of secretory products, usually proteins or proteins associated with other chemical compounds. It is, therefore, often associated with the events involved in cell growth and differentiation, in which proteins and protein complexes with other substances are so important.

In the exocrine cells of the pancreas, the granular endoplasmic reticulum has a very characteristic disposition. In the basal region of the cell the system consists of reticular sheets and fenestrated cisternae, often in parallel groups joined by branches and anastomoses. The parallel arrays are orientated in relation to the nuclear membrane, mitochondria or the plasma membrane, and may form concentric or whorl-shaped figures. In section, the reticulum appears as small circular or ovate profiles or elongated cisternae, the latter form predominating. These profiles measure 400–1000 Å in diameter and the elongated cisternae may be 5–10 μ long, with the parallel rows separated by spaces 1000–1500 Å wide. The cavity of the cisternae is either more or less adielectronic than the hyaloplasmic matrix and in some instances contains intracisternal, very adielectronic granules, in which case the reticular profiles tend to be organized at random and to be generally circular in shape.

In the apical region of the pancreatic cells the granular reticulum is mainly in the form of circles or ovals and is distributed at random throughout the hyaloplasmic matrix and between the zymogen granules, while in the nuclear region the random apical and orientated basal distribution merge. In mice the granular reticulum in the parotid acinous cells forms large net-like masses which originate from the nuclear membrane in one or more places. This arrangement is thought to be a precursor to the more usual orientated type (Fig. 4.7a, b).

The long slender profiles of the granular reticulum of the pancreatic cells are a feature of other cells also, e.g. liver cells and vertebrate neurones, and embryonic cells undergoing differentiation, such as the notochordal cells of *Rana* and *Amblystoma* in which, however, there is some widening of the cisternae and less well-marked parallelism. The same type of appearance of granular reticulum occurs in some invertebrates, e.g. the cnidoblasts of *Hydra* when actively synthesizing the nematocyst.

A different form and disposition of granular reticulum is observed in the plasma cell, the thyroid epithelium and epithelium of the mouse prostate and hen oviduct. In all these the reticular profiles are swollen and irregular in both shape and distribution (Fig. 4.8). In the plasma cell the cisternae are only moderately enlarged, and appear in section as a system of polymorphic "lakes" connected by narrow channels, the whole lying approximately in parallel with the plasma membrane and the nuclear surface. In the prostate the reticulum assumes a very extreme form with the cisternae dilated in a most pronounced fashion. In the apical region of the cell, the cisternae are elongate, oval or circular, and between them are narrow bands of cytoplasm, except for the region of the Golgi complex. In the mid and basal regions the cisternae lose their individuality and form freely communicating spaces between which the cytoplasm appears as thin strands, oval or circular profiles. The resulting impression is as if the reticulum and the hyaloplasmic

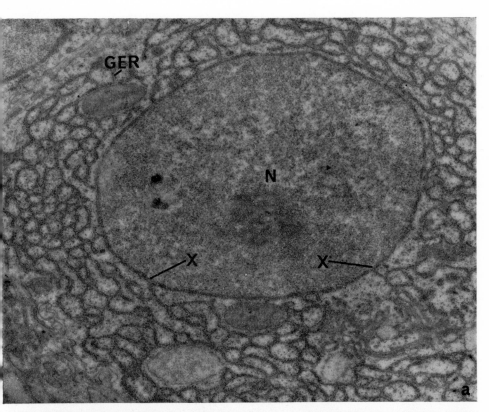

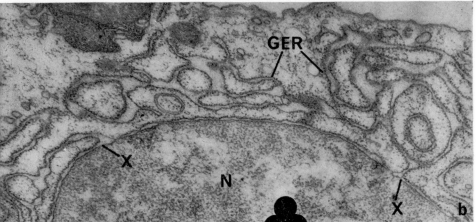

Fig. 4.7. (a) and (b) Parotid acinous cells of the mouse, showing the reticular granular reticulum (GER) connected to and originating from the nuclear membrane (at X); N, nucleus. (Courtesy Dr. H. F. Parks. (a) × 17,000. (b) × 24,000.)

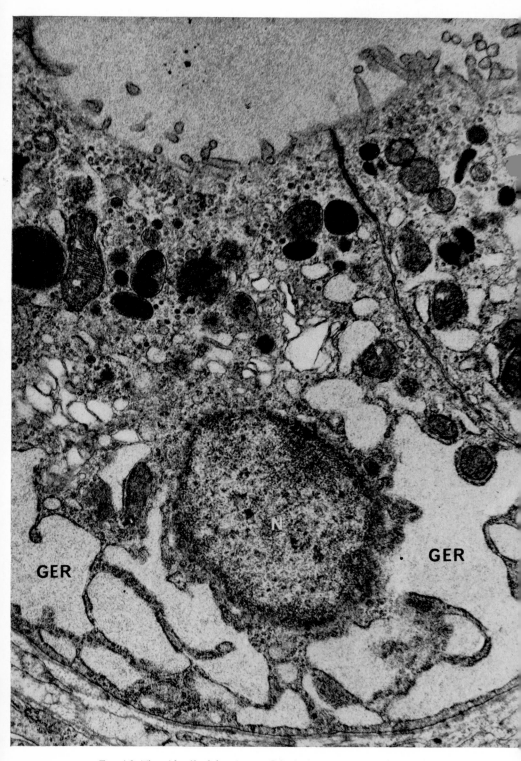

FIG. 4.8. Thyroid cell of the pigeon, *Columba livia,* containing greatly dilated cisternae of the granular endoplasmic reticulum (GER) in its basal cytoplasm. (Courtesy C. Lewis. × 20,000.)

matrix have changed places, the matrix, nucleus, mitochondria and Golgi complex appearing suspended in a homogeneous material. Only a narrow band of cytoplasm surrounds the nucleus and runs along the lateral and basal cell membranes. The dilated cavities of the cisternae have a homogeneous appearance and are less electron dense than the hyaloplasm. The cisternal contents are believed to have an albuminous character. The form and disposition of the granular reticulum in the hen oviduct epithelium resembles that of the prostate to a very great extent.

Another notable form of the granular reticulum is found in the "endoplasmic nebenkern" (so called to distinguish it from the type of nebenkern formed of mitochondria, which appears in insect spermatids). This "endoplasmic nebenkern" is formed of a series of approximately concentric reticular membranes organized into a generally spherical or elliptical shape. The membranes at the periphery of the sphere have attached ribosomes, but those more central are without these bodies. The structures give the appearance of "spinning off" membranes.

Functional Activity of the Endoplasmic Reticulum

It has been noted already that the endoplasmic reticulum of both the granular and agranular varieties, is known to be intimately involved in numerous cellular functions, including synthesis, intracellular transport, impulse conduction and metabolism, so that only a fraction of the known changes in this organoid with function can be mentioned.

The granular endoplasmic reticulum is known to be concerned with protein synthesis. The ribosomes are responsible for the character of the protein synthesized and can operate without the benefit of a membrane. The production of protein by free ribosomes, however, is for internal consumption; hence the frequent appearance of free ribosomes, but scarcity of granular endoplasmic reticulum, in embryos. When ribosomes are attached to membranes to form granular reticulum, the substances synthesized by this system are segregated within the lumina of the cisternae. Such substances are usually a secretion which is destined for the external environment of the cell.

In many cases the product segregated within the cisternae is diffuse and dielectronic and, therefore, pictorially indistinct. In the pancreas of the rat and guinea pig, however, this is not the case. During the period of gland recovery after secretion, relatively large adielectronic granules appear within the cisternae. The granules have a density similar to mature zymogen granules and, on isolation, have been shown to have the properties of zymogen as it is normally secreted from the cell. The product synthesized by the ribosomes is therefore separated from the cytoplasmic matrix and appears to move from the endoplasmic reticulum into the Golgi complex situated at the apical pole of the cell, where it is finally prepared for

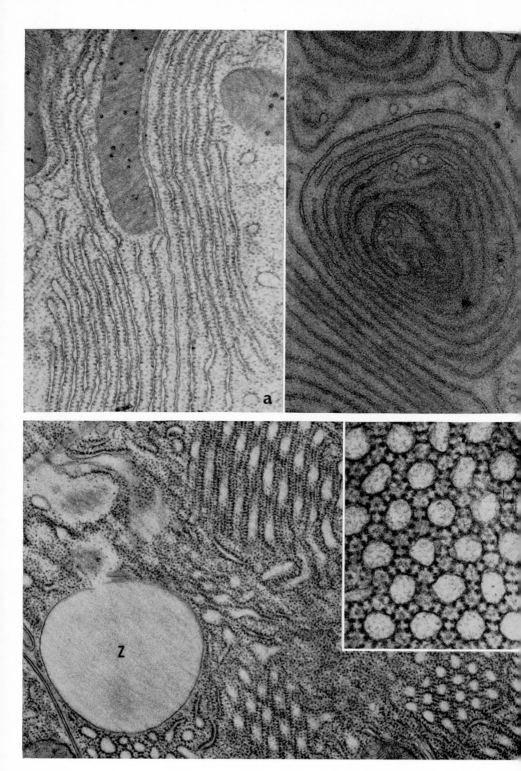

FIG. 4.9. (a) and (b) Granular endoplasmic reticulum in the bat pancreas. (a) from a starved animal, (b) from an animal 1 hr after feeding. Changes in the disposition of the reticulum are conspicuous. (Courtesy Dr. S. Ito. (a) × 20,000. (b) × 22,000.) (c) Granular reticulum in the chief cell of the bat stomach. The disposition of the ribosomes in groups of twelve evenly spaced around the circumference of the tubular reticulum is characteristic; Z, zymogen. (Courtesy Dr. S. Ito. × 26,000; insert × 67,000.)

secretion. Further details of this relationship between endoplasmic reticulum and Golgi complex will be given in a later chapter.

In the bat, the granular endoplasmic reticulum of the pancreas and chief cells of the stomach assumes a form which are different in fasting and fed animals. During fasting, the reticulum exists as closely packed cisternae which lie roughly parallel to the cell surface, but in fed animals the reticulum is reorganized into multi-layered concentric systems which have mitochondria, secretion granules or other formed elements in their centre (Fig. 4.9a, b). Whether the changes are due to the rapid formation of a new secretory product or to changes in the hydration, sol–gel transformation or other physico-chemical conditions of the cell, is not clear. In the chief cells of the stomach the granular reticulum is disposed in a similar way to that of the pancreas in the fed animal. In the hibernating animal, however, the cisternae are grouped in hexagonal arrays about 1200 Å in diameter. These arrays consist of 10–75 straight tubular cisternae in parallel. The associated ribosomes are arranged in straight rows along the cisternae, so that in cross-section six pairs of ribosomes appear arranged with a regular spacing round the circumference of the tubular reticulum (Fig. 4.9c).

Other examples of the relationship between the granular endoplasmic reticulum and protein synthesis occur in the albumen-secreting cells of the hen oviduct, the thyroid epithelium, and the coagulating gland of the mouse prostate. All these cells have cisternae which enlarge enormously during the secretory cycle of the cell, and although no granules appear in the cisternae lumen, protein has been shown to be present. Similarly, the extensive development of the granular reticulum at the time of the formation of a fibrillar sheath in the notochord of vertebrates, and in chondrocytes and fibroblasts during cartilage and collagen production, is suggestive of a correlation between endoplasmic reticulum and fibrillar, protein formations. The functional changes in the reticulum during the functioning of these cells will be dealt with in some detail in a later chapter.

The agranular endoplasmic reticulum is involved in non-protein synthesis. This organoid is abundant in cells concerned with lipid or steroid production and with glycogen metabolism.

The connection between glycogenesis, glycogenolysis, and agranular endoplasmic reticulum in both embryonic and adult liver cells is well documented. The liver cells have conspicuous granular cisternae disposed both in rows parallel to the nucleus and also elsewhere in the cytoplasm. In addition, small profiles of agranular reticulum occur, which are prominent along the cell periphery and in regions of stored glycogen. When animals are starved the agranular vesicles become prominent, many showing a dielectronic content (Fig. 4.10a). The glycogen units, about 1500 Å in maximum diameter and composed of smaller subunits, are confined to the marginal cytoplasm. The spaces between the residual glycogen are packed with expanded agranular cisternae pressing against the deposits. Some cisternae lie close to the plasma membrane, or may even appear to be

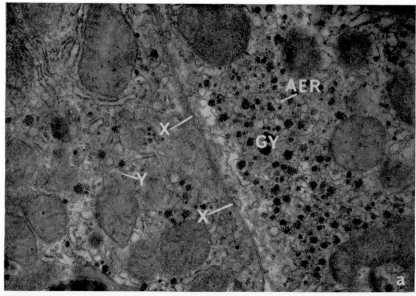

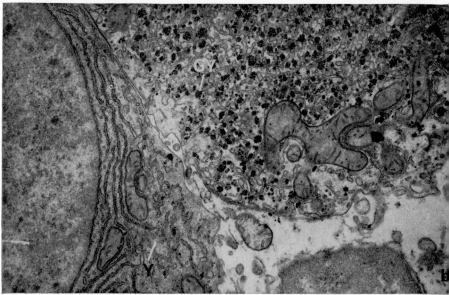

Fig. 4.10. (a) and (b) Liver cells of mice: (a) after a 24-hr fast; (b) re-fed 2 hr after a 24-hr fast. In (a) the glycogen is depleted, except in the peripheral cytoplasm, where swollen agranular reticulum and glycogen are closely associated. A close plasma membrane–agranular reticulum association is evident at X, and of agranular–granular reticulum at Y. In (b) glycogen is being restored and agranular cisternae have moderately electron dense contents. GY, glycogen; AER, agranular reticulum. (Courtesy D. K. Porter. (a) × 19,000. (b) × 16,000.)

fusing with it; this suggests a possible mechanism whereby the glucose is released from the liver cells. At the margins of the residual glycogen, the agranular reticulum is continuous with the granular endoplasmic cisternae.

When starved animals are re-fed, glycogen is resynthesized by the liver cells, and correlated with this is an hypertrophy of the agranular reticulum. The reticulum forms a lattice-work of irregular form composed of cisternae with a limited variation in diameter. Six hours after re-feeding, when stores of glycogen are maximal, the agranular vesicles are intermingled with the glycogen but are less numerous than in the earlier stage of glycogenesis (Fig. 4.10a).

From the above account it would appear that the agranular endoplasmic reticulum is involved in both glycogenesis and glycogenolysis, but cases in which glycogen storage occurs in the absence of agranular reticulum are known, e.g. diabetes mellitus and liver cells of young tadpoles. It appears, therefore, that agranular reticulum is concerned only with glycogenolysis, and this conclusion is supported by studies on the liver cells of pre- and postnatal mice. On the 15th day of gestation the liver cells have many free ribosomes and agranular and granular reticulum, although glycogenesis is not yet under way. By the 18th day glycogen is abundant in the liver cells, as are free ribosomes and granular endoplasmic reticulum (Fig. 4.11a, b). The agranular reticulum is only present in small quantities in various parts of the cytoplasm, including areas with glycogen. Glycogen accumulates rapidly until term when it exceeds the deposits in adult cells. Twenty-four hours after birth, however, a drastic reduction in glycogen content is evident in the liver cells. In areas with little or no deposit, an abundant lattice of agranular reticulum is present, and is continuous with the granular reticulum which bounds the deposits (Fig. 4.11b).

Experiments on fat absorption by intestinal cells of mammals, both *in vivo* and *in vitro,* have established the conducting function of the agranular and granular endoplasmic reticulum. In animals fed corn oil after a 24–40 hr fast, small fat droplets, 650 Å in maximum diameter, appear between the microvilli 20 minutes after re-feeding (Fig. 4.11c). The microvilli act as a filter, and at the same time fat droplets can be observed in pinocytotic vesicles which lie among the fibres of the cell web. In subsequent stages, larger, 500–2400 Å, fat droplets appear in the cisternae of the conspicuous and branching agranular reticulum which penetrates deep into the apical cytoplasm of the intestinal cells (Fig. 4.11d). As absorption progresses, fat droplets can be observed within the granular reticulum and even between the inner and outer nuclear membranes. Later droplets become clustered in dilated vacuoles lying laterally or basally between the Golgi complex and the intercellular spaces of the epithelium (Fig. 4.12a). Eventually droplets appear in the interstitial spaces of the connective tissue of the lamina propria and in the lacteals (Fig. 4.12b, c).

On the basis of this sequence in the position of the fat droplets, it is thought that they are filtered by the brush border, and enter the epithelial

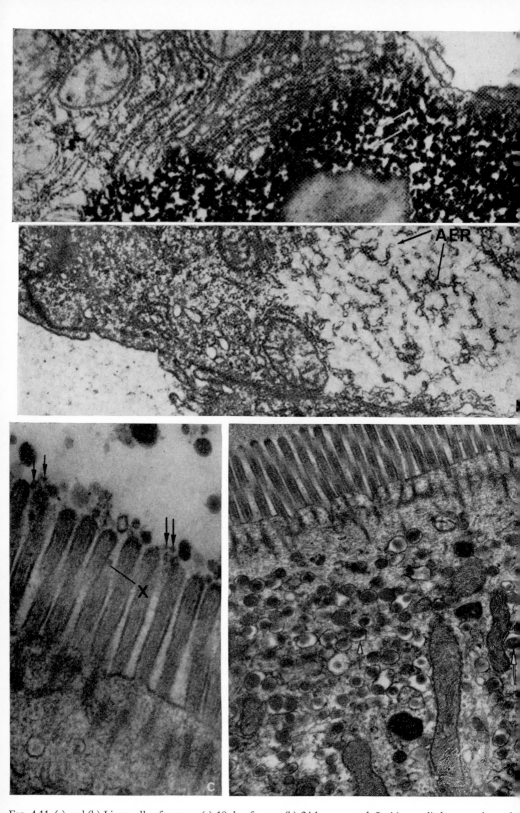

Fig. 4.11. (a) and (b) Liver cells of mouse: (a) 18-day foetus; (b) 24-hr postnatal. In (a) very little agranular retic is present (arrows) among the glycogen deposits, but the granular reticulum is prominent. In (b) the agranular retic (AER) is abundant in glycogen-depleted areas. (Courtesy Dr. V. B. Peters. (a) × 21,000. (b) × 33,000.) (c absorption by rat intestinal epithelium; early stage. Fat droplets less than 500 Å are arrowed and only a few dro appear between microvilli (at X). (× 45,000.) (d) Fat absorption by rat intestinal epithelium; later stage. Fat dro appear within the endoplasmic reticulum (arrows). (× 25,000.) ((c) and (d) by courtesy of Dr. P. F. Millingto

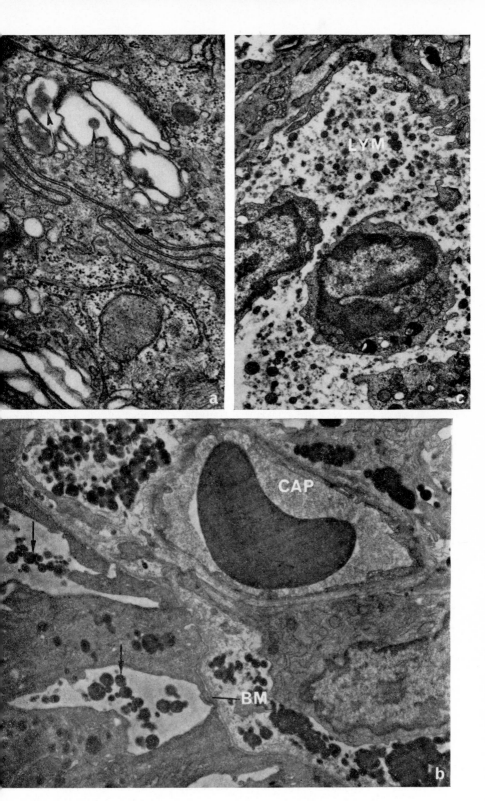

FIG. 4.12. (a) Fat absorption by rat intestinal epithelium; late stage. Fat droplets appear in the Golgi complex (arrows). (×47,000.) (b) Fat absorption by rat intestinal epithelium; late stage. Fat droplets appear laterally between adjacent cells (arrows), and below the basement membrane (BM); CAP, capillary. (×12,000.) (c) Fat absorption by rat intestinal epithelium; late stage. Lymphatic vessels of the villus (LYM) contain fat droplets. (×12,000.) ((a)–(c) by courtesy of Dr. P. F. Millington.)

cells by pinocytosis. The pinocytotic vesicles fuse with the agranular reticulum and the fat travels through the cisternae, passing into both the Golgi complex and through intermittently established openings in the lateral plasma membrane, into the intercellular spaces. The earliest stages in this theory of fat absorption are contentious, however, because sequences in the process of fusion between pinocytotic vesicles and the agranular reticulum have not been observed. Furthermore, some evidence suggests that fats are not absorbed as triglyceride droplets, but rather as particles of molecular size resulting from the hydrolysis of fats by pancreatic lipase and bile salts. Pinocytotic vacuoles are not found between the apical plasma membrane and the agranular reticulum with a frequency which would account for the total lipid intake. It is possible that both these modes of fat absorption occur in one and the same cell, for they are not mutually exclusive. It appears however, that molecular absorption contributes the major part of the total uptake of fats.

Cellular Inclusions

Fibrous and Tubular Elements

Fibrous elements† are common in animal cells and some of them have already been referred to in the descriptions of desmosomes, microvilli and cilia. All the fibrous elements appear to be related to the cell web which becomes very specialized in nerve and muscle cells. Electron microscopy has not only revealed the fibrous structures of the cell in greater detail, but has revealed fibres and tubular elements previously undetected.

The cell web, as observed by the electron microscope, has been described as a mass of fibrils extending between the zonula adhaerens and running up into the microvilli, and such fibres measure approximately 50 Å. Few observations, and apparently no research, have been carried out on the conspicuous and characteristic cell web in epithelial, secretory and other cells, perhaps because such fibres are not very evident in ultra-thin sections, in which they are often cut transversely or obliquely. Exceptions to this state of affairs are the Leydig cell of *Amblystoma* epidermis, the amphibian epidermis, and the connective tissue cells of the testis.

The Leydig cells of *Amblystoma* epidermis are large round cells forming in places a continuous layer between the basal and outer layers of the epidermis. They are characterized by large, pale mucous granules, a narrow juxta-nuclear zone of cytoplasm and a peripheral pale cytoplasm containing a cell net (Langerhans net) of a basket-like shape (Fig. 4.13a–c). This net is resolved in electron micrographs into bands approximately 5000 Å wide,

† All these elements of cells are in reality differentiations of the cytoplasm, as a result of functional adaptation. They may, therefore, be considered as merely specialized cytoplasm, although they are generally considered to be distinct cell organoids by most researchers.

composed of many closely aggregated fibres 50 Å thick and aligned roughly in parallel. The Leydig cells contact adjacent epidermal cells by numerous narrow truncated projections, and at these points are typical desmosomes with an adielectronic layer immediately below the plasma membrane, into which are inserted the fibres of the cell net. Langerhans net is, therefore, a specialization of the tonofibrils seen in the amphibian epidermis else-where. In the basal cells of the amphibian and mammalian epidermis, the 50 Å tonofibrils are attached to the half and full desmosomes of the basal and lateral plasma membranes respectively, and radiate out into the cyto-plasm in the form of "fountain-like" bundles (Fig. 4.13d).

The interstitial tissue of the human testis consists of Leydig (interstitial) cells, fibroblasts, blood vessels and nerves. Some of the fibroblasts are considered by certain authors to be immature Leydig cells or stages in the differentiation of fibroblasts into Leydig cells, but the majority are clearly connective tissue cells. These latter are large fusiform cells with round or indented nuclei, and their cytoplasm contains great numbers of fibres 50 Å thick and of indefinite length. The Leydig cells themselves also have bundles of fibres 50 Å thick dispersed between the lipids, pigments and other cell constituents.

In the previous descriptions of ciliary structure, the fibrous rootlets were included, although they really belong to the class of intracellular fibres. The protein fibres which form a pharyngeal framework below the mouth of gymnosomatous and some hypostomatous ciliates are perhaps derivatives of such ciliary rootlets. The fibres, 150–200 Å in diameter, form bundles which are arranged in a form typical of the species. In all cases, however, the fibres lie parallel, either loosely packed and irregular (Fig. 4.14a, b), or tightly packed and regular. The fibres are rigid and elastic, have a para-crystalline structure, are birefringent and stain with bromophenol blue, all characteristics which make them comparable with scleroprotein. Their function appears to be more structural than contractile.

Recently, the use of improved fixation using aldehydes and epoxy embedding media has revealed that the microtubule is a universal cellular constituent. Some structures previously described as fibres have been revealed as tubules, e.g., myofilaments, the sperm manchette, and the fibres penetrating the microvilli, and it is readily conceivable that many more so-called fibres will eventually be shown to have the bipartite features of the microtubule†. The microtubules observed in interphase cells other than muscle and neurones, are 210–230 Å in diameter, with adielectronic walls (Fig. 4.15a, b). The tubules are made up of 10–13 subunits, very much in the manner of ciliary subfibres. It is clear that the microtubule,

---

† There are difficulties in interpretation concerning tubules. The presence of adielectronic "walls" may only be evidence of a difference in physico-chemical properties or molecular architecture of the outer part of a solid tube or fibre, compared to the inside, or core. The word tubule implies an empty core, that is, a more or less complete absence of substance or structure in that region.

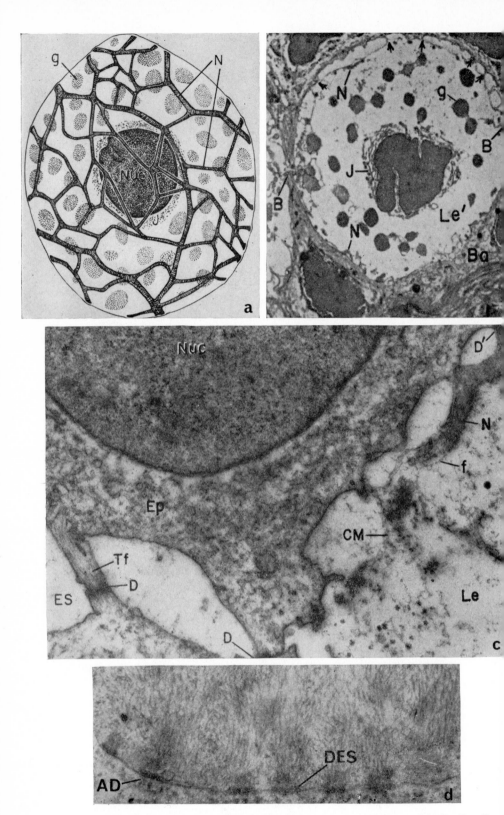

FIG. 4.13. (a)–(c) Langerhans net in the Leydig cell of *Amblystoma* epidermis. (a) Diagram of the Leydig cell and (b) Electron micrographs of the whole Leydig cell in section (×12,000). (c) Part of Leydig cell and adj epidermal cell (×15,000). N, fibrous network; G, granule; Ba, basement membrane; Le, Leydig cell; Tf, fibrils; D, desmosome; J, juxta-nuclear cytoplasm. (Courtesy Dr. E. D. Hay.) (d) Half-desmosomes (DES) radiating tonofibrils; basal cells of amphibian larval epidermis. AD, adepidermal membrane. (Courtesy I Weiss. ×37,000.)

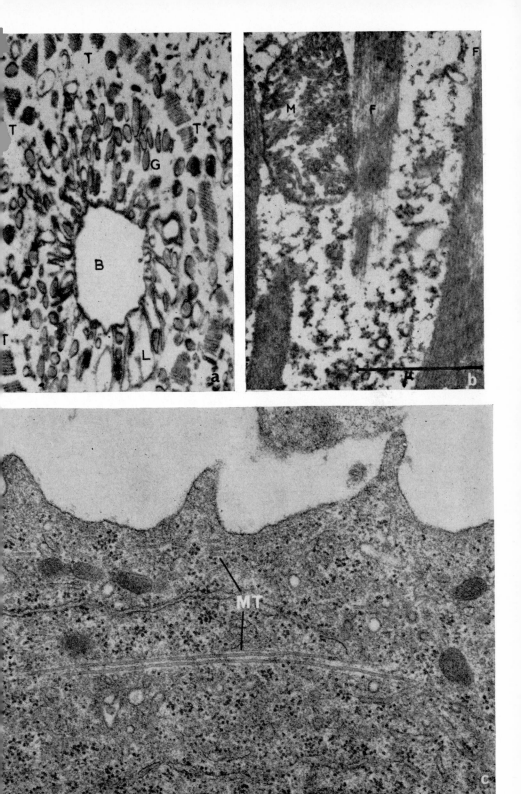

Fig. 4.14. (a) and (b) Pharyngeal protein fibres in ciliates. (a) *Coleps hirtus*, in which the trichites (T) round the buccal cavity (B) are composed of fibres. (b) *Frontonia marinus*, in which the pharyngeal fibres (F) are seen longitudinally. (Courtesy Dr. C. Rouiller. (a) ×23,000. (b) ×33,000.) (c) Microtubules (MT) in the epithelial cells of the small intestine of the foetal rat. (Courtesy Dr. O. Behnke. ×40,000.)

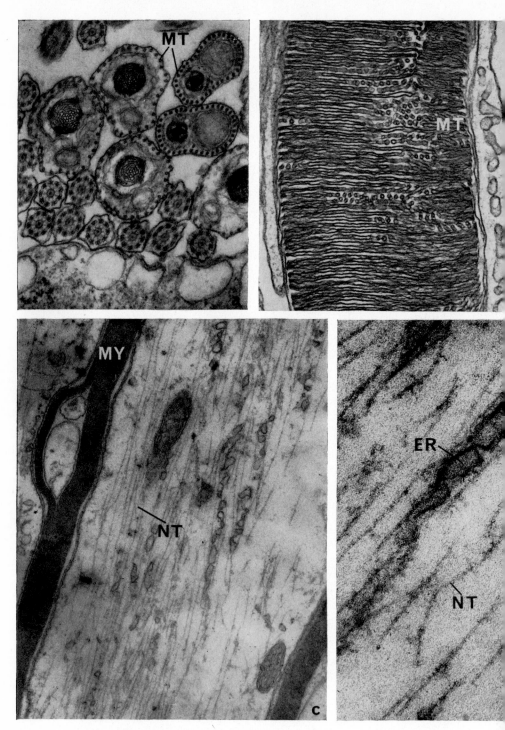

FIG. 4.15. (a) and (b) Microtubules (MT) in (a) planarian spermatozoa, transverse section, (b) kangaroo rat spermatozoa, longitudinal section. (Courtesy Dr. K. Porter. (a) × 14,000. (b) × 50,000.) (c) and (d) Neurofilaments (NT) in a nerve axon. MY, myelin; ER, endoplasmic reticulum. (Courtesy Dr. J. Metuzals. (c) × 27,500. (d) × 97,000.)

ciliary subfibre, myofilament, spindle fibre and perhaps cell web and neurofilament are closely related and may have a common origin. All these tubular elements are concerned with either movement or cell shape.

Neurofibrils

Although neurofibrils can only be observed in light microscopy after special techniques have been applied, they are readily apparent in electron microscopy. Smears of squid axon show fibrils ranging from 150 to 500 Å and there may be faint indications of internal spirals. In the extruded axoplasm of other animals, smooth fibrils of indefinite length and 100–400 Å thick occur. In sections, two main types of fibrils can be seen in some neurones, thin filaments 100 Å thick, and thick tubules 200–300 Å in diameter. In the axons of the central nervous system of the frog are fibrils, either nodose or smooth, of indefinite length, and ranging from 75–200 Å in thickness (Fig. 4.15c, d). It has been suggested that the large diameter tubular fibrils are part of the endoplasmic reticulum, although typical endoplasmic reticulum also occurs within the axon. It seems certain that the neurofibrils of the light microscope are due to the clumping of the thick tubules and the deposition of silver upon their surface.

Fibrils occur also in the neuroglial cells. They are 100 Å or less in diameter and form bundles ranging from a few fibrils to masses 2500–5000 Å in diameter. Definite identification of the type of glial cells in which these fibres appear is not possible, but they are probably astrocytes of the fibrous type.

Myofilaments

The myofibrils of the light microscope are composed of yet finer filaments, the myofilaments, and these are conspicuous elements throughout the sarcoplasm of muscle cells when observed by electron microscopy. In smooth muscle, the myofilaments are all identical, longitudinally arranged, and in parallel. In the smooth muscle of the urinary bladder the filaments are 100–200 Å thick and are spaced 200 Å apart.

The myofilaments of striated muscle present a more complex picture, and vertebrate muscle generally conforms to the following pattern. The myofilaments are of two types; the primary, thick filaments are 100 Å in diameter and 15,000 Å long, and the secondary thin filaments are 50–70 Å thick and 20,000 Å long, extending from the Z line to the edges of the H band (Fig. 4.16). Both the primary and secondary filaments are in hexagonal array, the primary being spaced 450 Å apart (Fig. 4.17a,c). In the A band, primary and secondary filaments interdigitate (Figs. 4.16; 4.17b), but the I band has only secondary filaments (Figs. 4.16; 4.17c). Each primary filament is surrounded by six secondary filaments, and each secondary filament is placed equidistant from three primary filaments (Fig. 4.17b, d).

The primary and secondary filaments are connected by cross-bridges 20–30 Å thick (Fig. 4.16). These bridges occur every 60–70 Å along a given thick filament, and each bridge is rotated 60° to form a helical structure. A primary filament is therefore joined to each of its six surrounding secondary filaments every 400 Å of its length. The primary filaments are

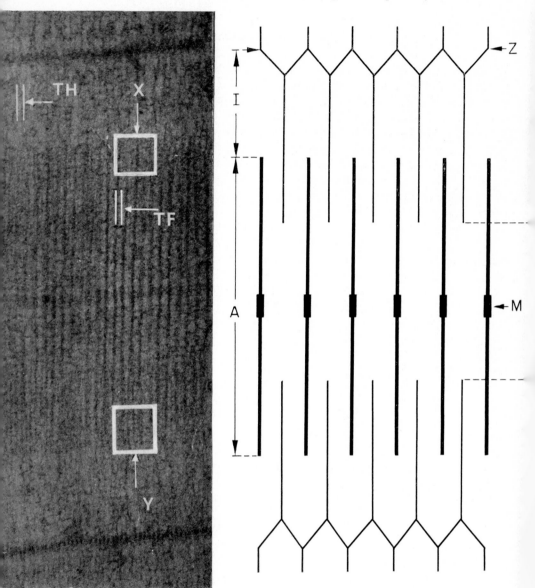

FIG. 4.16. Myofilaments in a single muscle sarcomere. Interdigitations of thick (TF) and thin (TH) myofilaments can be seen at X, and lateral connections between the two filament types at Y. (Courtesy Dr. G. G. Knappeis. × 80,000.)

myosin and the secondary actin and, perhaps, tropomysin. The bridges are actomysin linkages and correspond to the actomysin complex present in muscle.

The Z line often appears amorphous and the secondary filaments apparently pass through it. Recent research on frog skeletal muscle, however,

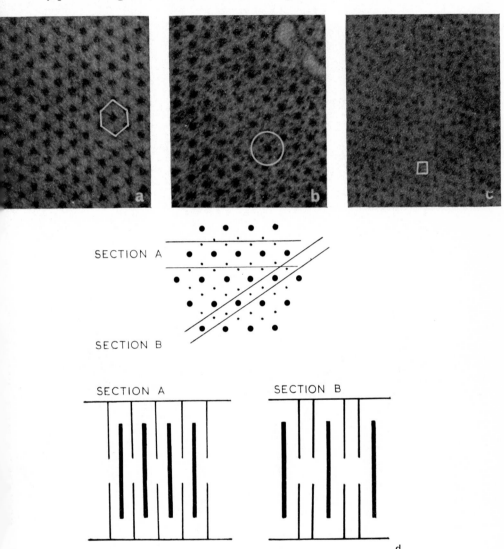

FIG. 4.17. (a)–(c) Transverse sections through (a) *H* band, thick filaments only; (b) *A* band, mixed thick and thin filaments; (c) *I* band, thin filaments only. Note also the hexagonal packing of filaments in (a) and square packing in (c) and (encircled), the 6:1 thin:thick ratio. (Courtesy Dr. G. G. Knappeis. All × 120,000.) (d) Diagram showing the relationship of thick and thin myofilaments, and the influence of the plane of section on this relationship. (Original.)

6*

has shown that each secondary filament on one side of the Z line faces the centre of the space between four secondary filaments on the opposite side (Fig. 4.18a, b). The secondary filaments near the Z line are 220 Å apart, and therefore form the corners of a square and are not hexagonally arranged as elsewhere in the sarcomere (Fig. 4.17c). Each secondary filament is

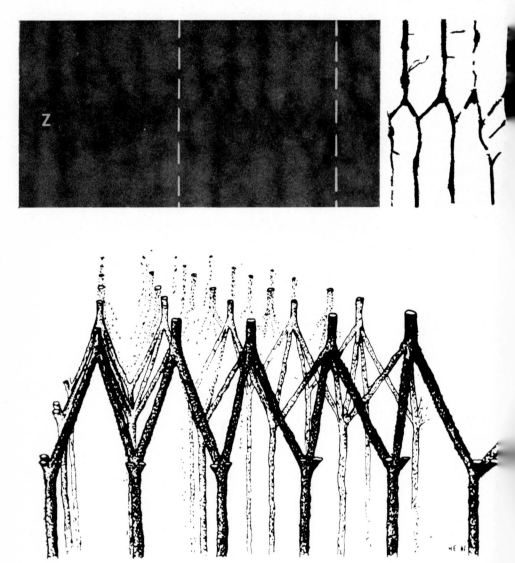

Fig. 4.18. (a) and (b) Photo and drawing showing the relationship of thin myofilaments of adjacent sarcomeres on each side of the Z line. (Courtesy Dr. G. G. Knappeis. × 38,000.)

joined to four of the Z line filaments, each of which is 50 Å thick, and is thereby connected to four of the secondary filaments on the opposite side (Fig. 4.18b). Between the Z line and the A band the secondary filaments are displaced and rotated 90–100° to change their square pattern to an hexagonal one.

The mechanism of muscle contraction is still controversial, but a theory which resolves most of the major points of the controversy has been put forward and is as follows. In the first stage of contraction, from 100 to 79 per cent of rest length, the secondary filaments slide into the A band between the primary filaments, occluding the H band and drawing the Z lines together (Fig. 4.19a, b). In the next stage, 79 per cent of rest length, the myofilaments coil or fold. The secondary filaments fold close to the Z line, and an unidentified dense substance accumulates between the secondary filaments, resulting in a dense contraction band at this level. The primary filaments coil on each side of the M line at about the level of the former H band boundary (Fig. 4.19c–f). At 63 per cent of rest length these changes result in an increasingly wide secondary anisotropic band (A-II band) in place of the original H band, and a narrow secondary I band (I-II band) appears on each side of the A-II band (Fig. 4.19d, e). These A-II and I-II bands and the M line gradually acquire a similar density, although how is not clear, until at 58 per cent of rest length these three bands are hardly distinguishable from each other (Fig. 4.19f).

The arrangement of the myofilaments as described above applies to most vertebrates and some invertebrates, but other invertebrates have different patterns. In the scorpion the primary filaments are 150 Å thick and are spaced 450–500 Å apart in an hexagonal array. The secondary filaments are 50 Å thick and they outnumber primary filaments by 10–12 to 1, instead of 6 to 1 (Fig. 4.20a, b). In the King crab, there is an inconstant number of secondary filaments, and the arrangement of primary and secondary filaments is very irregular. In a number of *Cyclops* species the primary filaments are 120 Å thick and 15,000 Å long, and the secondary filaments are 40 Å thick. The primary filaments are spaced 250 Å apart in hexagonal array and are surrounded by six secondary filaments, but at this point the similarity with vertebrate muscle ends. The proportion of primary to secondary filaments is not 1:2 as in vertebrate muscle, but 1:3 because each secondary filament does not lie equidistant from three primary filaments (Fig. 4.20c). Instead, if three primary filaments are considered as the apices of an equilateral triangle, a secondary filament lies in the middle of each side. The secondary filaments are, therefore, also the apices of a triangle, although this is smaller than the primary triangle, and this secondary triangle is inverted within the primary one (Fig. 4.20c). Any section cut parallel and through a row of primary filaments will never show more than one secondary filament between each primary pair, although the latter may be 250 or 430 Å apart, depending on the plane of section (Fig. 4.20c).

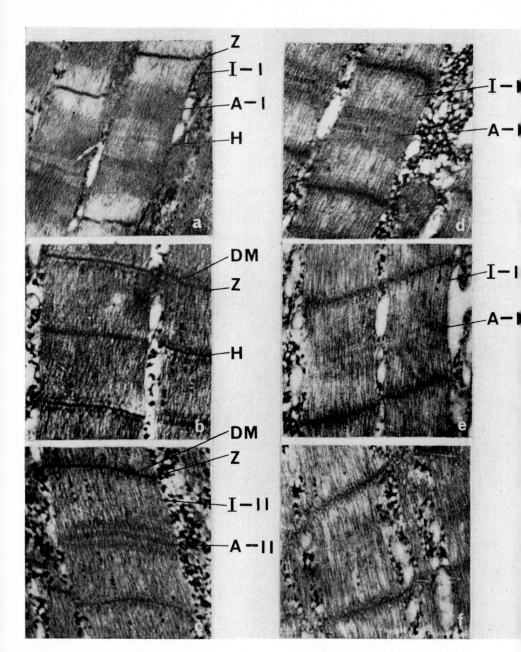

FIG. 4.19. (a)–(f) Stages in the contraction of a sarcomere. (a) 100 per cent; (b) 79 per cent; (c) 74 per cent; (d) 63 per cent; (e) 63 per cent; (f) 58 per cent relaxed length. *A*-I and *I*-I, original *A* and *I* bands; *A*-II and *I*-II, secondary *A* and *I* bands due to folding of myofilaments. DM, dense material adjacent to the *Z* line due to folding of thin filaments. (Courtesy Dr. V. P. Gilev. All photos × 25,000.)

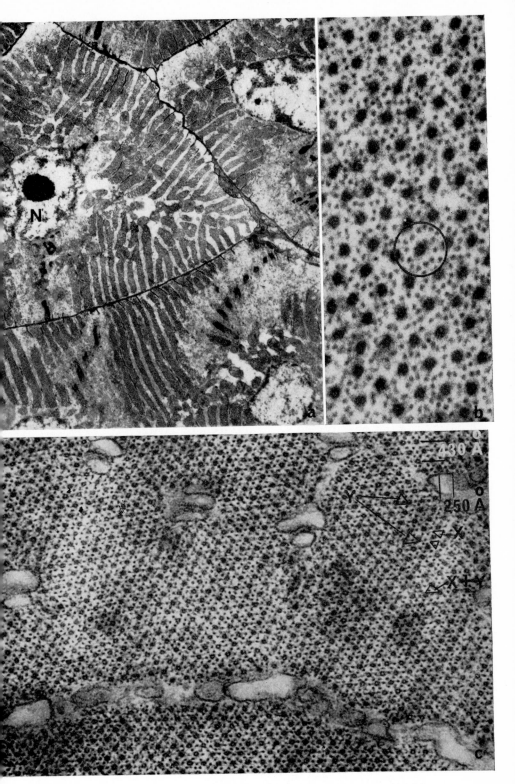

FIG. 4.20. (a) and (b) Scorpion muscle. (a) Low magnification to show the central nuclei and myofilaments. (b) Enlarged part of the myofilaments to show the thick:thin ratio of approximately 1:12. (Courtesy Dr. M. Auber. (a) × 5280. (b) × 145,000.) (c) Cyclops muscle showing the relationship of thick:thin myofilaments, the latter forming a triangle (at X) inside a triangle of the former (at Y). (Courtesy Dr. Y. Bouligand. × 100,000.)

Paraplasms or Cell Inclusions

The paraplasms are morphologically, chemically and physically such a large and diverse group, that it is not possible to cover them adequately in this text, even if a complete coverage served a useful purpose, which is doubtful. Some paraplasms, e.g. neurosecretory granules or the secretory product of anterior pituitary cells, are simply adielectronic round or oval bodies, while many other secretions are very similar except for the presence or absence of an enclosing membrane, while yet other inclusions show distinctive morphology but cannot be identified chemically. In the face of these difficulties, only a relatively few examples of paraplasms will be described, including examples of proteins, lipo- and mucoproteins, carbohydrates, lipids and phospholipids, and two recently discovered inclusions, the lysosomes, originally a biochemical concept, and annulate lamellae, an electron-microscope discovery. Some other paraplasms are described in Chapters 5 and 6 in relation to morphological correlates of cellular activity.

Proteins

Paraplasms solely of protein are rare, because reserve protein is accumulated in the muscle and blood and not within cells. Proteins do, however, occur in secretory granules, zymogen, for example, and neurosecretory granules. A most readily observable form of protein is the food reserves present in embryos, i.e. yolk. In *Planorbis* the yolk globules are $0 \cdot 5 – 3 \cdot 0 \ \mu$ in diameter and are enclosed in a single or double membrane. The globule is a heterogeneous complex, with a dielectronic structureless background substance in which are embedded small crystalline bodies (Fig. 4.21a, b). The crystals are composed of 60 Å adielectronic granules (composed in turn of smaller granules containing iron) in hexagonal array (Fig. 4.21b). Clear areas occur in some yolk globules and have an electron density only slightly greater than that of the background, but with the addition of faint striations.

In amphibian eggs and embryos, the yolk platelets are bipartite structures surrounded by a single membrane. Oval bodies lie in the interior and are composed of adielectronic 50 Å granules spaced 70 Å centre to centre in a crystalline lattice. The material surrounding the crystals is adielectronic and made up of 50Å granules, randomly distributed (Fig. 4.21c, d).

In the eggs and embryos of the domestic chicken, yolk is complex and of a variety of types. In the unincubated egg the primary yolk (so called to distinguish it from the secondary intracellular yolk) is arranged in alternating layers of white and yellow bands, the latter owing its colour to yellow pigment. The yolk is an emulsion, the continuous phase being a fluid in which float yolk spheres and lipid droplets. White yolk spheres measure 4–7 μ and yellow 35–100 μ, and both contain lipid subdroplets,

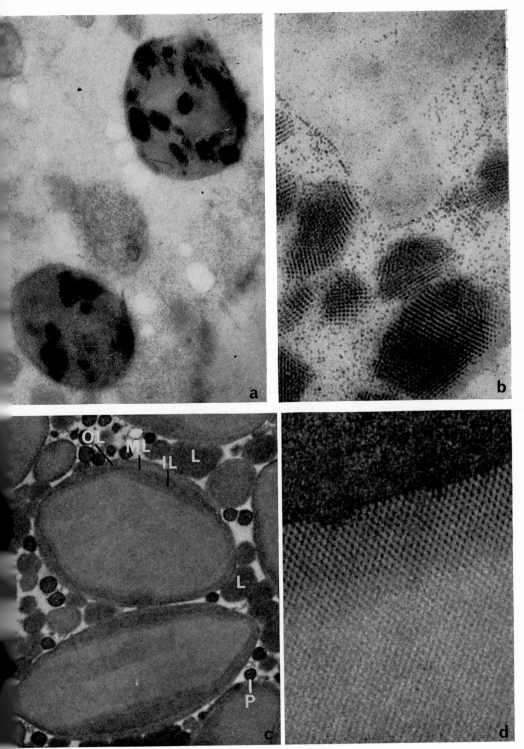

Fig. 4.21. (a) and (b) Yolk platelets of *Planorbis* oocytes. The crystalline protein aggregates within the platelets are clear and are surrounded by free granules and amorphous areas. (Courtesy Dr. P. Favard. (a) ×25,000. (b) ×135,000.) (c) and (d) Yolk platelets in the frog, *Rana pipiens*. A membrane encloses the platelet (not clear in this photo) and the platelet consists of outer (OL), middle (ML), and inner (IL) layers. The inner layer is crystalline. L, lipid; P, pigment. (Courtesy Dr. R. T. Ward. (c) ×8,000. (b) ×233,000.)

though these are larger and more numerous in white yolk (Fig. 4.22a, b). The continuous phase and the yolk droplets less their lipids are largely protein or, possibly, lipoproteins in an aqueous solution. In electron

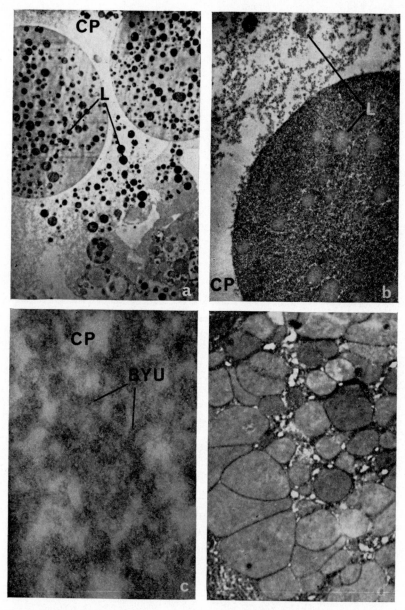

FIG. 4.22. (a)–(c) Yolk from the egg of the domestic hen. (a) white yolk; (b) yellow yolk; (c) basic yolk unit, BYU. CP, continuous phase; L, lipid. (Courtesy Dr. R. Bellaires. (a) × 17,500. (b) × 7800. (c) × 85,000.) (d) Mucoprotein bodies in a mucous cell from the grill of *Salmo salar*. (Original. × 3000.)

micrographs two types of yolk droplets are recognizable, despite the fact that the fluid component of the yolk and both types of yolk droplets are composed of the same basic units. This basic unit is a small round profile

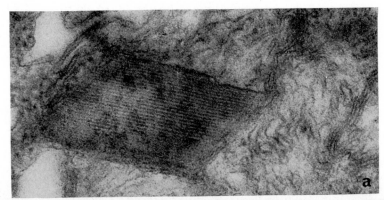

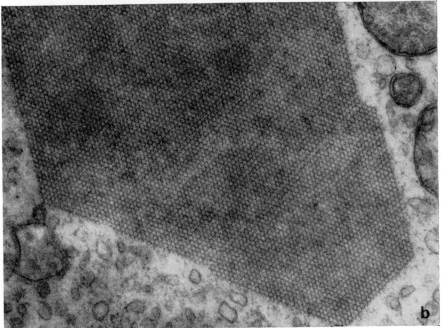

Fig. 4.23. (a) Protein crystalloid in a retinal rod cell of the frog, showing striations. (Courtesy Dr. E. Yamada. × 104,000.) (b) Protein crystalloid from the interstitial, Leydig, cell of the human testis. (Courtesy Dr. E. Yamada. × 56,000.)

250 Å in diameter, which may be a section of a small tube or a sphere (Fig. 4.22c). The units in the yolk sphere may be surrounded by a lamellated capsule due to hydration changes during egg storage, or a single unit

membrane, or be naked at the surface. In the continuous phase the unit particles form rings or chains and are generally more packed than in the yolk droplets. In white yolk the inclusions of lipid have a greater electron density than the remainder of the yolk droplet, whereas in the yellow yolk the reverse is true, the lipid droplets being less adielectronic than the surrounding yolk. The free lipid droplets are about 2·0 μ in diameter, more electron dense than the continuous phase, and made up of subunits of 30–60 Å in diameter.

In the chick embryos the secondary yolk is of three types. Type A is 0·6–3·0 μ in diameter, has either an adielectronic core surrounded by a less dense zone, or is granular and of uniform adielectronicity throughout, the granules being the same unit particles as in the primary yolk. The type B yolk measures 0·5–1·0 μ in diameter and is identical with the lipid droplets of the primary yolk. The third type of yolk, type C, is a complex droplet which has an enclosing membrane and contains both the type A and B droplets within it, as well as mitochondria, vacuoles and various other particles. It is postulated that the type A yolk is derived from the granular material of the primary yolk, and in turn gives rise to the cytoplasmic circular bodies which may contribute to the endoplasmic reticulum and microparticles presumed to be precursors of RNA.

Mucoproteins are readily recognizable in goblet and mucus secreting cells because of their position and compaction, but are not so easily identified elsewhere. The granules vary in shape from oval to polymorphic, depending on the extent of their packing. They have a homogenous appearance, with some mottling, and an electron density ranging from moderately adielectronic to dielectronic (Fig. 4.22d). The globules are without limiting membranes, although they may be outlined by adjacent endoplasmic reticulum or microsomes.

Crystalloids, probably of a protein or lipoprotein nature, occur in the inner segment of the retinal rods of the frog. The long crystalline rods, which have sharp angular outlines, lie amongst the mitochondria and are bounded by a membrane 80 Å thick. Internally these bodies are composed of 45 Å wide adielectronic lines separated by a 50 Å interspace. The dense lines are beaded, giving the crystalloid a striated appearance (Fig. 4.23a).

The crystalloids of Reinke are protein bodies peculiar to the Leydig (interstitial) cells of the human testis. They are rod, rectangular, or trapezoid in shape, often with rounded ends. At high resolution the crystalloids are observed to have a complex and highly ordered structure, being composed of bundles of long parallel tubules 180 Å in diameter. The tubules are connected by slender lateral bridges, and there are points of continuity between the bundles and the agranular endoplasmic reticulum, which is so extensive throughout the cytoplasm of Leydig cells. The crystalloids are, therefore, local differentiated regions of agranular endoplasmic reticulum (Fig. 4.23b).

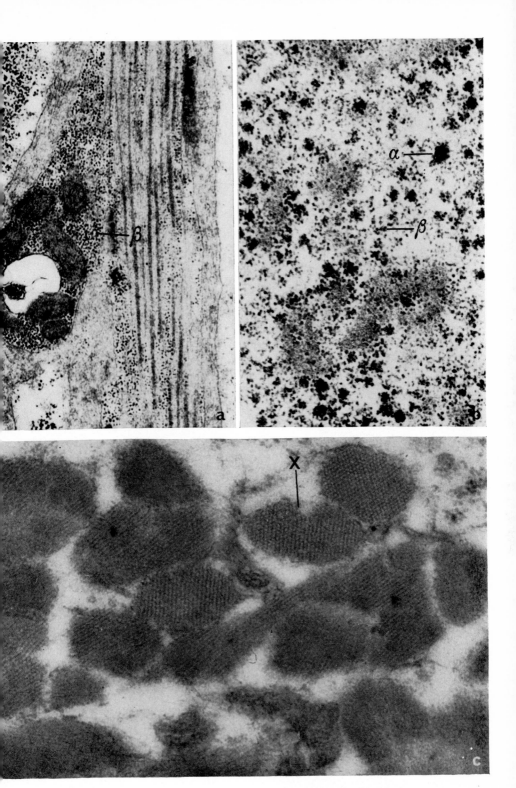

FIG. 4.24. (a) and (b) α- and β-glycogen in the muscle and parenchymal cells of the liver fluke, *Fasciola hepatica*. (Courtesy Miss S. S. E. Gallagher. (a) ×30,000. (b) ×40,000.) (c) Polysaccharide crystalloids from the blastocyst stage of the rabbit embryo. Hexagonal packing is evident at X. (Courtesy Dr. R. Hadek. ×75,000.)

Carbohydrates

Glycogen is widely distributed in animal cells, being an especially prominent component of the adult liver and muscle cells, and the brown adipose tissue of foetal mice. Without staining, the glycogen of rat liver cells has a low electron density and a diffusely mottled appearance, and at high magnification appears either as an amorphous cloudy mass or as closely packed small granules of low electron density. In frog liver the glycogen is more particulate, the granules occurring singly, in clusters, or in branching strands, while in frog muscle the granules 150–300 Å in diameter are relatively adielectronic. After fixation in osmium, glycogen is not retained in certain tissues, although after glutaraldehyde fixation and staining with lead salts, the glycogen appears as distinct granules, very adielectronic and measuring 150–400 Å in diameter (Figs. 4.24a, b).

In the blastocyst stage of the rabbit embryo, polysaccharide crystalloids are a common occurrence. These are spherical to elongate in shape, 0·1–1·0 μ wide and up to 10 μ long. At high resolution the crystalloids are observed to be limited by a smooth membrane, sometimes incomplete. In longitudinal section the bodies show parallel rows of alternating adielectronic and dielectronic lines (Fig. 4.24c). In cross-section the crystalloids are composed of circular units 100 Å in diameter, with a dielectronic centre and hexagonal parking.

Lipids and Phospholipids

Fat or lipid droplets are present in many cells and characteristically are very adielectronic when tissues are fixed in osmium-containing fluids (Fig. 4.25a). The droplets are round, crenated or very irregular in shape, the latter two forms probably being due to shrinkage during preparation. The bodies are without a limiting membrane and may be very adielectronic throughout, or have an adielectronic core surrounded by a less dense rim. Some have circular regions of low density in a generally dense matrix, giving a frothy appearance. In spleen, kidney, and embryonic tissues are bodies apparently completely lipid, which have a distinct ordered pattern and a limiting membrane. In mouse kidney these granules are 0·3–1·2 μ in diameter and are enclosed by a single membrane 20–40 Å thick. Between the granule proper and the membrane is a dielectronic space 23 Å wide, and the outer limit of the granule itself has a thin rim of very adielectronic particles. The granule has two basic patterns within it, an outer zone of parallel alternating adielectronic and dielectronic lines with a centre-to-centre spacing of 40–50 Å (Fig. 4.25b, c). The dark band is 16 Å wide and the light 27 Å. The central region of the granule is composed of a granular matrix of medium electron density containing very adielectronic granules, 20–50 Å in diameter which are packed closely together in some areas and loosely in others.

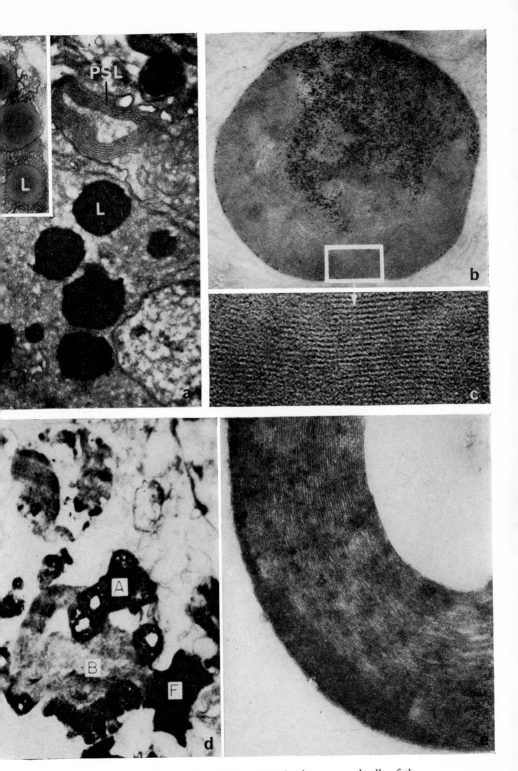

Fig. 4.25. (a) Lipid granules and phospholipid (PSL) in the tegmental cells of the tapeworm *Proteocephalus pollanicoli*. *Insert*, lipid droplets after OsO₄ fixation and double staining with uranyl-lead. (Original. (a) ×12,000; insert ×10,000.) (b) and (c) Fat droplets from the epithelial cells of the mouse kidney. (b) The peripheral striations and central area of dense granules are evident; (c) enlarged part of the peripheral striations. (Courtesy Dr. W. Thoenes. (b) ×88,000. (c) ×320,000.) (d) and (e) Phospholipids from the ovotestis of a snail. (d) Anhydrous condition (A); (e) hydrated state (B). F, fat. (Courtesy Dr. E. H. Mercer. (d) ×12,000. (e) ×64,000.)

Phospholipids show an even more complex and variable morphology than lipids. In an anhydrous condition, the phospholipid is amorphous, very adielectronic, and has small vacuoles or areas of low density within it (Fig. 4.25d, e). In the hydrated state the phospholipids form myelin bodies, often crescentric in shape, but whatever their shape, the bodies always consist of more or less closely packed parallel membranes, 60 Å thick and 120 Å apart. These two forms, anhydrous and hydrated, may occur separately in the cytoplasm, or together within a membrane-limited, presumably watery, vacuole. The hydrated type forms caps, crescents or complete shells on or around the inner surface of the vacuole, or forms other complex shapes within the vacuole.

Inorganic Inclusions

Haemosiderin, a ferric complex with protein, is present as granules in the choroid plexus of the guinea pig. Such granules may number 2–25 per cell and range from $0·5–5·0$ μ in diameter. The smaller forms are dense round or oval granules, and the larger ones generally appear as round frothy bodies with dielectronic circular areas of various sizes lying in a homogeneous material of great electron density (Fig. 4.26a). The larger bodies tend to be situated in the basal part of the cell.

Mineralized granules have been observed in the Malpighian tubules of *Rhodnius* and the calciferous gland of *Lumbricus*. The granules are presumed to be phosphates or carbonates of calcium or magnesium. In *Rhodnius* the fully formed granules are composed of concentric rings of various thickness, which have alternations of electron density between adielectronic and dielectronic. The central part of the granule is usually very dielectronic and the periphery very adielectronic. Incompletely formed granules have a narrow adielectronic granular outer ring, a wide granular and less electron-dense inner ring, and a dielectronic centre (Fig. 4.26b, c).

The melanin granules of the epidermal melanocytes of man and cat range from $0·1–0·4$ μ in size and are lozenge shaped. They are of two types, the light and the dark. The light type has a crystalline lattice structure of dense granules with a 70 Å spacing, and no limiting membrane (Fig. 4.26f). The dark granules have the same lattice structure as the light type, but this is masked by an adielectronic diffuse substance around it (Fig. 4.26d). In addition, the dense granules are surrounded by a shell of relatively coarse granular material. After permanganate staining, the shell and diffuse substances are removed and the essential crystalline structure of the dark granules is unmasked (Fig. 4.26e).

The test cells (specialized follicle cells) of tunicates become enclosed with the oocyte within the vitelline membrane, and in *Stylea plicata* such cells accumulate a yellowish orange pigment. This pigment arises within vacuoles of the young test cell and is at first a series of fine beaded filaments randomly oriented. Later, the filaments thicken and assume an orientation

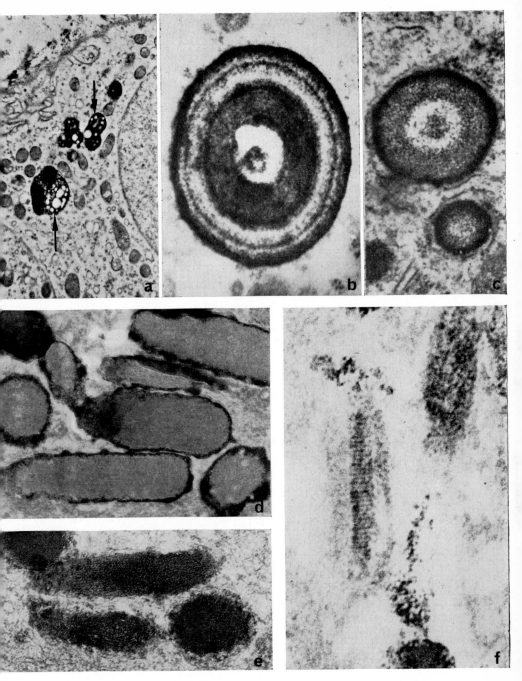

FIG. 4.26. (a) Haemosiderin granules in the choroid plexus epithelium of the guinea pig (arrows). (Courtesy Dr. M. Case. ×3900.) (b) and (c) Mineralized granules (Ca or Mg phosphates?) in the Malpighian tubules of *Rhodnius*. (Courtesy Sir V. B. Wigglesworth and Dr. M. Perry. (b) ×27,000. (c) ×38,000.) (d)–(f) Melanin granules from epidermal melanocytes. (d) Dark type granule. (e) Dark type granule after permanganate treatment, which reveals the essential striations. (f) Light type granule. (Courtesy Dr. P. Drochmans. (d) ×65,000. (e) ×65,000. (f) ×150,000.)

parallel to the long axis of the vacuole. The filaments are composed of chains of small spheres 38–40 Å in diameter, with a dielectronic centre. These masses of beaded filaments become progressively more electron dense and eventually fill the cell and compress the nucleus.

Lysosomes

The lysosome was originally a biochemical concept, being defined as a granule rich in hydrolytic enzymes, especially acid phosphatase. Subsequently, lysosomes were shown to contain acid ribonuclease and acid desoxyribonuclease, cathespin and β-glucuronidase. Lecithinase and proteolytic enzymes release the activity of the lysosomatic enzymes which are normally impermeable to their substrate. It was deduced, therefore, that the lysosome was enclosed in a lipoprotein membrane. Lysosomes have been identified from a wide variety of tissues and animal species and must now be considered as a distinct class of cellular inclusion.

The cytological identification of lysosomes is difficult, both because of their heterogeneity and the short time since their discovery. At the present time the universal characteristics of lysosomes in electron micrographs appear to be the presence of a single bounding membrane and of acid phosphatase. Other variable features of lysosomes are their narrow size range, ferritin granules and moderate electron density. In electron micrographs lysosomes have been identified with some certainty in liver and kidney. In the former they are homologous with the pericanalicular or peribiliary dense bodies, have a single bounding membrane enclosing many adielectronic grains resembling ferritin, and accessory vacuoles. They differ from micro-bodies in lacking the latter's crystalline inclusions. In kidney, droplets with a single limiting membrane and an amorphous content of medium electron density are considered to be lysosomes.

There is some evidence that four broad groups of lysosomes can be characterized: (a) the storage granule ("unused" lysosome) with a relatively homogeneous content and a peripheral localization of enzyme (Fig. 4.27a), (b) the digestive vacuole with a heterogeneous or frothy content and a random distribution of enzymes (Fig. 4.27b), (c) the autophagic vacuole with mitochondria or endoplasmic reticulum in process of degeneration and a randomly distributed enzyme (Fig. 4.27c), (d) the residual body containing myelin-like bodies and a peripheral distribution of enzymes (Fig. 4.27d). Of these four types the last two are most easily distinguished, but many intermediate forms make for difficulties in classification (Fig. 4.28a).

Other structures which have been identified as possible morphological representations of lysosomes are: (a) single membrane-bound bodies derived by the pinching off of swollen Golgi sacs, (b) pinocytotic and phagocytotic vacuoles, (c) multi-vesicular bodies, 0·5–0·25 μ in diameter, with a membrane boundary, sometimes incomplete, enclosing small vesicles

200–500 Å in diameter; such bodies have been observed in glomerular epithelium, neurones, sperm of various vertebrates and invertebrates, and mouse lymphocytes, to mention but a few tissues and cells.

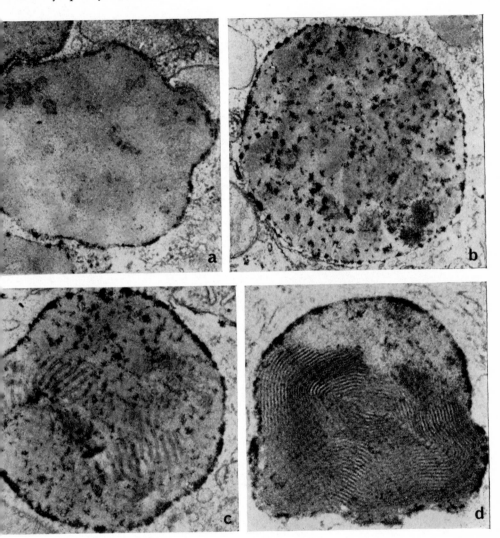

Fig. 4.27. (a)–(d) Lysosomes. (a) Lysosome; (b) digestive vacuole; (c) autophagic vacuole; (d) residual body. The dense granules show sites of acid phosphatase activity. (Courtesy Dr. F. Miller. All photos × 55,000.)

Annulate Lamellae

Annulate lamellae were unknown until the advent of electron microscopy. They appear to be confined to rapidly growing and differentiating cells

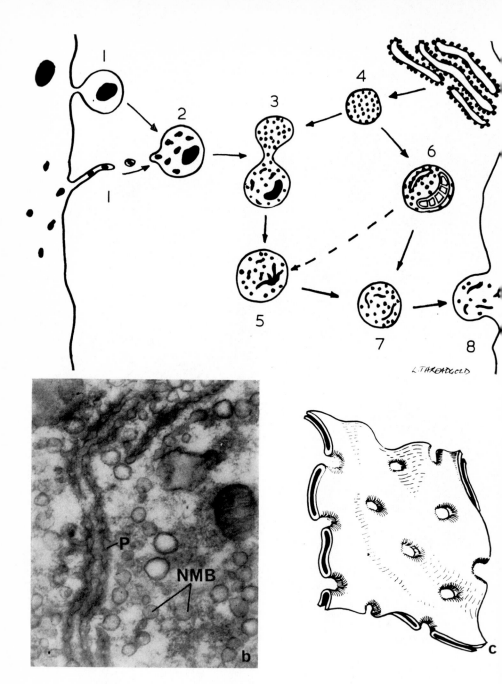

F IG. 4.28. (a) Diagram to show the interrelationship of the various types of lysosomes. 1, Formation of phagocytic and pinocytotic vacuoles by the plasma membrane; 2, vacuoles lying free in the cytoplasm; 3, fusion of lysosome (4) with the cytoplasmic vacuole; 4, lysosome derived from the endoplasmic reticulum, or Golgi complex; 5, digestive vacuole; 6, autophagic vacuole; 7, residual body; 8, defaecation vacuole. (Original, after Dr. C. de Duve.) (b) Annulate lamellae from the oocyte of *Necturus*. NMB, nuclear membrane blebs; P, pore. (Courtesy Dr. R. G. Kessel. × 31,600.) (c) Tridimensional drawing of annulate lamellae. (Courtesy Dr. S. Wischnitzer.)

such as oocytes, embryonic cells and spermatocytes. They have been observed in rat tissues, *Amblystoma* larvae, and in invertebrate and amphibian oocytes, in all of which they are morphologically similar. The annulate lamellae greatly resemble a portion of the nuclear membrane. Individual lamellae consist of two membranes in parallel, about 200–400 Å apart, and united at their ends (Fig. 4.28b, c). The membranes are perforated by pores with annulae identical with nuclear pores. The lamellae may occur singly but are sometimes stacked. They may lie close to and parallel with the nuclear membrane, or lie anywhere within the cytoplasm (Fig. 4.28b, c). They are strongly basophilic and contain RNA, although this is not in the form of ribosomes such as occur in the granular endoplasmic reticulum.

Further Reading List

1. Huxley, H. E., Muscle Cells, *The Cell*, Vol. IV, edit. Brachet, J. and Mirsky, A. E., Academic Press, London, 1961.
2. Porter, K. R., The Ground Substance, *The Cell*, Vol. II, edit. Brachet, J. and Mirsky, A. E., Academic Press, London, 1961.
3. Sjostrand, F. S., Endoplasmic Reticulum, *Cytology and Cell Physiology*, 3rd ed., edit. Bourne, G. H., Academic Press, London, 1964.
4. Haguenau, F., The Ergastoplasm: Its History, Ultrastructure and Biochemistry, *Int. Review of Cytology*, Vol. 9, edit. Bourne, G. H. and Danielli, J. F., Academic Press, London, 1957.
5. Weiss, P., Cell Contact, *Int. Review of Cytology*, Vol. 7, edit. Bourne, G. H. and Danielli, J. F., Academic Press, London, 1957.
6. Oberling, C., The Structure of the Cytoplasm. *Int. Review of Cytology*, Vol. 8, edit. Bourne, G. H., and Danielli, J. F., Academic Press, London, 1958.
7. The Sarcoplasmic Reticulum, *J. Biophys. Biochem. Cytol.*, **10**, Suppl. 1961, edit. Porter, K. R., Rockefeller Institute Press, New York.
8. Porter, K. R., The Endoplasmic Reticulum: Some Current Interpretations of its Form and Function, *Biological Structure and Function*, edit. Goodwin, T. W., *Proc. of the first IUB/IUBS International Symposium*, Academic Press, London.

CHAPTER 5

THE ULTRASTRUCTURE OF THE CYTOSOME

III. The Golgi Complex and the Mitochondrion

The Golgi Complex

The Golgi complex, which was such a controversial structure when it could only be observed with the light microscope, has emerged from electron microscopy with a distinct and characteristic fine structure which makes it readily recognizable in all cells. It is now generally agreed that the vertebrate Golgi complex and the invertebrate dictyosome are homologous structures, and that the Golgi complex intervenes in some secretory processes.

At low magnification the Golgi complex appears as a series of alternating adielectronic and dielectronic lines (lamellae) $0 \cdot 5$–$3 \cdot 0$ μ long, resembling a section of a myelin sheath or a phospholipid inclusion (Fig. 5.1a). These lamellae may be in flat sheets but more often are curved, so that their three-dimensional shapes may vary from a shallow saucer to a narrow-necked bowl (Fig. 5.1a, b). Associated with the lamellae may be vacuoles ranging in size and number.

In sections observed at high magnification and resolution the Golgi complex in fully differentiated and actively secreting cells is composed of three elements: first, a stack of flattened sacs which are united pairs of the adielectronic lamellae seen at low magnification; second, large vacuoles; and third, small vesicles. The flattened sacs generally have a narrow lumen which is sometimes slightly expanded at its ends (Fig. 5.1c). The contents of the lumen have an electron density about equal to that of the hyaloplasm, though it may vary from more adielectronic to less adielectronic, depending on the functional state of the Golgi complex and the preparative techniques used. The lumen is enclosed by a smooth membrane which, under suitable conditions, can be resolved into the unit membrane structure (Fig. 5.1c) of a type resembling the endoplasmic rather than the plasma membrane, i.e. it is symmetrical and has a lipid layer with a globular pattern (Fig. 5.2a). The sacs usually lie in parallel, but may diverge anywhere along their length, especially at the periphery of the stack. In the more curved type of Golgi complex, the more central sacs are shorter than the outer ones, and even in almost straight complexes, a few sacs may be shorter than the others, or may even run from one stack to form part of another stack.

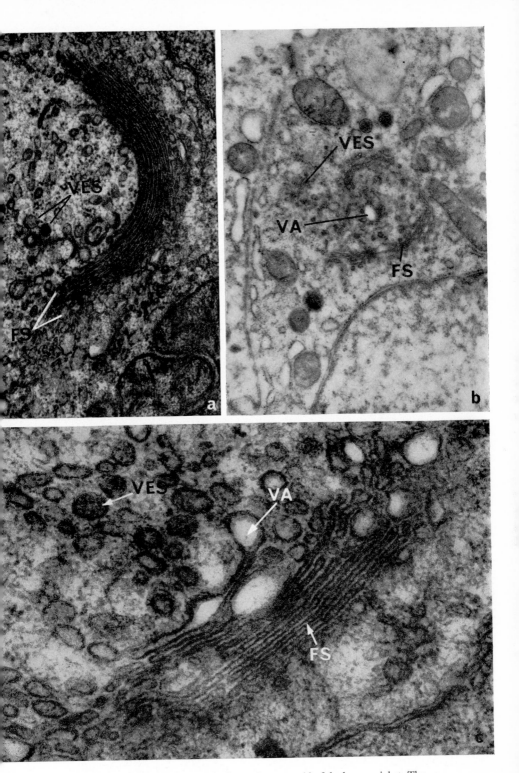

FIG. 5.1. (a) Golgi complex (dictyosome) of an early spermatid of the house cricket. The shallow saucer shape is due to the grouping of the flattened sacs (FS). VES, vesicular component of the complex. (Courtesy Dr. J. Kaye. ×36,000.) (b) Golgi complex of the pancreas of a 16-day incubated chick embryo. The complex is flask-shaped. VA, vacuolar component of the complex. (Courtesy Dr. R. F. Zeigel. ×21,000.) (c) Golgi complex (dictyosome) of the primary spermatocyte of the house cricket. The tripartite nature of the sac and vesicle membranes is apparent. Swollen ends of the sacs give rise to vacuoles (VA), the third component of the Golgi complex. (Courtesy Dr. J. Kaye. ×93,000.)

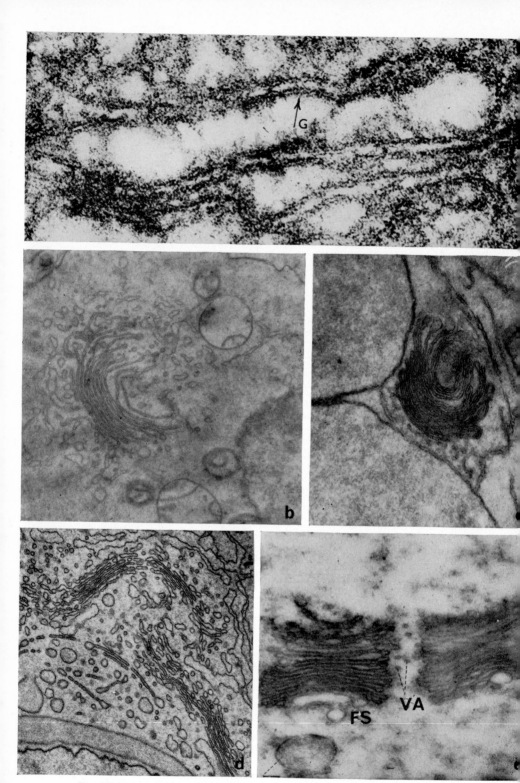

FIG. 5.2. (a) Membranes of the Golgi complex showing the globular pattern of the lipid component (arrow at G). (Courtesy Dr. F. Sjostrand. ×230,000.) (b) and (c) Golgi complex (dictyosome) of a spermatogonium of the camel cricket, *Ceuthophilus*. The number of sacs per complex is approximately 11. (Courtesy Dr. T. N. Tahmisian. (b) ×21,000. (c) ×14,500.) (d) Golgi complex of a spermatocyte of the guinea pig (KMnO₄ fixation). Average number of sacs is 6. (Courtesy Dr. H. Mollenhauer. ×19,000.) (e) Golgi complex (dictyosome) of *Trichonympha*, containing an average of 14 sacs. (Courtesy Dr. M. P. Grasse. ×41,000.)

The number of sacs in a Golgi complex varies considerably, depending on function and species, but generally invertebrate dictyosomes have more sacs than vertebrate complexes. In the camel cricket *Ceuthophilus*, the spermatocyte dictyosome has 10 sacs and the spermatid acrosome 17 (Fig. 5.2b, c), whereas in mammalian spermatogenital cells the number of sacs varies from 6 to 9 in the rat and from 5 to 6 in the guinea pig (Fig. 5.2d). Similarly, the parabasal body of the flagellate *Trichonympha agilis* has 14 sacs (Fig. 5.2e) while the Golgi complex of the convoluted tubules of the mouse kidney has only 4–6 sacs. There are, however, some exceptions, e.g. the dictyosomes of the neurones and epithelial cells of the limpet, *Patella vulgata,* have only 4–6 sacs.

The sacs are the origin of both the large vacuoles and the vesicles. The large vacuoles with their dielectronic centres are conspicuous only in the Golgi complex of active or secretory cells, so that in other inactive or fully differentiated non-secretory cells the vacuoles may be absent, the Golgi complex then consisting only of sacs and vesicles. The vacuoles are situated mainly at the periphery of the sacs, but may occupy the area bounded by the curvature of the complex or the middle region of the stack. Most vacuoles clearly originate by a considerable, but localized, swelling of the lumen of a sac and the lumen of such vacuoles may be continuous with the narrow lumen of the remainder of the sac. The free vacuoles are derived by the pinching off of swollen ends of sacs and are, therefore, completely enclosed by a membrane identical with that appearing elsewhere in the Golgi complex. Some vacuoles, especially if they lie against the outermost sac of a stack, have either a single limiting membrane or the double membrane of the sac running along part of their margin, the remaining limits of the vacuole being indistinct. These vacuoles give the appearance of not having arisen from an expansion of a sac, but rather in relation to the outer surface of one of the sac membranes. However, careful examination of the relationship of vacuole to sac shows that such vacuoles do arise within a sac lumen, but that subsequently part or all of their limiting membranes become lost, and consequently indistinctly limited vacuoles come to lie close against or between the double membranes of adjacent sacs. The foregoing descriptions of vacuoles are derived from studies of material fixed in osmium or chrome-osmium solutions. With potassium permanganate fixation, however, the vacuoles are not so prominent a feature of the Golgi complex and their lumen often has an electron density the same as the narrow lumen of the sacs. The enclosing membranes are distinct for all vacuoles and these are more obviously merely expanded portions of sacs.

The vesicles appear in sections as small elliptical, oval, or circular bodies and have a limiting membrane identical with that of the sacs. The contents of the vesicles have an electron density similar to the lumen of the sacs, although it may be less dense in some of the larger vesicles or have a central adielectronic granule, e.g. *Patella* neurones. The vesicles are grouped and may lie aligned with the ends of the sacs, or within the area enclosed by the curvature of the sacs, or in the immediate vicinity of the outermost sac, i.e. the sac with the least curvature. Although the vesicles farthest from the Golgi complex probably represent sections through spheres or ellipsoids, those aligned with the periphery of the sacs, or lying within the stack, are probably sections through fenestrated parts of the sacs. This interpretation is supported by observations on oblique sections of sacs at their periphery, for these show electron-dense anastomosing strands with round dielectronic areas between them (Fig. 5.3a). The extent to which this fenestration of the sacs at their edges is due to fixation or other preparative techniques is not known.

The dimensions of the Golgi complex depend upon a variety of factors which have been mentioned already, but some conception of the range in dimensions can be gained by reference to measurements of a few complexes. In the limpet, *Patella vulgata*, the sacs are 150–300 Å wide, with adjacent sacs separated by 50–200 Å. The smooth membranes of the sacs measure 50–100 Å in thickness and the lumen are 50–100 Å wide. The large vacuoles vary from about 750 Å to about 6000 Å and the vesicles from 300 Å to 1000 Å. In the convoluted tubules of the kidney the sacs are 160–210 Å wide, with adjacent sacs separated by spaces 50–200 Å. The sac membranes are 60 Å in diameter and the lumina 90 Å. The large vacuoles range from 500–2000 Å, and the vesicles are about 500 Å in diameter with walls 60 Å thick. Other species have sac widths ranging from 120 to 300 Å, with membranes 50–100 Å thick and lumina 60–150 Å wide. Similarly, sacs separated by distances ranging from 50 to 500 Å, vacuoles 500–6000 Å and vesicles from 250 to 1000 Å in diameter have been recorded.

Functional Activity of the Golgi Complex

The Golgi complex and its structural changes have been correlated with secretory activity in cells from the earliest studies of this organoid. This correlation has been amply supported by the results of numerous electron-microscope studies. Examples of alterations in the ultrastructure of the Golgi complex with function could be drawn from a great many sources. Three examples will suffice to show the range of involvement of the Golgi complex in secretion, namely, the formation of intracellular crystals in the midgut glands of a marine crustacean, milk protein droplet form-ation in the mouse mammary gland, and the parafollicular cells of the thyroid.

The isopod, *Limnoria lignorum,* burrows into wood pilings or drift wood. It has the ability to digest cellulose and convert it into simple sugars. Involved in this process are the midgut glands which produce a cellulase, and some of the cells of these glands contain crystals ranging up to 30 μ long and 15 μ thick. The appearance of crystals is sporadic, some glands have no crystals, others have small crystals lying between the nucleus and secretory pole of the cell, and yet other cells have large crystals

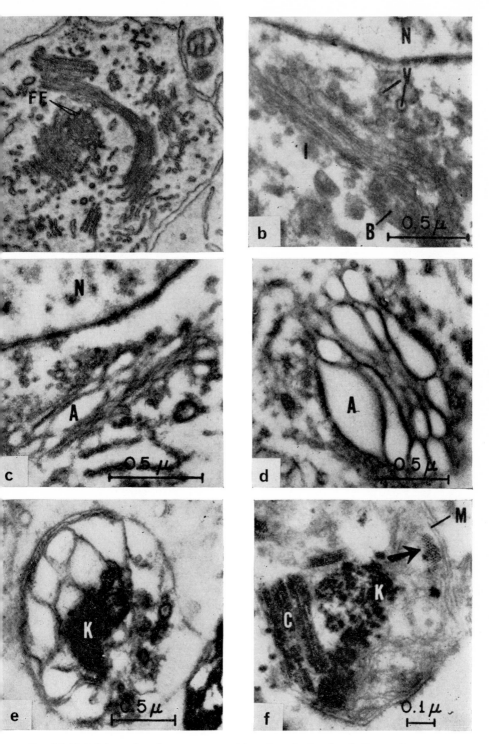

Fig. 5.3. (a) Golgi complex of a spermatocyte of the guinea pig showing the fenestrations (FE) at the periphery of the sacs. (Courtesy Dr. H. Mollenhauer. ×24,000.) (b)–(f) Sequence showing the secretion of iron–protein crystals by the Golgi complex of the mid-gut gland of *Limnoria lignorum*. GA, Golgi complex; A, dilated Golgi sacs; K, iron-containing particles; C, iron-containing granules aligned on membranes; arrow, hexagonal packing of iron-containing particles. (Courtesy Dr. S. W. Strunk.)

which may lie anywhere in the cytoplasm. Originally the crystals were considered to contain uric acid, but they are now known to contain protein and iron.

The Golgi complex of the mid-gut glands has a variety of morphologies which can be arranged in a series thought to represent the successive stages in the elaboration of the crystals. In stage 1 the Golgi complex lies close to the nucleus, is 1–2 μ long and up to 0·5 μ thick. It consists of the typical stack of flattened sacs and associated vesicles (Fig. 5.3b). The distance between adjacent sacs is 70–1000 Å and between membranes of a single sac 70 Å. In stage 2 the Golgi complex has dilated oval sacs, either arranged in parallel or in an arc about a central focus (Fig. 5.3c, d). The enlarged inter-filamentous areas contain a fine fibrillar material. By stage 3 the Golgi complex is about 2·0 μ in diameter, has an elliptical shape and lies relatively far from the nucleus. The complex is composed of a single large vacuole enclosing a number of smaller vesicles packed together so as to give them irregular shapes due to reciprocal pressure (Fig. 5.3e). Dense granular material lies between the vesicles. In stage 4 the Golgi complex is up to 3·0 μ in diameter and may lie in any part of the secretory pole of the cell. The complex is surrounded by limiting membranes presumably derived from swollen Golgi sacs, but difficult to trace. Within these membranes the large vacuoles have become flattened and their membranes are apparently in-creased by elaboration to form orderly parallel arrays (Fig. 5.3f). Concurrent with the changes in membrane arrangement, loose aggregates of iron-containing particles accumulate within the vesicles (Fig. 5.3f) and later come to lie in an ordered pattern on the pairs of flattened membranes which lie in parallel. These rows of granules on the membranes may be connected to a dense mass of iron-containing particles at one end (Fig. 5.3f). It has been suggested that the particles may "flow" along the membranes. Later the membranes are either concealed or they disintegrate and the particles become hexagonally packed to form a small crystal (Fig. 5.4a). The crystal is without an enclosing membrane, and its particles are spheroidal, being about 60 Å in diameter and spaced 90 Å apart centre to centre. Probably the larger crystals are due to the fusion of smaller ones.

The lactating mammary gland of mice secretes both large fat droplets and smaller, 300–4000 Å in diameter, protein droplets. The latter are related to the Golgi complex which is usually composed of several flattened sacs. Some of these flattened sacs have broad, oval or elliptical dilations at their extremities which contain fine vesicles 100–300 Å in diameter (Fig. 5.4b). Similar vesicles occur in closed vacuoles close to the Golgi complex and appear to be pinched off portions of the swollen sacs (Fig. 5.4c). Between the Golgi complex and the apical cell membrane are numerous vacuoles similar in all aspects to those near the Golgi complex and showing all degrees of concentration of their contents, until they resemble the mature protein droplets. Mature droplets are relatively adielectronic and contain a fine, particulate substance. These droplets appear to open on to the cell surface,

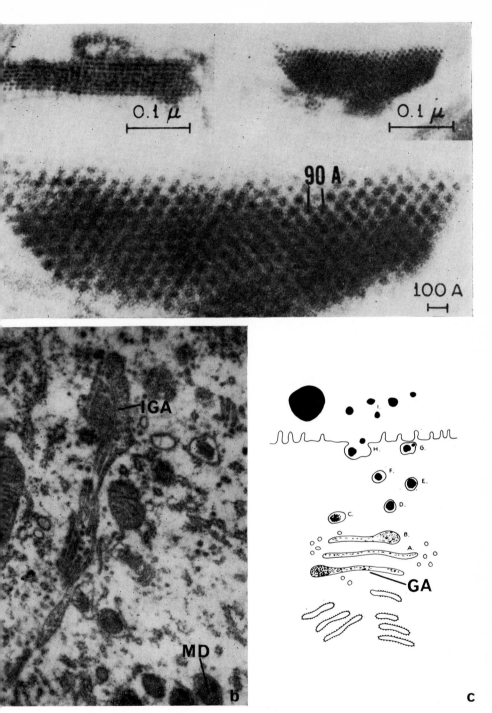

Fig. 5.4. (a) Hexagonal packing of iron–protein complexes in crystals arising in the mid-gut glands of *Limnoria lignorum*. (Courtesy Dr. S. W. Strunk.) (b) and (c) Secretion of milk droplets by the Golgi complex in the mammary epithelium of the mouse. IGA, swollen ends of Golgi sacs with protein secretion in the lumen; MD, milk droplets. (Courtesy Dr. S. R. Wellings. (b) × 19,000. (c) Drawing of the secretory process.)

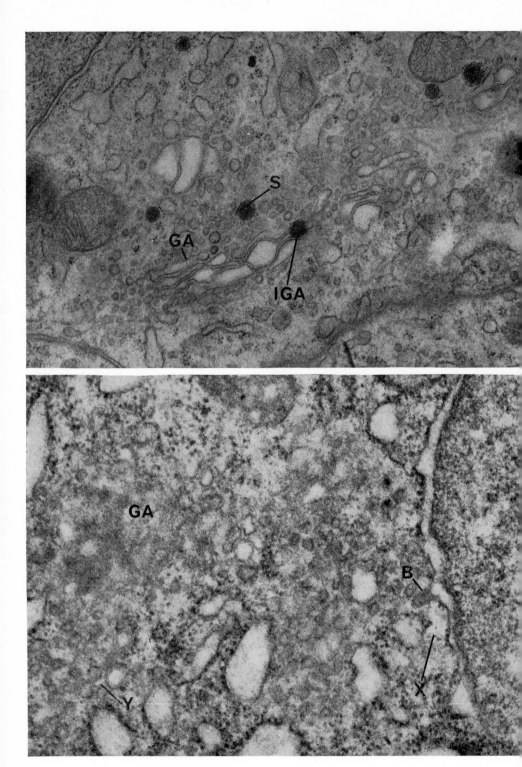

Fɪɢ. 5.5. (a) Secretion of dense granules by the Golgi complex of the parafollicular cells of the rat. GA, Golgi complex; S, secretion; IGA, intra-Golgi secretion. (Courtesy Dr. S. L. Wissig. × 28,000.) (b) Murine plasma cells (neoplasm) showing the blebbing of the nuclear membrane (B) and the close association of the blebs to the Golgi complex (GA). Intimate nucleus–endoplasmic reticulum and Golgi–endoplasmic reticulum relationships are also evident at X and Y respectively. (Courtesy Dr. R. F. Zeigel. × 69,500.)

presumably by the fusion of their enclosing membrane with the plasma membrane (Fig. 5.4c).

The thyroid gland of the rat contains in addition to the thyroid epithelium a second type of cell, namely the parafollicular cell. These cells are rare, occurring in small groups, and have an ellipsoidal shape, their long axes being parallel to the circumference of the follicular basement membrane. Parafollicular cells are always separated from the colloid by overlying thyroid follicle cells.

The parafollicular cells are characterized by an abundance of spherical vesicles approximately 2000 Å in diameter. Each vesicle is limited by a single membrane and contains a matted substance of intermediate electron density, although some vesicles contain an adielectronic substance (Fig. 5.5a). The Golgi complex consists of large flattened sacs, with large local central and terminal expansions, and small vesicles. The 2000 Å diameter vesicles are intermingled with the Golgi complex and appear to be derived from pinched off parts of the Golgi sacs (Fig. 5.5a). Adielectronic granules occur within the lumina of some of the Golgi sacs, so supporting the association between this cell organoid and the spherical vesicles. The parafollicular cells, therefore, are a separate endocrine epithelium in the thyroid, and the Golgi complex is involved in the secretion of an unknown substance.

The frequent juxta-nuclear position of the Golgi complex in conjunction with the appearance of small outpocketings and vesiculation of the adjacent nuclear membrane, have initiated the idea that under certain circumstances the nuclear membrane may contribute to the membranes of the Golgi complex. Cells in which this nuclear–Golgi complex relationship is very evident are in a murine plasma cell neoplasm (MPC-2 (Fig. 5.5b), and other tumour cells. In addition, the plasma membrane may give rise to smooth surfaced membranes which transform into Golgi membranes, and such a situation has been suggested from observations on the absorptive cells of the rat ileum.

More frequently observed than the nuclear–Golgi or plasma membrane–Golgi relationship is the linkage, both functional and structural, between the Golgi complex and the endoplasmic reticulum. This association has been observed in the uterine epithelium, ciliary body, parotid gland and *Epistylis* (Fig. 5.6a), to mention but some of the known examples. An intimate structural and functional association between the Golgi complex, the endoplasmic reticulum and the plasma membrane has been observed in the formation of the secretory product of the A type cell in the anterior lobe of the pituitary of 18–21-day-old rat *in utero*.† In these cells the granular endoplasmic reticulum in the vicinity of the Golgi complex, and also elsewhere in the cytoplasm, has local outpocketings free of ribosomes (Fig. 5.7b). Many small vesicles of a diameter similar to the evaginations

† The cells of the anterior lobe of the pituitary are divided into A type with secretion granules 3200–3500 Å in diameter, and B type with granules 1600 Å in diameter.

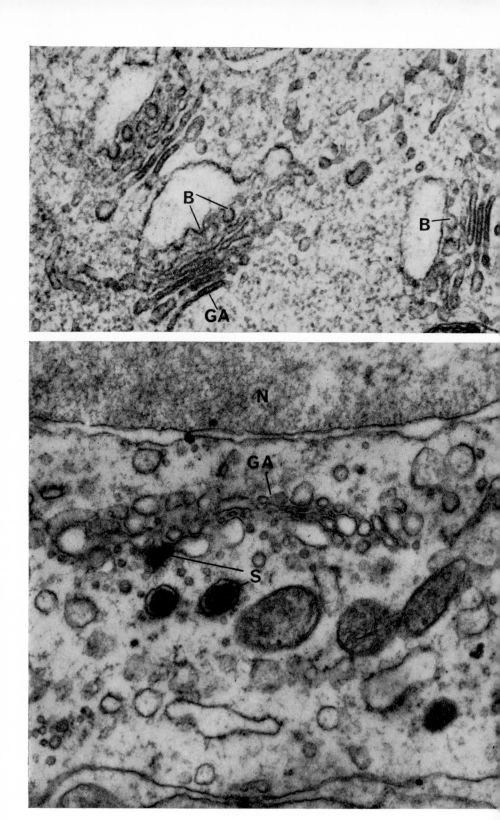

FIG. 5.6. (a) Intimate relationship between the Golgi complex (GA) and the granular endoplasmic reticulum in *Epistylis anastatica*. B, blebs from the reticulum passing to the Golgi complex. (Courtesy Dr. E. Faure-Fremeit. × 56,000.) (b) Secretion production (S) by the Golgi complex (GA) in the A type cell of the foetal rat hypophysis; N, nucleus. (Courtesy Dr. M. Maillard. × 41,000.)

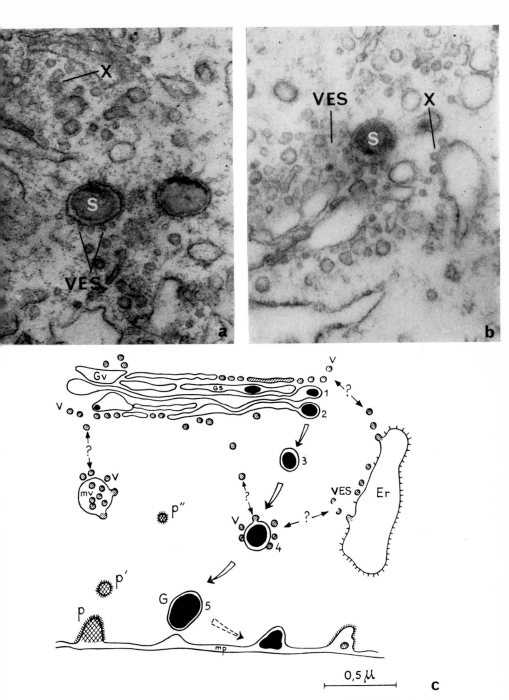

Fig. 5.7. (a) and (b) Small vesicles (VES) fusing with the secretory bodies (S) in the A type cell of the foetal rat hypophysis. The vesicles appear to arise from the granular endoplasmic reticulum (see at X). (Courtesy Dr. M. Maillard. (a) × 47,000. (b) × 47,000.) (c) Diagram showing the possible relationship between the various cell organoids in the A type cell of the foetal rat hypophysis; GS, Golgi sac; GV, Golgi vacuole; V, vesicles; G, secretory granule; MP, intercellular space; ER, endoplasmic reticulum; p, p' and p", pinocytotic vesicles; Ves, vesicles. (Courtesy Dr. M. Maillard.)

on the reticulum lie around that structure and the Golgi complex. Some vesicles appear to be in the process of adding themselves to the flattened sacs of the Golgi complex, while others are apparently fusing directly with the maturing secretory granules (Fig. 5.7a–c). Within the Golgi sacs are adielectronic granules, sometimes central but more often terminal (Fig. 5.6b). Membrane-bound, adielectronic secretory granules budded from the Golgi sacs lie around the complex and between it and the plasma membrane (Fig. 5.6b). Certain secretory granules lie in contact with the plasma membrane and others appear to have merged their membranes with the plasma membrane, so that their adielectronic contents lie as an amorphous mass in the intercellular space (Figs. 3.31a–c, 5.7b).

In general, the function of the Golgi complex seems to be the concentration of secretory products by the withdrawal of water from them. This process may occur within the Golgi complex itself, where membrane-bound secretory bodies budded off from the flattened sacs gradually decrease in size and their contents become progressively more adielectronic, or by withdrawing water from the endoplasmic reticulum, an idea which has been suggested on the basis of some observations on the albumen-secreting cells of the hen oviduct. It is possible therefore that in terrestrial animals, in addition to the conservation of water carried out by the urinary system, all cells in the body may also conserve intracellular water by means of Golgi function.

Mitochondria

The basic ultrastructural similarity of all mitochondria was demonstrated soon after electron microscopy of thin sections of animal tissues started. On the basis of ultrastructure, the mitochondrion can be most simply defined as a cell organoid with a smooth limiting membrane and an inner, infolded membrane, the infolds being called cristae. Between the two adielectronic membranes is a dielectronic outer chamber, which is continuous with the core of the cristae, and enclosed by the inner membrane is an inner chamber or matrix. Small adielectronic granules may occur within the matrix (Fig. 5.8a).

The limiting and inner membranes each measure 35–60 Å thick and the outer chamber is 40–70 Å wide. The inner membrane forming the cristae measures 40–70 Å and the continuation of the outer chamber into the cristae is 40–80 Å wide (Fig. 5.8a, b). Each limiting and inner membrane can be resolved into a typical unit membrane, the central dielectronic component, 20–23 Å being flanked on each side by an adielectronic component 15–17 Å thick, as measured on human leucocyte mitochondria. These mitochondrial membranes are of the symmetrical type, and have a lipid layer with a globular pattern as do the Golgi and endoplasmic membranes (Fig. 5.9a). Although the limiting and inner membranes appear structurally identical, there is evidence for considering them different. The limiting membrane shows the same smooth form in all mitochondria and is apparently very

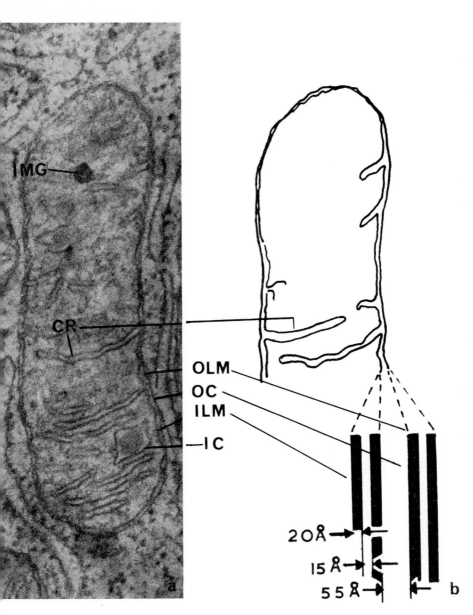

FIG. 5.8. (a) A mitochondrion from the mucoid cell of the fundic gland of the mouse stomach. OLM, outer limiting membrane; ILM, inner membrane; OC, outer chamber; IC, inner chamber (matrix); CR, cristae; IMG, intramitochondrial granule. (Courtesy Dr. H. F. Helander. × 112,000.) (b) Diagram of part of the mitochondrion in (a) interpreted to show the average dimensions and molecular structure of the membranes. (Original.)

stable. The inner membrane is labile and appears in a variety of forms within the same mitochondrion, in mitochondria of the same cell undergoing different functions, and in different cells and animals, as will shortly be described. The limiting membrane may be absent in some mitochondria, although many recorded instances of this phenomenon are probably the result of poor fixation, resolution or other preparative technique. The limiting membrane is considered to be highly permeable, while the inner membrane has a restricted permeability and its structure is not destroyed or altered in mitochondria isolated from tissues. Furthermore, careful measurements of the liver mitochondria of normal rats show that the limiting and inner membranes average 45 Å and the cristae 50 Å in diameter. After thyroxin stimulation, however, the limiting and inner membranes measured the same as in normal rats, although the outer chamber increased from 60 to 80 Å, whereas the cristae membranes had increased in thickness to 55 Å. In the mitochondria of the ciliate *Epistylis anastatica* the limiting membrane measured 40 Å and the inner one 70 Å. Such observations support the idea of differences in the function and structure of limiting and inner membranes.

The inner chamber matrix shows various electron densities, depending on tissue and animal species. It is generally composed of fine granules 40–50 Å in diameter, but may appear homogeneous or so dielectronic in localized areas as to resemble a vacuole. The matrix is considered by some electron microscopists to be a fluid, but its electron density, its granularity, and the presence of large intramitochondrial granules and crystals suspended in the matrix suggest that it is viscous and semi-solid. In the mitochondrial matrix of many species are fibres 20–50 Å in diameter or clumps about 100 Å wide which are often attached to the inner membrane. These fibres are circular DNA molecules 4·7–5·4 μ long. Mitochondria also have ribosomes 120–150 Å in diameter, and t RNA. Although m RNA has not yet been demonstrated, mitochondria can incorporate amino acids into insoluble, structural proteins, but apparently not into soluble, enzymatic ones, indicating they possess the complete DNA–RNA–protein system.

The very adielectronic mitochondrial granules within the matrix are 300 Å in diameter on average. Their number per mitochondrion varies, granules being absent or few in the mitochondria of protozoans, myocardial cells, and resting thyroid cells whereas in liver, pancreas, duodenal absorbing, bronchial epithelial and kidney brush border cells, and in myeloblasts and leucocytes, the granules are very numerous. The granules appear to be the sites for the binding of divalent ions of magnesium and cacium, elements which are important in the molecular structure of enzymes (Fig. 5.9c).

The matrix in the inner chamber of the mitochondrion is considered to be a continuous phase, although the interconnections of the different parts may be tenuous and temporary. In some electron micrographs individual cristae are clearly joined to the inner membrane on opposite sides of the mitochondrion, thereby forming a true septum and individual compartments within the matrix. Such cristae, however, may incompletely partition the matrix in subsequent sections (Fig. 5.9d, e) and, even if complete, may exist in life only temporarily. Physiological processes within the mitochondrion would be facilitated by a continuous matrix in the inner chamber, just as these processes benefit from the increased surface area provided by the cristae and the continuation of the inner membrane into the cristae. Doubtless, the extent of the inner chamber varies between mitochondria and in a particular mitochondrion with time and function.

The fine structure of the mitochondrion as described above, with all the mitochondrial membranes smooth and of the unit membrane type, and with the organoid consisting of limiting and inner infolded membrane, and of an outer chamber and inner chamber with granules, is derived principally from the study of material fixed in osmium. Nevertheless, it has been accepted as a true picture of mitochondrial morphology. A number of recent observations, however, suggest that some of the above features are artefacts, or if not artefacts, at least give an incomplete picture of the true structure of the mitochondrion. To date, there is insufficient research to support and confirm these observations beyond doubt, but the improved techniques and special circumstances in which the observations have been made are good reason for believing that such features may eventually be observed in most mitochondria.

Certain observations suggest that the outer chamber may be an artefact, due to swelling during preparation. Exocrine cells of the cat pancreas fixed in potassium permanganate and embedded in Vestopal show mitochondria in which the outer chamber is absent. The limiting and inner membranes are fused, the two tripartite membranes forming a pentapartite structure with a central adielectronic component flanked on each side by a dielectronic and adielectronic component, respectively (Fig. 5.10a). The cristae may also show this pentapartite structure, but in parts enclose an outer chamber of limited dimensions, giving the usual seven-layered appearance of two unit membranes separated by a dielectronic space.

Such observations are supported in some measure by the appearance of mitochondria specially treated by fixation in formalin, ultra-rapid dehydration followed by lipid extraction and epoxy embedment. These organoids give a generally negative image except for the cristae which show a central adielectronic layer 50–60 Å thick. This layer must be proteinaceous since it resists lipid extraction and is not visible in the mitochondrial envelope. It may be that this protein layer within the cristae is equal to the remnants of the outer chamber, but could equally well be the central fused line of a pentapartite structure.

Certain special modifications of the relationship between the limiting and inner mitochondrial membranes have also been seen. In the exocrine cells of the pancreas, the limiting membrane of the mitochondrion is not always continuous, but appears in places to invaginate into the matrix to

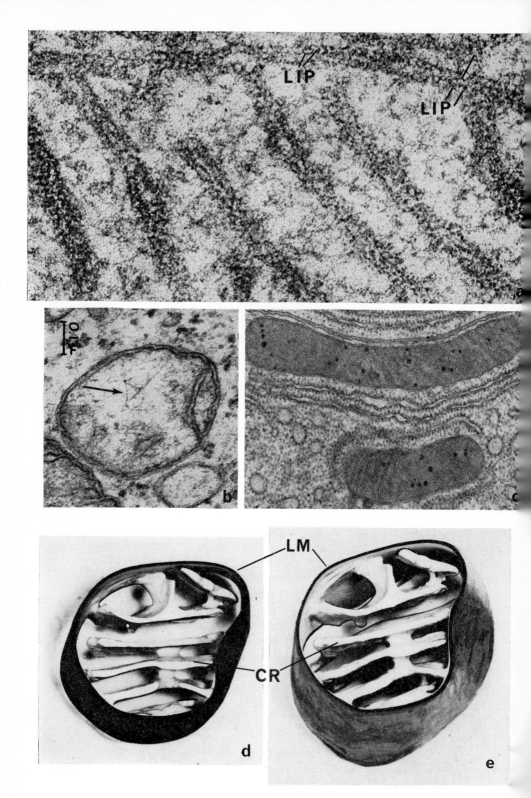

FIG. 5.9. (a) Mitochondrial membranes to show the globular pattern of the lipid component (LIP) of the membranes. (Courtesy Dr. F. Sjostrand. × 400,000.) (b) Mitochondrion containing DNA fibres (arrow) from a developing chick embryo. (Courtesy Dr. M. M. K. Nass. × 80,000.) (c) Intramitochondrial granules in the mitochondria of the bat pancreas. (Courtesy Dr. S. Ito. × 20,000.) (d) and (e) Tridimensional reconstruction of the mitochondrion in the terminal axon branchlet of mouse muscle. LM, limiting membranes; CR, cristae. (Courtesy Dr. E. Andersson-Cedergren.)

form a crista. Such invaginations must either pierce or pass through a pore in the inner membrane, or a pore must exist in the limiting membrane opposite and in line with a normal crista. In any of these cases the core of the crista would be open to the cytoplasm (Fig. 5.10b).

In the liver and kidney cells of the day-old hamster, and in the cells of the striated duct of the human salivary gland, the limiting and inner membranes "cross-over". One of the two membranes is continuous at the point of "cross-over", and so reverses from being a limiting to being an inner membrane. The other membrane either loses density and grades into a less dense area at the "cross-over" point, or is broken, ending abruptly as either a limiting or an inner membrane. Such an observation detracts from any theories that the inner and limiting membranes are essentially different, for in some cases they are parts of one membrane (Figs. 5.10c; 5.11a). As in the previous modification, the mitochondrial matrix is in contact with the cytoplasm at the "cross-over" by a channel 100 Å wide. It has been suggested that swelling of the mitochondria could occur without disruption of membranes by the relative sliding of the two membranes and the unfolding of the cristae.

Another modification of the limiting mitochondrial membrane has been observed in the mitochondria of the synaptic bodies of the rod cells in the cat. The mitochondria occur in pairs or small groups which are intimately associated, so that the opposed membranes of adjacent mitochondria lie only 125 Å apart. In such areas of contact the outer adielectronic component of the limiting membranes has a beaded appearance with a periodicity of 160 Å. Where adjacent membranes diverge there is an abrupt change to the normal smooth limiting membrane (Fig. 5.11b).

As previously indicated, the limiting mitochondrial membrane is a more stable structure than the cristae membranes, so that modifications in mitochondria are mainly apparent in the latter, although some changes in mitochondrial matrix, intramitochondrial granules and the limiting membrane do occur, as has already been shown. The number of cristae per mitochondrion varies greatly, and there appears to be a correlation between the number of cristae per mitochondrion and the general activity of the tissue. For example, in insect flight muscle and mammalian cardiac muscle, tissues which have high rates of oxidative metabolism, the number of cristae in the mitochondria is very high (Fig. 5.12a). Other cells with similar types of mitochondria to muscle are spermatozoa, brown fat, mammalian striated muscle, retinal rods, oxintic cells and distal convoluted tubules of the kidney. The number of cristae may be such that the matrix is almost occluded, the cristae lying close together in parallel array. Conversely, in ciliated, brush and bronchiolar cells of the trachea and lungs, and rat hepatic cells, the mitochondria have few cristae, and even the cristae present seem to partition incompletely, revealing large areas of matrix running as a wide central band throughout the organoid. In parasitic helminthes, mitochondria frequently have only one crista running

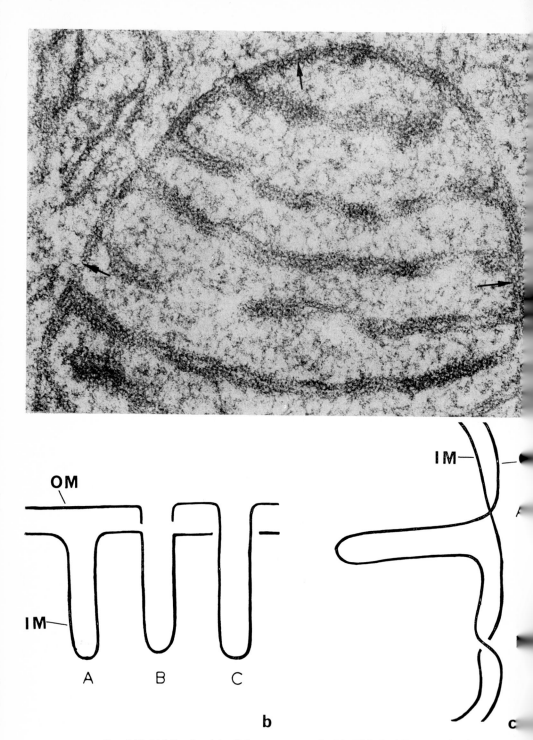

FIG. 5.10. (a) Mitochondria of the cat pancreas fixed in KMnO₄. The outer chamber is absent in places (arrows) due to contact of the inner and outer mitochondrial membranes. (Courtesy Dr. F. Sjostrand. × 230,000.) (b) Diagram of the possible relationships between the inner (IM) and outer mitochondrial (OM) membranes of mitochondria in the exocrine pancreas of the mouse. (Original, after Dr. S. K. Malhotra.) (c) Diagram of the relationship of reversed inner (IM) and outer (OM) mitochondrial membranes in the mitochondria of the liver of day-old hamsters (see Fig. 5.11a.) (Original, after Dr. S. Chandra.)

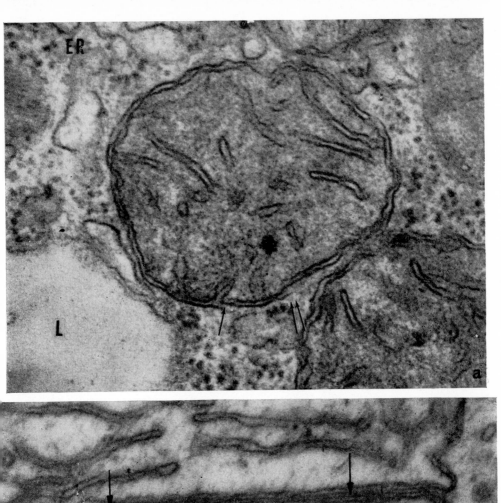

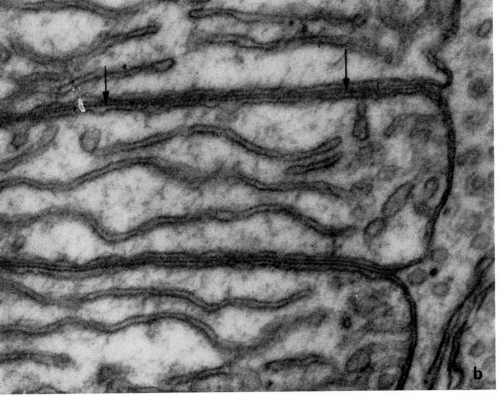

FIG. 5.11. (a) Mitochondrion from the liver of a day-old hamster showing the cross-over (reversal) of the mitochondrial membranes (arrows). (Courtesy Dr. S. Chandra. ×100,000.) (b) Mitochondria from the synaptic bodies of cat rod cells showing the beading of the closely opposed outer mitochondrial membranes (between the arrows). (Courtesy Dr. D. C. Pease. ×98,000.)

longitudinally, and sometimes apparently no cristae are present; this situation is probably related to the ability of such parasites to survive in environments poor in oxygen (Fig. 5.12b).

Cristae can be classified as either (a) septate, complete or incomplete,

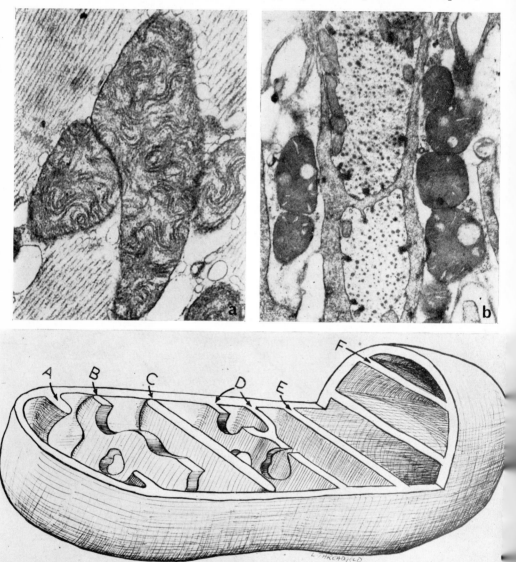

Fig. 5.12. (a) Locust muscle mitochondria showing an abundance of cristae. (Original. × 30,000.) (b) Mitochondria the parenchyma of the liver fluke, *Fasciola hepatica,* showing very few cristae. (Original. × 10,000.) (c) Tridimens drawing of some of the possible (A–F) types of septate cristae and their relationship to the inner membrane. A, perip type; B, fenestrated, unattached type; C, non-fenestrated unattached type; D, fenestrated, continuous with the inner r brane type, with branching; E, non-fenestrated, continuous with the inner membrane type; F, longitudinal type, con with A–E, which are all transverse. (Original.)

and (b) tubular or villous. The septate cristae are those which are usually described as typical and appear as triple-layered, parallel-sided partitions, more or less complete, regardless of the plane at which the mitochondrion is sectioned. The partitions are, of course, composed of two unit membranes separated by a continuation of the outer chamber which may vary in width. The complete type of septate crista must be approximately circular or oval in outline, the two unit membranes being continuous at the circumference of the partition with the inner mitochondrial membrane (Fig. 5.12c). The incomplete type must fall within one of the following categories (Fig. 5.12c) (a) almost identical with the complete type, except for being fenestrated by holes of various sizes and shapes, (b) a partition having part or all of its circumference in contact with, but not fused to, the inner membrane, (c) a partition which forms a narrow shelf projecting from the inner membrane and partly or wholly inscribed around the inner wall of the mitochondrion, (d) a partition of almost any conceivable shape and size, isolated in the matrix and not in contact with the inner mitochondrial membrane at any point.

Septate cristae are usually single and straight, but variations occur. In the cricothyroid muscle and pancreas of bats, the chloride cells of the gills of *Fundulus*, frog gastric mucosa, the nervous system of the leech, *Hirudo medicinalis*, and salamander liver, another modification, called angulation, occurs. Instead of the crista having the usual parallel sides, one of the unit membranes diverges from the other and then forms a clearly defined angle of 90° or more that restores the normal distance separating it from its opposite unit membrane which has continued on undeflected, or only slightly curved, with its convexity towards the angulation (Fig. 5.13a). Further along the same crista the same angulation occurs but this time to the other, formerly normal, unit membrane. This alternation of angulation gives the crista a zigzag course, and such zigzag cristae may lie close together in parallel, because of the synchrony of their form.

An extreme form of the angulated type of crista is the prismatic, which have been described only from the cricothyroid muscle of the bat larynx. The mitochondria in this muscle have closely packed septate cristae orientated transversely and occasionally fenestrated. In addition, however, triangular profiles can be observed either singly or in groups of 6 arranged radially with their sides parallel. The sides of the triangles are about 600 Å long and sometimes slightly concave. Other sections show that the triangles are cross-sections of prismatic tubules, which appear as parallel stripes when cut longitudinally. The prismatic tubules may run straight, but may also bend at right angles, thus giving triangular and striped profiles in a single section. These prismatic tubules occupy a local area within the mitochondrion, the area being limited by normal septate cristae. Transitional forms between septate and prismatic cristae occur, and one form may grade into the other along one crista, showing clearly that the prismatic cristae are derived from the septate type (Fig. 5.13b).

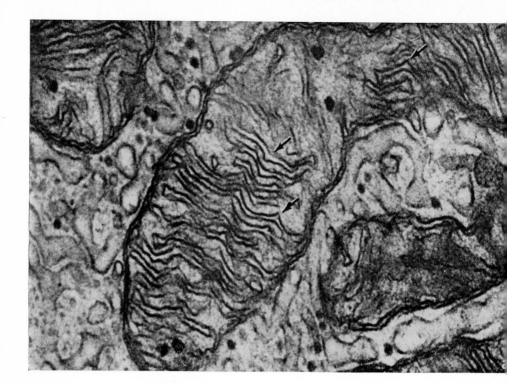

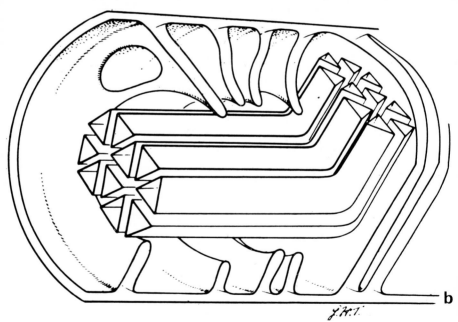

b

FIG. 5.13. (a) Angular cristae (arrows) in the mitochondria of the chloride cells of *Fundulus*. (Courtesy Dr. C. W. Philpott. × 70,000.) (b) Tridimensional drawing of prismatic cristae from the cricothyroid muscle of the bat. The cristae are hexagonally packed. (Courtesy Dr. D. Fawcett.)

In the majority of mitochondria the septate cristae are orientated more or less transversely to the length of the organoid, but in the U-shaped mitochondria of striated muscle and the mitochondria of neurones, synaptic endings and some invertebrate spermatids, the cristae run longitudinally (Fig. 5.14a). In the cells of the convoluted tubules of the kidney of new born mice, the lobster axon, the spermatids of snail and opossum, and in cardiac muscle, the mitochondria have concentrically arranged cristae. Such cristae parallel the contour of the mitochondrion, each successive crista from the outermost inwards having a smaller radius. The immediate central area of the matrix may be free of cristae, leaving a central canal. Although not always clearly demonstrated, it is presumed that the series of concentric cristae is derived from a relatively few long cristae which all originate from the inner mitochondrial membrane. Another form of the concentric cristae is a modification of the angular cristae. Instead of alternating, successive angulations occur on only one of the two unit membranes, the other having only a smooth curving outline. The result of successive angulations is to produce a concentric crista with sharp turns on its outer side (Fig. 5.14b). A section across a free end of such a concentric crista gives a square outline. Such cristae appear in the mitochondria of the neurones of the leech.

Finally, the septate cristae may form not only simple partitions but also complex ones. The cristae may branch, or fork, or interconnect, to give rise to a complex network of partitions or a honeycomb pattern. These patterns have been observed in the mitochondria of human leucocytes, tracheal epithelium of rat, striated muscle, scorpion spermatids and the axons of the lobster. It should be noted that in any one tissue or mitochondrion, one or more of the above types of septate cristae may occur simultaneously, e.g. in the spermatocytes of *Viviparus*, skeletal muscle and distal convoluted tubules of the kidney, transverse, longitudinal and oblique orientations occur within the same mitochondrion.

The tubular (villous) type of crista occurs in the mitochondria of most protozoans, mammalian steroid secreting cells (adrenal, and corpus luteum), insect Malpighian tubules, lung endothelium and occasionally in kidney brush border cells, liver cells and neurones. Sections of mitochondria with tubular cristae show tortuous profiles of narrow, parallel-sided villi and small round profiles which are cross-sections of such tubules (Fig. 5.14c, d). The terminal part of the tubule may be expanded to form a bulbous area, such cristae sometimes being termed saccular or vesicular cristae. In many mitochondria the tubules appear to be arranged completely at random, crossing and interweaving in a complex manner (Fig. 5.15a). In other cases a regular orientation occurs, when the tubules lie nearly in parallel. An excellent example of orientation in tubular cristae has been observed in the mitochondria of *Pelomyxa carolinensis*, the giant amoeba. At one end of the mitochondrion the cristae are few, irregularly shaped and interspersed with densely packed fibres, but the other end contains

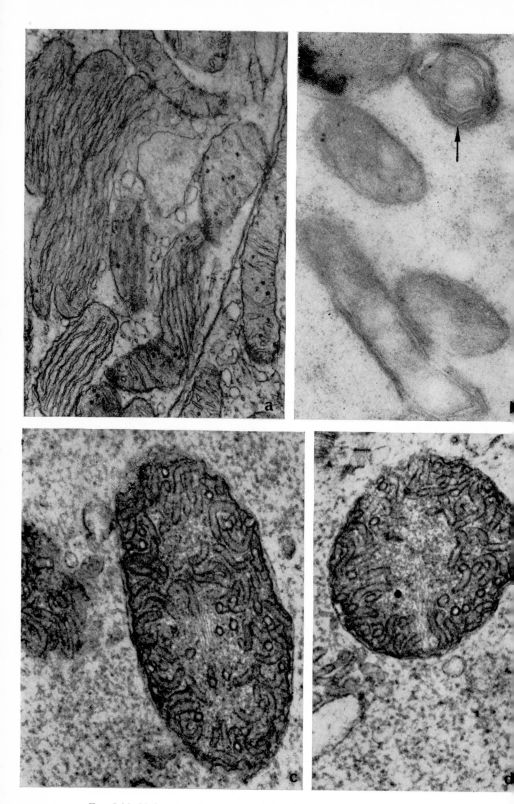

Fig. 5.14. (a) Septate cristae orientated longitudinally in a mitochondrion from the kidney of a starved frog. (Courtesy Dr. M. Karnovsky. ×36,000.) (b) Circular cristae (adaptation of the angular type), at arrow, from the ovotestis of *Planorbis*. (Courtesy Dr. N. Carasso. ×39,000.) (c) and (d) Tubular cristae in mitochondria from *Epistylis anastatica*. (Courtesy Dr. C. Faure-Fremeit. ×156,000.)

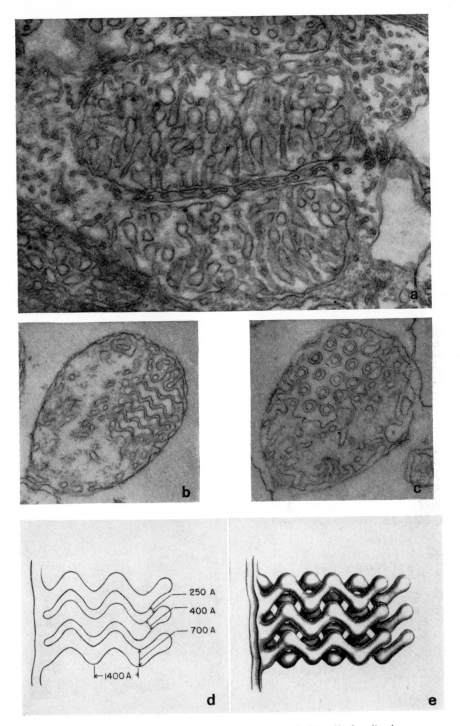

Fig. 5.15. (a) Tubular cristae in mitochondria from the chloride cell of sardine larvae. (Original. × 29,000.) (b) and (c) Mitochondrion of *Pelomyxa carolinensis* showing (b) zigzag cristae; (c) fenestrated cristae. (Courtesy Dr. G. Pappas. (b) × 25,200. (c) × 33,600.) (d) and (e) Diagrams giving the dimensions and tridimensional relationships of the zigzag cristae. (Courtesy Dr. G. Pappas.)

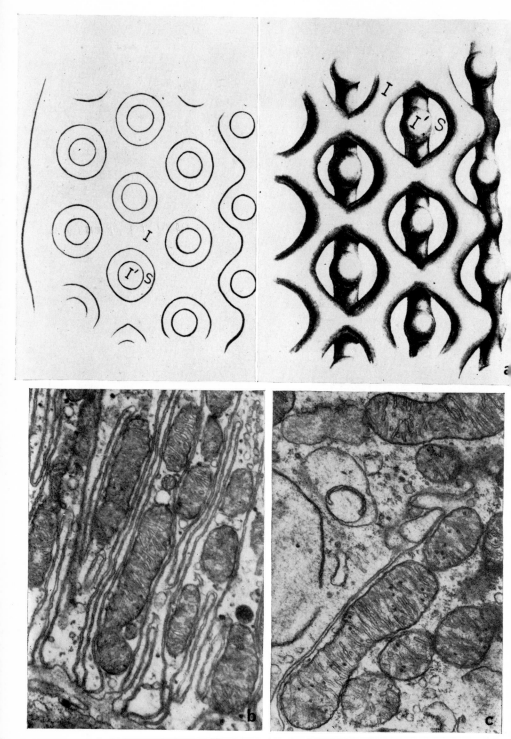

FIG. 5.16. (a) Diagram to show the relationship between the zigzag and fenestrated cristae in *Pelomyxa* mitochondria. I, crista; I', bulbous enlargement; S, space. (Courtesy Dr. G. Pappas.) (b) Mitochondria from the distal tubule of the nephron of the fed summer frog. Cristae are of the transverse septate type. (Courtesy Dr. M. Karnovsky. × 19,000.) (c) Mitochondria from the proximal tubule of the nephron of the fed summer frog. Cristae are of the transverse septate type. (Courtesy Dr. M. Karnovsky. × 25,000.)

cristae organized into at least three patterns. First, zigzag tubules, 400 Å in diameter, with bulbous enlargements 700 Å in diameter at the apex of each angle of the zigzag and at the end of the tubule (Fig. 5.15c). The peak to peak distance of the apex of the zigzag is about 1400 Å, and zigzags may lie in parallel rows, although successive rows may be out of phase (Fig. 5.15b, d, e). Second, out-of-phase rows of zigzag cristae which have between and at right angles to them thin 300 Å straight elongated villi (Fig. 5.15d). Third, a fenestrated membrane formed by the fusion of the bulbous apical enlargements of out-of-phase zigzags. At right angles to such sheets are rows of in-phase zigzags, the bulbous parts of which project into the fenestrations (Figs. 5.15b; 5.16a). This arrangement can give rise to sections showing a membrane with a hexagonal array of circular holes, each hole having a circular profile within it. The centre-to-centre spacing of the circular profiles is naturally equal to that of the apical bulbous enlargements, i.e. 1400 Å.

Functional Activity of Mitochondria

The significance and role of mitochondria in cellular metabolism are well known. Such enzymatic activities, however, are at a molecular level which electron microscopy cannot reveal, although the sites and presence of enzymatic activity can be shown by electron-microscope histochemistry. More obvious changes of mitochondrial structure with function have been frequently observed with the light microscope, and many of these have been confirmed with the electron microscope. Changes in the ultrastructure of mitochondria are relatively gross aspects of mitochondrial function, but are of great interest where they can be correlated with enzymatic observations.

In the convoluted tubules of the frog nephron correlated alterations in cytochrome oxidase activity and mitochondrial structure can be observed between summer and winter animals, and between starved and fed animals in the summer. In the distal convoluted tubules the cytochrome oxidase activity is constant throughout the year, and the mitochondria have a constant form with transverse septate cristae (Fig. 5.16b). In the proximal tubules, however, cytochrome oxidase activity is high in summer and virtually absent in winter, and in starved animals in the summer. The mitochondria in the proximal tubules of fed summer frogs have transverse septate cristae (Fig. 5.16c), but in winter animals and in those starved in summer, the cristae run longitudinally (Fig. 5.17a). Some mitochondria have mixed transverse and longitudinal cristae, while others assume a ring shape, with the cristae parallel to the circumference of the ring. Intramitochondrial granules are less evident in the mitochondria of winter and starved frogs than in others. Clearly the decline in cytochrome oxidase activity in the proximal convoluted tubules is not due to a decrease in mitochondrial numbers, but to the reorientation of the cristae within the organoid.

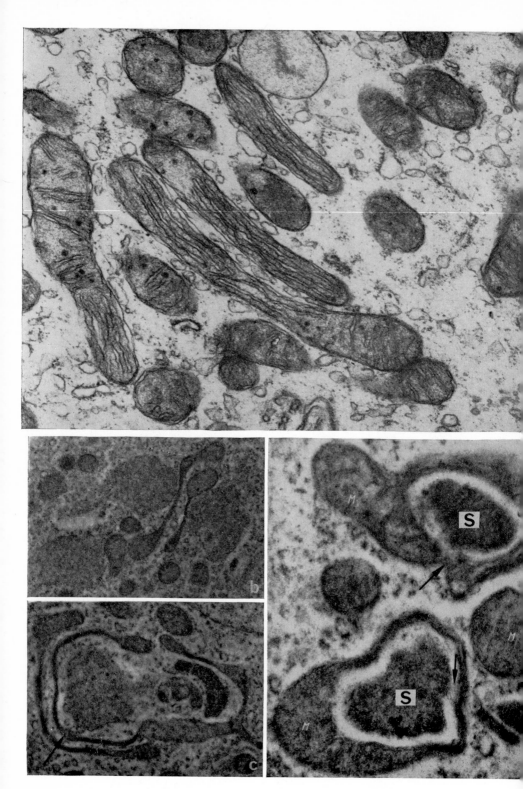

Fig. 5.17. (a) Mitochondria from the proximal tubule of the nephron of a starved summer frog. Cristae are of the longitudinal septate type. (Courtesy Dr. M. Karnovsky. × 60,000.) (b)–(d) Mitochondria from the epithelial cells of the rabbit submandibular gland. (b) and (c) Hypertrophied mitochondria in the synthesizing stage of secretion; (d) deformed mitochondria (M) intimately related to the secretory product (S) at arrows. (Courtesy Dr. K. Kurosumi. (b) × 9600. (c) × 11,400. (d) × 53,000.)

A more direct involvement of mitochondria in the secretory activity of the cell can be observed in the rabbit submandibular gland. This is a tubulo-alveolar gland lined by simple cubical or columnar secretory epithelium. In the resting state the mitochondria are few, small and slender, and scattered randomly through the cytoplasm. The cristae are of the transverse septate type and are crowded together. Secretion granules are absent. In their synthesizing stage the gland cells have secretory granules of moderate electron density, and these lie in close relation to the mitochondria which have increased their diameter two or three times compared to the previous state, although some mitochondria are still small and slender. These hyper-trophied mitochondria have a voluminous matrix and cristae are sparse, suggesting the accumulation of material within the mitochondrion (Fig. 5.17b–d).

In the active secretory stage the mitochondria are deformed, being elon-gated and constricted in their middle region (Fig. 5.17c, d). The granular or homogeneous secretory product is located adjacent to the thinned areas of the mitochondria. Some mitochondria become horse-shoe shaped or annular, and warp themselves around a mass of secretory granules. The ends of such mitochondria have a normal structure with transverse cristae and distinct limiting membranes, but their middle portions are sometimes adielectronic and the cristae run longitudinally. In places the secretory product is in contact with the mitochondrion, at which point the limiting membrane of the organoid is obscure or diffuse in appearance (Fig. 5.17d). These observations strongly suggest that the secretion product is segre-gated or synthesized within the mitochondria, and later becomes free in the cytoplasm.

Another example of the direct intervention of mitochondria in the production of a cell paraplasm is the formation of yolk in the ovotestis of the pulmonate snail, *Planorbis corneus*. The cytoplasm of the young oocyte contains numerous mitochondria but no yolk, while later oocytes have yolk platelets with the characteristic protein crystalline pattern, and numerous mitochondria in process of conversion into yolk platelets. In the first stage of this conversion, the mitochondrial cristae become either diffuse and break down, or are reorganized concentrically parallel to the outer mito-chondrial membrane (Fig. 5.18a). After these changes, adielectronic granules 60 Å in diameter appear in the matrix of the mitochondria and are identical with the granules of the mature yolk platelets (Figs. 5.18b). The granules may be dispersed, but are more often in small groups or larger masses with a distinct crystalline pattern (Fig. 5.18c). The production of yolk granules is not uniform even within a single mitochondrion, for cristae are lost completely in some before granules appear, while in others areas of normal cristae remain as granules arise elsewhere in the mitochondrial matrix. The granules finally form larger groups, ribbons and crystals, and grow into young yolk platelets. Doubtless the yolk granules arise within the mitochondrial matrix, though this does not eliminate the possibility

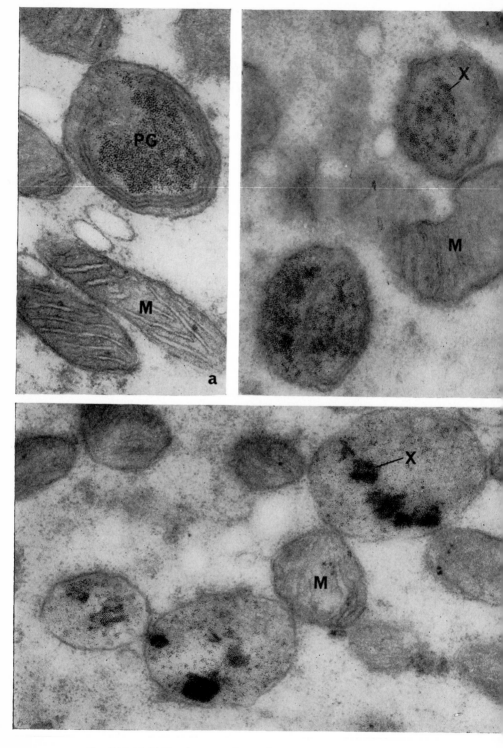

Fig. 5.18. (a)–(c) Development of crystalline yolk platelets within mitochondria of the ovotestis of *Planorbis corneus*. (a) Stage of accumulation of protein granules (PG) in the matrix; (b and c) formation of crystalline and hexagonal packing of the granules (at X). M, mitochondrion. (Courtesy Dr. N. Carasso. (a) × 57,900. (b) × 39,000. (c) × 39,000.)

that the precursor materials are produced elsewhere; for example, the protein moiety might well be synthesized by the granular endoplasmic reticulum.

In *Planorbis,* yolk platelets are formed not only within the mitochondria, but also by mitochondria in conjunction with the agranular endoplasmic reticulum and the cytoplasm. In this complex mode of yolk formation, small smooth-surfaced vesicles in the cytoplasm fuse together into long narrow cisternae, which come to encircle a portion of the cytoplasm containing one or more mitochondria (Fig. 5.19a). The agranular reticulum completely encircles the cytoplasm and mitochondria, the latter forming yolk granules in the manner already detailed. In addition, the reticulum buds off swollen vesicles which come to lie among the mitochondria, and within the vesicles and the surrounding cytoplasm yolk granules also appear (Fig. 5.19b). Eventually the membranes enclosing the internal vesicles and mitochondria break down and the intramitochondrial and intracisternal granules become part of one yolk platelet, which is still encircled by the membranes of the agranular reticulum (Fig. 5.19c).

The origin of mitochondria has been the subject of much speculation, but despite continued research on this organoid little detail of the process has been discovered, and the only generally accepted theory of their origin is that which involves binary fission. Recent electron-microscope investigations have provided observations which strongly suggest two other modes of mitochondrogenesis other than by fission. The first example is from spermatogenesis in the rat and the second from the development of photoreceptors in the guppy.

In the rat, spermatogonia are poor in mitochondria, whereas the primary spermatocyte at the end of the growth period has a rich mitochondrial population. During this growth stage mitochondria are not scattered randomly in the cytoplasm, but are organized into compact groups. A diffuse adielectronic material lies in the centre and between the mitochondria of some groups, rather like a cement, while in other groups an incomplete or small mitochondrion occupies the central position (Fig. 5.20a, b). As growth of the spermatocyte progresses, the number of mitochondria per group increases in such a way that the groups give every appearance of being the centres of mitochondrogenesis. The diffuse cement material is possibly derived from ribosomes which occur as compact masses of various sizes surrounded by diffuse adielectronic material. Some diffuse masses lie free in the cytoplasm or adjacent to one or two mitochondria. Another common occurrence is the contact of the endoplasmic reticulum with individual mitochondria, the contact being so intimate in some instances that the membranes of both the reticulum and the mitochondrion are indistinct in the region of contact. It appears, therefore, that the endoplasmic reticulum and ribosomes play a part in the supply of materials necessary for new mitochondria and that these materials are assembled

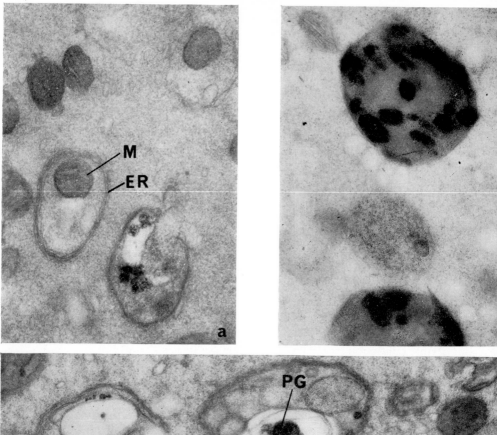

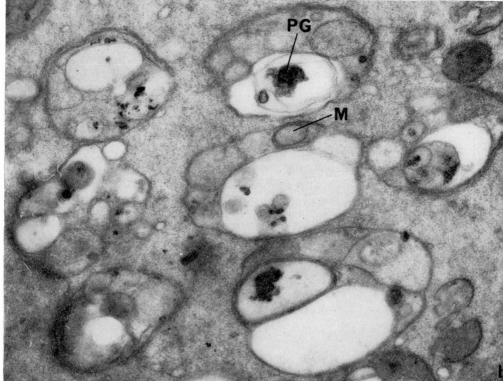

Fig. 5.19. (a)–(c) Second mode of yolk platelet formation in *Planorbis corneus,* involving both mitochondria and endoplasmic reticulum. (a) Endoplasmic membranes encircling protoplasm and mitochondria; (b) complex bodies formed from budded endoplasmic reticulum, mitochondria and protoplasm, with some protein granules (PG) present; (c) mature yolk platelets with crystalline proteins. (Courtesy Dr. N. Carasso. (a) × 25,500. (b) × 85,000. (c) × 25,000.)

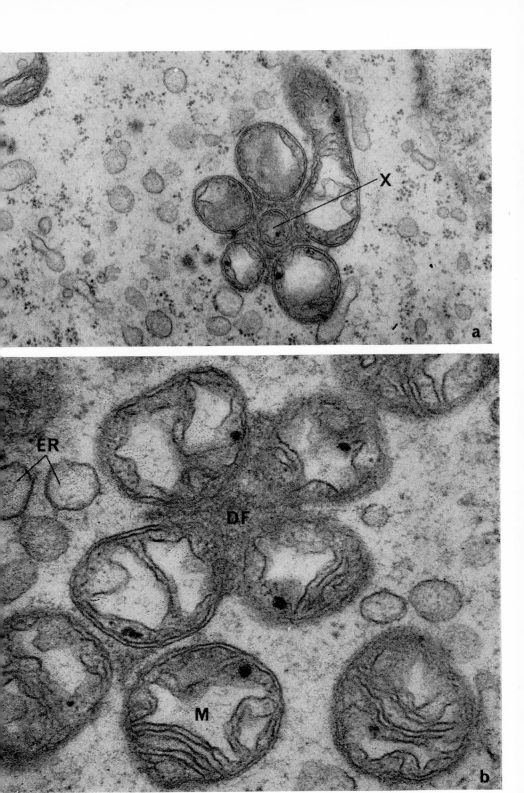

Fig. 5.20. (a) and (b). Genesis of mitochondria in the spermatocytes of the rat. (a) At X a small mitochondrion is developing in the dense material between the surrounding mitochondria; (b) dense, diffuse material (DF) between four mature mitochondria; this material may be derived from the associated endoplasmic reticulum (ER). (Courtesy Dr. J. Andre. (a) ×40,000. (b) ×70,000.)

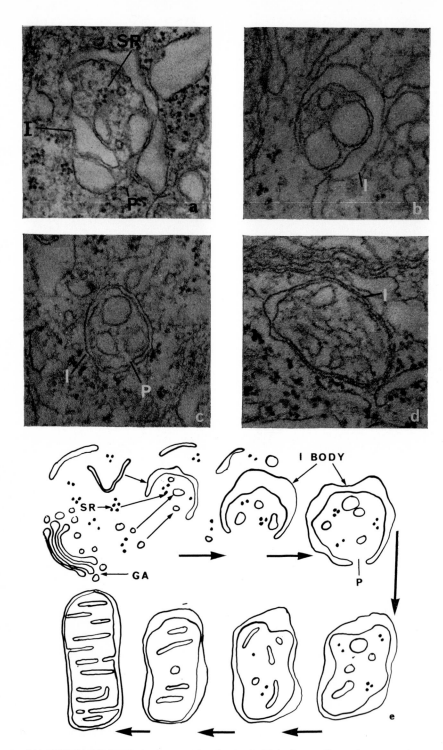

FIG. 5.21. (a)–(d) Stages in the genesis of mitochondria from cell membranes in the twin cones of the guppy retina. I, I structure; P, pore; SR, ribosomes; (d) is a late stage before cristae appear. (Courtesy Dr. E. R. Berger. (a) × 70,000. (b) × 105,000. (c) × 94,000. (d) × 112,000.) (e) Diagram showing the proposed sequence of mitochondrogenesis from the Golgi complex derivatives (GA), ribosomes (R), and cellular membranes in the perinuclear cytoplasm of the twin cones of the guppy retina. (Original, after Dr. E. R. Berger.)

to form new mitochondria under the influence of pre-existing mito-chondria.

In the twin-cone type of photoreceptor in the guppy,† the inner segment is filled by the ellipsoidal body which consists of an aggregation of many mitochondria and little non-mitochondrial cytoplasm. During neonatal development of the retina the ellipsoidal body occupies about 50 per cent of the inner segment and the mitochondria are arranged, for the most part, in a linear size gradient, increasing in size from the vitreal to the scleral end of the cone.

Mitochondria are absent in the perinuclear cytoplasm but this region has a prominent Golgi complex, lamellar membranes (flattened sacs) and vesicles about 800 Å in diameter. Peculiar to the perinuclear cytoplasm and always located within $1·0 \mu$ of the developing ellipsoidal body are I structures (Fig. 5.21a–e). These are spherical, invaginated, membranous sacs averaging 3400 Å in diameter. The structures are bounded by a double membrane, the outer one being continuous with the inner, so forming a pore through which the matrix of the I structure and the cytoplasm are continuous (Fig. 5.21a–c). The interspace between the bounding mem-branes is highly irregular and the matrix contains vesicles 1200 Å in dia-meter and sometimes ribosome-like bodies (Fig. 5.21a). More than one I structure per cone cell is rare and some cells do not have any. In addition some structural differences occurred between individual I structures, e.g. some had large pores whereas others had none (Fig. 5.21a, d), in some the intermembranous space was wide and irregular and in others narrow and regular (Fig. 5.21b, c), in some the ribosomes were conspicuous and in others absent (Fig. 5.21a, b).

Mitochondria immediately outside the perinuclear zone had outer chambers of irregular dimensions and their cristae were vesicular and distributed at random. With increasing proximity to the scleral end of the ellipsoid, mitochondria assumed a more normal appearance with septate cristae arranged in a high degree of order.

From these observations the following stages in mitochondrogenesis have been proposed (Fig. 5.21c). Membranes in the perinuclear region form I structures by engulfing cytoplasm containing vesicles derived from the Golgi complex and ribosomes. The ends of the membranes are almost in contact, but leave a pore. Subsequently the pore is reduced in size and closed, giving a discrete body with a wide, irregular inter-space between its limiting double membrane and containing small vesi-cles. The further development of this I structure into a mitochondrion involves the formation of an interspace (outer chamber) of constant width and the organization of the vesicles into cristae with a regular pattern.

---

† The guppy retina, like that of other surface teleosts, has three types of photoreceptors, rods, single cones, and twin-cones, research being concentrated on the latter.

Further Reading List

1. DALTON, A. J., Golgi Apparatus and Secretion Granules, *The Cell,* Vol. II, edit. BRACHET, J. and MIRSKY, A. E. Academic Press, London, 1961.
2. NOVIKOFF, A. B., Mitochondria, *The Cell,* Vol. II, edit. BRACHET, J. and MIRSKY, A. E., Academic Press, London, 1961.
3. POLLISTER, A. W. and POLLISTER, P. F., The Structure of the Golgi Apparatus, *Int. Review of Cytology*, Vol. 6, edit. BOURNE, G. H. and DANIELLI, J. F., Academic Press, London, 1956.
4. LEHNINGER, A. L., *The Mitochondrion (Molecular Basis of Structure and Function)*, W. A. Benjamin, Inc., New York and Amsterdam, 1964.

CHAPTER 6

ULTRASTRUCTURAL CHANGES IN CELLS DURING EMBRYOGENESIS, DIFFERENTIATION AND SECRETION

THE intimate relationship between changes in structure and function by individual cell organoids has been demonstrated in previous chapters. Electron-microscope studies have been made, however, on structural changes during the functioning of the cell as a whole, e.g. during cell differentiation in embryos and adult animals, during the production of secretory products and during spermatogenesis and oogenesis. Some examples from each of these fields are given in this chapter, so as to give a view of whole cells operating as an integrated unit.

Embryogenesis

The Development of the Vertebrate Notochord

Undoubtedly embryonic cells show some of the most profound changes in structure during differentiation to the adult condition. An excellent example of such differentiation, and one which has been studied by a number of researchers, is the development of the notochord in vertebrates, although it must be noted that this structure only functions temporarily and is replaced in the adult by the vertebrae. The following account has been taken mainly from observations on notochord development in urodeles and the chick.

In the neural plate and neural groove stage of embryogenesis the notochordal cells are loosely packed, with large intercellular spaces between them. Only over short distances are the cells in contact, and such contacts are without desmosomes (Fig. 6.1a). The cytoplasm is finely granular, and contains smooth-surfaced yolk bodies and lipid droplets of irregular outline. In some vertebrates, pigment granules, singly or in groups, are also present. Mitochondria are few and widely scattered, and although only small amounts of endoplasmic reticulum occur, ribosomes are plentiful. The Golgi complex, of typical form, lies in a juxta-nuclear position (Fig. 6.1a). The nucleus is often lobed, due to the presence of between 5 and 10 finger-shaped cytoplasmic invaginations with mitochondria, which project deep into the main mass of the nucleus. Such lobed nuclei are probably present in cells which have divided recently, as the nuclei in other cells are

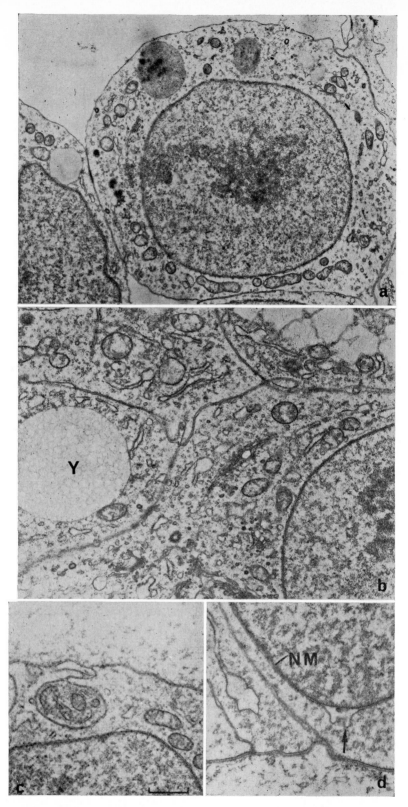

FIG. 6.1. (a)–(d) Development of the notochord; chick. (a) Peripheral cells with little endoplasmic reticulum. Adjacent cells are only in limited contact. (b) Central cells showing their close opposition; Y, partly digested yolk granule. (c) Interdigitations of adjacent cells. (d) Nuclear blebbing (arrow) to form granular endoplasmic reticulum. NM, nuclear membrane. (Courtesy Dr. A. Jurand. (a) × 9000. (b) × 15,000. (c) × 7500. (d) × 12,000.)

round with a smooth outline. The double nature of the nuclear membrane is conspicuous because of the frequent distension of the inter-membranous space into strings of vesicles. Cytoplasmic vesicles lie close to the nucleus and elsewhere within the cytoplasm.

In the next developmental stage the notochord is a cylindrical rod. The area of contact between cells is increased and becomes progressively greater with development until the intercellular spaces are occluded and adjacent cells throughout the notochord are in contact over their whole surface (Fig. 6.1b). At the periphery of the notochord the cell base of one cell may project as a tongue of protoplasm over the base of its neighbour (Fig. 6.1c). The nucleus is similar to the earlier stage, except that invaginations into the nucleus are rare. Nucleoli are now conspicuous elements in the nucleus and have a dielectronic core and an adielectronic periphery. The nucleoli often lie against the nuclear membrane in regions where the outer nuclear membrane is considerably evaginated and is apparently giving rise to granular endoplasmic reticulum (Fig. 6.1d). The granular endoplasmic reticulum within the notochordal cells has increased greatly by this stage and may appear as stacks of flattened cisternae, amply covered with ribosomes, although free ribosomes are still plentiful.

The notochord in its later stages of development has a "pile of coins" configuration. The nuclei are morphologically similar to the previous stage. The plasma membranes in the lateral regions of the cell show modifications, however. Vesicles arise immediately below the plasma membrane, in contact with it, and as pinocytotic-like invaginations (Fig. 6.2a). Such observations suggest pinocytosis, but the tight junction along most of the lateral cell surfaces argues against a flow of fluid between and into the cells. Probably the vesicles are discharging fluid into the intercellular space, an assumption borne out by the reappearance of intercellular clefts, though these are much smaller than those observed at earlier stages of development.

During the late stages of notochord development the central and peripheral cells diverge during differentiation, a divergence for which the endoplasmic reticulum is principally responsible. In the central cells the endoplasmic reticulum enlarges into vesicles of irregular shape (Fig. 6.2b). Such vesicles apparently merge to form large intracellular vacuoles, the walls of which do not have attached ribosomes. The endoplasmic reticulum in the cells is gradually reduced, as is the number of ribosomes. Eventually, the vacuoles occupy the greater part of the cell and the cytoplasm is reduced to a thin peripheral layer, which is compressed against a similar layer of the adjacent cell, forming septa which divide the notochord into compartments (Fig. 6.2c). The cytoplasm of these septa is composed of a meshwork of fine fibres, but the nucleus and other cell organoids do not show any specialization or further differentiation. The central area, therefore, develops into a mass of swollen turgid cells which contain very little endoplasmic reticulum.

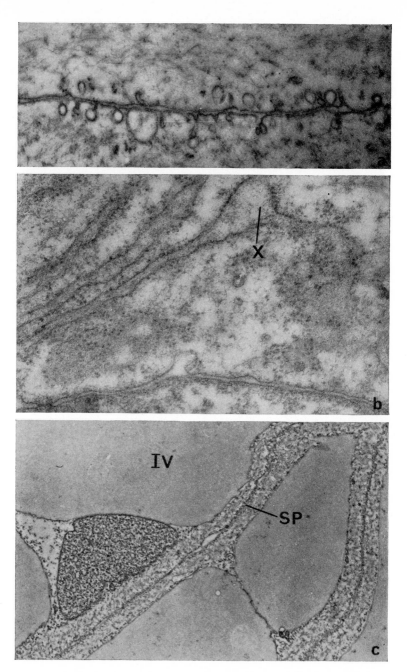

Fig. 6.2. (a) Blebbing of the plasma membranes of adjacent cells of the notochord of *Triturus*. This process gives rise to intercellular vacuoles. (Courtesy Drs. C. H. Waddington and M. Perry. × 40,000.) (b) Beginning of intracellular vacuole formation from enlarging endoplasmic cisternae (at X). (Courtesy Dr. A. Jurand. × 30,000.) (c) Large intracellular vacuoles (IV) causing the appearance of protoplasmic septa (SP). (Courtesy Drs. C. H. Waddington and M. Perry. × 4200.)

The peripheral cells develop endoplasmic reticulum from the nuclear membrane in a similar manner to the central cells. In its final form this endoplasmic reticulum consists of stacks of flattened cisternae which anastomose by cross bridges or fork. The membranes are covered with ribosomes forming whorls or circles. The cisternal cavities are filled with a granular material which has an electron density greater than the cytoplasm (Fig. 6.3a). In certain parts of the cells, the granular endoplasmic reticulum is ringed with small vesicles, multivesicular bodies, and the Golgi complex. The granular endoplasmic reticulum of the peripheral cells never develops into large vacuoles but, the surrounding cytoplasm does contain fibrils about 50 Å thick which lie close to the plasma membrane.

Concurrently with the differentiation of the granular endoplasmic reticulum in the peripheral cells, fibres 85–100 Å thick are laid down outside the plasma membrane of the cells (Fig. 6.3b, c). The fibres run circumferentially round the notochord and a fully formed sheath is 8–10 μ thick, with a narrow, beaded adielectronic outer band (Fig. 6.3a). The origin of the sheath is still in doubt, but the correlation between the formation of abundant granular endoplasmic reticulum in the peripheral cells and the appearance of the sheath fibres suggests that the pro-fibre material is produced within the endoplasmic reticulum and then secreted, although the latter process has not been seen. Fibrillar material is formed also inside the cytoplasm of the notochordal cells and the notochord is surrounded by mesenchyme cells. Either cell type could, therefore, be the origin of the sheath fibres.

Cytogenesis of Chick Pancreas

The exocrine cells of the chick pancreas differentiate at the ends of ducts which invaginate into the mesenchyme. Initially, acini are scarce and organized as small spherical or tubular groups of cells, which are little different from duct cells. At 6 or 7 days of incubation, the acinar cells have small, 5 μ, round nuclei, the pores of which are closed by a diaphragm. The nucleolus is doughnut-shaped, 1·5–3·0 μ, and composed of adielectronic granules 180 Å in diameter. Such large nucleoli are the first sign of differentiation between duct and acinar cells (Fig. 6.3d). Mitoses are common at this time. Mitochondria 0·4–1·5 μ long, are rod shaped with a dense matrix, have transverse septate cristae, and are distributed randomly through the cytoplasm. The Golgi complex is supra-nuclear and small (Fig. 6.3d). It is composed of flattened sacs and a few small vesicles, and has a generally cup or open-ring-like form. The granular endoplasmic reticulum is sparse but widely distributed, and has cisternae with dense contents. Free ribosomes are numerous in the cytoplasm, generally appearing in clumps. Inclusions are either lipid droplets of stellate shape, relatively large and numerous, or prozymogen granules 0·1–0·3 μ in diameter, with an angular profile

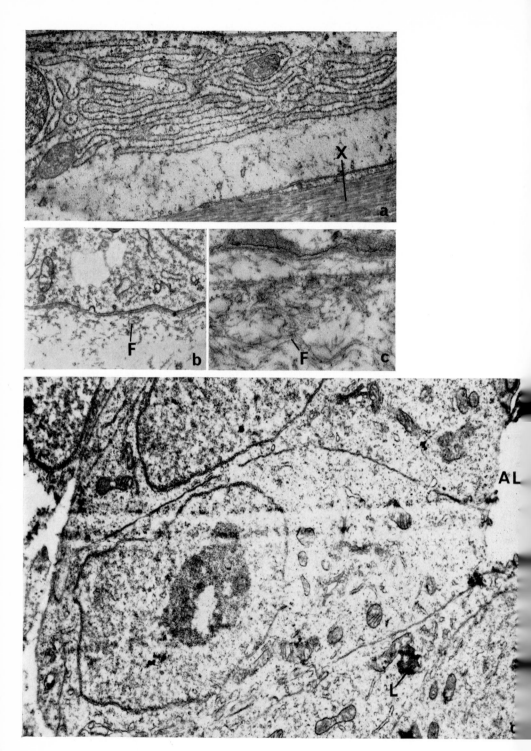

Fig. 6.3. (a) Peripheral notochordal cells of *Triturus* with stacked granular reticulum. The fibrous notochordal sheath is at X. (Courtesy Drs. C. H. Waddington and M. Perry. × 16,000.) (b) and (c) Formation of the notochordal sheath in the chick. (b) Early stage; (c) late stage. F, fibres being laid down. (Courtesy Dr. A. Jurand. (b) × 15,000. (c) × 16,000.) (d) Acinar cell of the chick after 7 days' incubation. AL, acinar lumen; L, lipid. Zymogen granules are not visible in this particular area of section. (Courtesy Dr. R. F. Zeigel. × 10,400.)

and considerable adielectronicity, but few in number. Adjacent plasma membranes have typical zonula occludens at the luminal ends of their lateral surfaces, but zonula adhaerens are rare, unlike the adjacent duct cells in which they are common. The plasma membrane at the luminal surface has small microvilli, and this feature and the zonula occludens were constant structures throughout the incubation and post-hatched periods.

By the 9th day of incubation the Golgi complex has enlarged, the granular endoplasmic reticulum has increased in extent, and zymogen granules measuring up to 0·75 μ are more numerous (Fig. 6.4a). By the 12th day the nucleus shows evaginations of its outer membrane to form granular endoplasmic reticulum (Fig. 6.4b), with which RNA particles become increasingly associated. Mitochondria are large, 4–7 μ, filamentous, and sometimes branched, with a dense matrix and numerous cristae. Generally the mitochondria are orientated parallel with the long axis of the cell, and mitochondria of this type are present from 12 days until hatching. In intimate association with the Golgi vacuoles and vesicles are zymogen granules, suggesting the origin of the latter from the former. The endoplasmic reticulum is further increased, whereas lipid droplets are smaller and have decreased in number. Zymogen granules up to 1·0 μ in diameter occur, are more numerous and randomly scattered, except that the smaller granules tend to be near the plasma membrane.

By the 16- to 18-day stage the Golgi complex is extensive and prominent. It again shows a relationship with the zymogen granules which now range from 0·2 to 1·0 μ in diameter. Other cell features are as previously described, with continued proliferation of the endoplasmic reticulum. At 20 days the reticulum is closely spaced but mainly basal in position, and shows an intimate relationship with both the Golgi complex and the nuclear membrane. Free ribosomes are concentrated apically, and along with them are mature zymogen granules, adielectronic, homogeneous and bounded by a membrane (Fig. 6.4c).

In the 3- and 8-day post-hatched chicks the acinar cells are like those in the adult mammalian pancreas. The nucleus has true pores which are patent and without diaphragms, and distinct connections between the nuclear membrane and the endoplasmic reticulum are visible (Fig. 6.5a). Mitoses are not seen at this stage. Mitochondria are long and filamentous, but differ from the mitochondria in pre-hatched cells in having intramitochondrial granules, 250–450 Å in diameter, as well as smaller 100 Å granules.

The Golgi complex is composed of small circular profiles or vesicles, pairs of smooth membranes and large membrane-bound vacuoles. The Golgi membranes are almost twice as thick as those of the endoplasmic reticulum. Granules with a variety of densities lie amongst the Golgi membranes, suggesting the maturation of the prozymogen granules in their development into mature zymogen (Fig. 6.5a). The entire cytoplasm is packed with granular endoplasmic cisternae, having ribosomes 130–180 Å

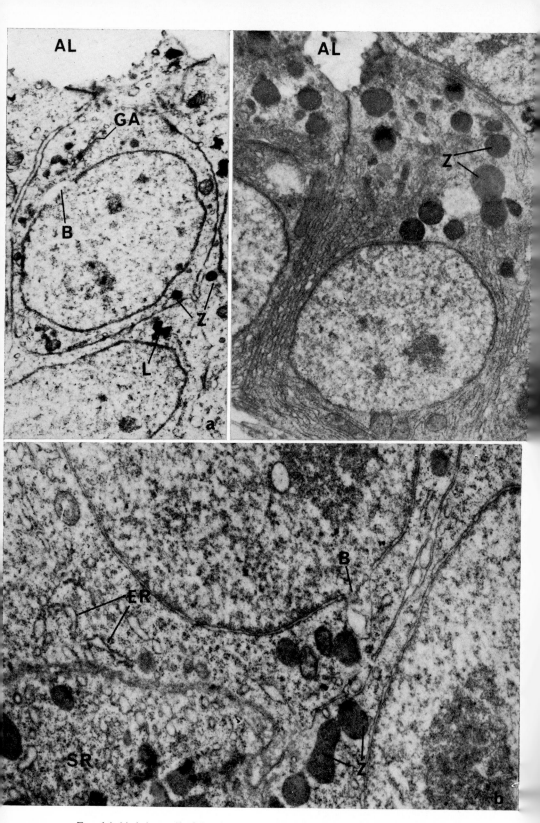

FIG. 6.4. (a) Acinar cell of the chick after 9 days' incubation. Z, zymogen granule; B, nuclear bleb. L, lipid; GA, Golgi complex. (Courtesy Dr. R. F. Zeigel. ×10,400.) (b) Acinar cell of chick after 12 days' incubation. Free ribosomes (SR) are abundant and the granular reticulum (GER) increased. (Courtesy Dr. R. F. Zeigel. ×26,000.) (c) Acinar cell of the chick after 20 days' incubation. Abundant granular endoplasmic reticulum and zymogen granules (Z) are evident. AL, acinar lumen. (Courtesy Dr. R. F. Zeigel. ×4800.)

in diameter; free RNA particles lie elsewhere in the cytoplasm. The endo-plasmic membrane adjacent to the Golgi complex sometimes lacks ribo-somes on its surface and is evaginated into small projections. Furthermore, small vesicles occur between the endoplasmic membranes and the Golgi sacs. All these observations strongly suggest the transfer of material between the endoplasmic reticulum and the Golgi complex, and the con-centration of material so transferred within the Golgi sacs. Zymogen granules are concentrated apically and material of medium electron density appears in the lumina of the acini.

Cellular Differentiation in Adult Animals

Nematocyst Development in Hydra

The nematocyst of *Hydra* consists of a capsule containing a coiled filament with a smooth or barbed end. The capsule has a lid, or operculum, which remains closed until the nematocyst is triggered by stimulation of a hair-like structure, the cnidocil, at which time the coiled filament is shot out. The nematocysts are, therefore, expendable and must be replaced by the continuous production of new nematocysts within special cells called cnidoblasts.

The cnidoblasts are derived from interstitial cells which lie singly or in pairs at the base of the epidermis, and between the musculoepithelial cells (Fig. 6.5b). Their nuclei have a variety of shapes but are always smooth in outline and homogeneous at low magnification. At high magnification, the nucleoplasm is revealed as poorly defined granules, 100–208 Å in diameter, while the more adielectronic nucleolus is made up of adielectronic sharply defined granules 80–120 Å in diameter.

Mitochondria are sparse, rod-shaped and randomly distributed. The Golgi complex is small, juxta-nuclear in position and typical in structure (Fig. 6.5b). One or more small lipid droplets may be present in the cyto-plasm. The endoplasmic reticulum, however, is either entirely lacking, or present as only a few small vesicles widely scattered. The cytoplasm contains an abundance of ribosomes.

The interstitial cells commence their differentiation into cnidoblasts by mitoses, so forming clusters of 4–16 cells (Fig. 6.6a). A peculiar feature of interstitial cell division is the incomplete cytogenesis, resulting in temporary intercellular bridges. Early cnidoblasts are polygonal and have reduced cytoplasm, due to the division of the original interstitial cell cytoplasm without subsequent growth. The RNA granules in the nucleoplasm increase, but those in the cytoplasm appear to remain constant. Mitochondria are slightly larger in size than previously and have increased numbers of cristae. The Golgi complex is greatly enlarged and forms within one of its vacuoles the nematocyst primordium (Fig. 6.6c). This latter is pear-shaped and

8*

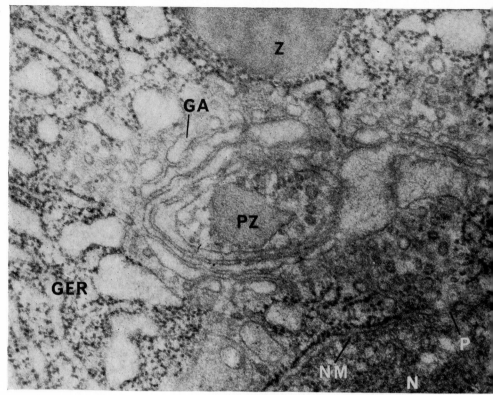

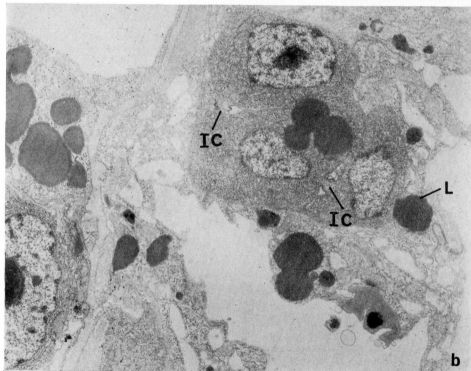

FIG. 6.5. (a) Acinar cell of the chick post hatched 8 days. Note the intimate relationship between the nuclear membrane (NM), Golgi complex (GA), and granular reticulum (GER). PZ, prozymogen granule; P, pore; Z, zymogen granule. (Courtesy Dr. R. F. Zeigel. × 62,000.) (b) Interstitial cells at the base of the ectoderm of *Hydra*. L, lipid; IC, intercellular bridge. (Courtesy Dr. D. B. Slautterback. × 7000.)

enclosed in a thick capsule except at its apex where it is bounded by a thin membrane. The nematocyst interior is fine textured and dielectronic. The endoplasmic reticulum increases rapidly, first by the production of more of the type of vesicles seen in interstitial cells, and subsequently by the elongation and coalescence of vesicles to form narrow cisternae which meander in the cytoplasm (Fig. 6.6b). Ribosomes become attached to the membranes of the cisternae, resulting in the origin of typical granular endoplasmic reticulum from the previous agranular type. The cytoplasm, however, still contains many free ribosomes.

In the more advanced cnidoblasts, the mitochondria continue to enlarge. The granular endoplasmic reticulum becomes very extensive, the broad cisternae lying in parallel array and intercommunicating (Figs. 6.6c, 6.7a). Ribosomes become increasingly located on the reticular membranes and free ribosomes are consequently rare. The lumen of the endoplasmic reticulum is dielectronic, its material probably not preserved. The endoplasmic reticulum is continuous in places with both the Golgi membranes and the nuclear membrane, and its lumen opens into the membrane-limited cavity in which the nematocyst is being formed (Figs. 6.6c, 6.7a). The latter eventually becomes so large as to displace the nucleus peripherally.†

In late cnidoblasts, the Golgi complex remains in close contact with the apical end of the nematocyst (Fig. 6.7b). The Golgi region just lateral to the tip of the nematocyst is composed of flat vesicles distended in parts into vacuoles. At the nematocyst apex the Golgi complex is composed of a dense aggregation of minute tubules and vesicles and thin-walled irregularly-shaped vacuoles, the contents of which vary in electron density between dielectronic to that approaching the adielectronicity of the nematocyst. It appears that the Golgi complex segregates and concentrates the nematocyst material in vacuoles (expanded and nipped off Golgi sacs), which later fuse with the nematocyst and contribute their contents to its growth (Fig. 6.7b).

When the nematocyst attains definitive size, the apex continues to grow into a tapering process coiled in the cytoplasm and thought to be homologous with the external tube of the light microscope observations on nematocyst structure. During this growth process the Golgi complex is carried farther and farther away from the nematocyst proper, and eventually comes to lie in the peripheral cytoplasm. The coiled process must later invert and lie within the nematocyst capsule as the internal tube, but this process was not observed.

In late cnidoblasts the nucleus is crescentric shaped and peripheral in position. The nucleoplasm has only a few RNA granules, although clumps of larger granules occur. The mitochondria are less numerous than in earlier stages, have a less adielectronic matrix and few cristae. The Golgi complex has regressed to flattened sacs and small vacuoles and is not

† Four types of nematocysts are produced by *Hydra,* but could not be identified in electron microscopy.

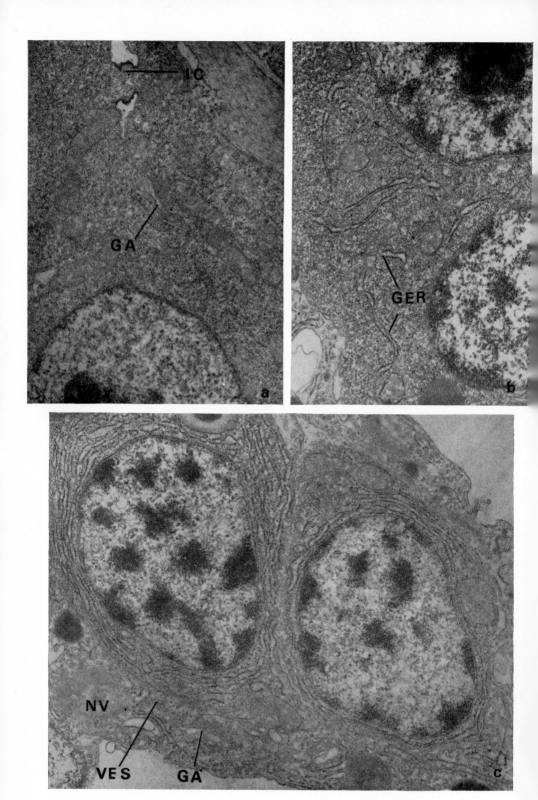

FIG. 6.6. (a) Differentiating cnidoblast with Golgi complex (GA) and abundant ribosomes but no endoplasmic reticulum. IC, intercellular bridge, due to incomplete cytokinesis. (Courtesy Dr. D. B. Slautterback. ×19,000.) (b) Differentiating cnidoblast showing a gradual increase in endoplasmic reticulum (GER). (Courtesy Dr. D. B. Slautterback. ×20,000.) (c) Two well-differentiated cnidoblasts with abundant granular endoplasmic reticulum. GA, Golgi complex giving off vesicles (VES) to form the nematocyst vacuole (NV). (Courtesy Dr. D. B. Slautterback. ×17,000.)

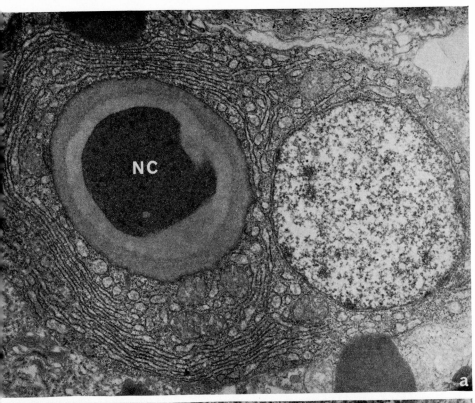

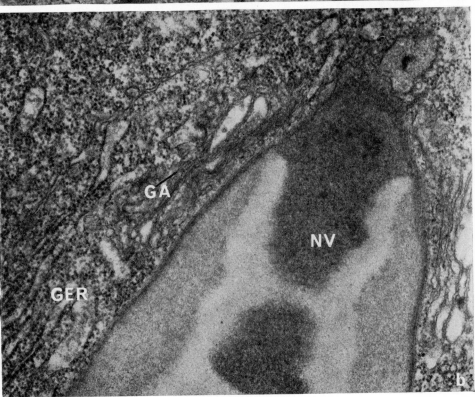

FIG. 6.7. (a) Mature cnidoblast with partly formed nematocyst (NC) sectioned transversely. (Courtesy Dr. D. B. Slautterback. × 23,000.) (b) Late stage of nematocyst formation showing the relationship between the Golgi complex (GA), the granular reticulum (GER), and the nematocyst vacuole (NV). (Courtesy Dr. D. B. Slautterback. × 42,500.)

spatially related to the nematocyst. The granular endoplasmic reticulum is reduced in extent and is fragmented into isolated vesicles with few ribosomes. In very old cnidoblasts only a few large vesicles occur, apparently derived from the fusion of the small vesicular remnants of the endoplasmic reticulum. The formation of the internal tube, barbs, the operculum, and the cnidocil were not observed in this study.

Differentiation of White Adipose Tissue

Between birth and 9 days old, white adipose tissue differentiates in the inguinal and epididymal fat pads of rats. In this period, therefore, the sequence of lipid accumulation can be conveniently studied, along with the morphological alterations which occur during the change-over from fibroblast to adipose cell.

Pre-adipose Fibroblasts

The adipose stem cells are spindle shaped with a number of protoplasmic projections directed in the cells' long axis. These tenuous projections are without inclusions or cell organoids. The nuclei are round or oval, with one or two small nucleoli in a homogeneous granular nucleoplasm. Mitochondria are small and spherical with a few transverse septate cristae. The endoplasmic reticulum is of the granular type and its narrow cisternae lie in parallel groups or form concentric loops or branching systems. The material within the cisternae is more adielectronic than the hyaloplasm. Typical Golgi complexes of small size, and free ribosomes lie in the dielectronic cytoplasm. These stem cells closely resemble fibroblasts, and it is postulated, therefore, that the adipose cells at these sites are derived directly from fibroblasts, rather than from cells of the reticuloendothelial system, i.e. macrophages.

Early Adipose Cells

The first cells to which the term adipose can be applied are like the pre-adipose cells in general appearance, but have fewer protoplasmic extensions and a concentration of small lipid droplets near the nucleus at one or both poles of the cell (Fig. 6.8a, b). The lipid droplets are crenated, without a limiting membrane, and are adielectronic to varying degrees, characteristics they retain throughout further differentiation.

The nucleus is round or oval, sometimes centrally placed, sometimes polar. It is without conspicuous morphological change during the later stages of cell differentiation. The granular endoplasmic reticulum is randomly distributed and its cisternae may have local dilations and be filled with a granular material of moderate electron density. The Golgi complex is juxta-nuclear and small, and mitochondria are generally spherical, but may also be filamentous in form.

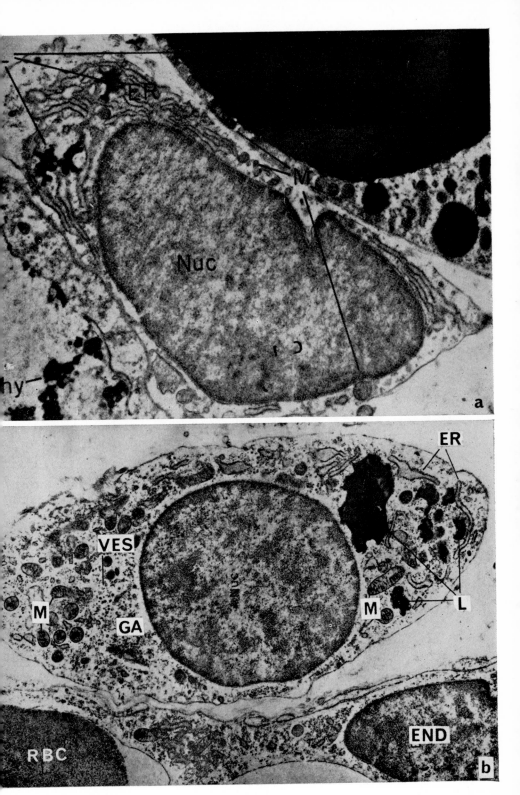

Fig. 6.8. (a) Adipose stem cell (differentiating fibroblast). L, lipid droplet; ER, granular endoplasmic reticulum; NUC, nucleus; CHY, chylomicrons in capillary lumen; M, mitochondrion. (Courtesy Dr. L. Napolitano. × 20,000.) (b) Early adipose cell. L, lipid; ER, granular endoplasmic reticulum; RBC, red blood cell; END, endothelium; GA, Golgi complex; VES, vesicles; M, mitochondrion. (Courtesy Dr. L. Napolitano. × 12,000.)

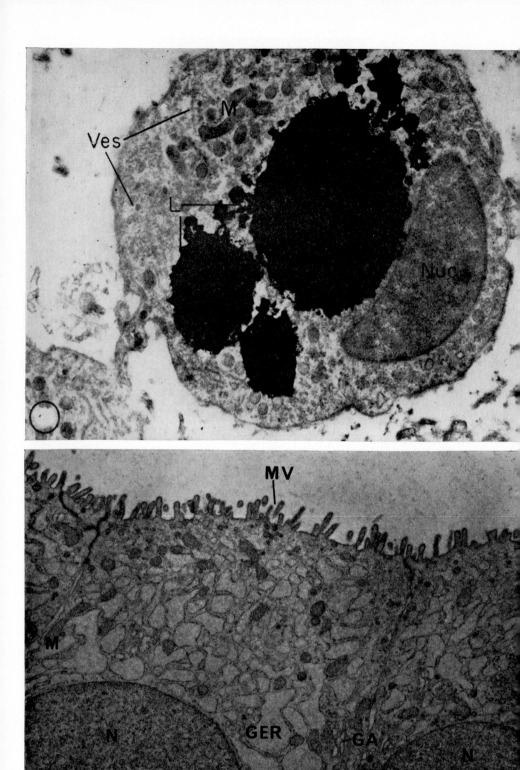

Fig. 6.9. (a) Advanced adipose cell, with large lipid inclusions (L). VES, vesicles; M, mitochondrion; NUC, nucleus. (Courtesy Dr. L. Napolitano. × 15,000.) (b) Apical part of a follicular epithelial cell of the thyroid of the normal rat. GA, Golgi complex; GER, enlarged endoplasmic cisternae; MV, microvilli; N, nucleus; M, mitochondrion. (Courtesy Dr. S. L. Wissig. × 9000.)

Conspicuous in these early adipose cells are numerous smooth-surfaced vesicles of different sizes, which may contain a material of moderate adi-electronicity. The plasma membrane, which has at this stage a pitted appearance due to the presence of many pinocytotic vesicles, is overlaid by a thin dielectronic layer of basement membrane. The small vesicles could arise by either pinocytosis at the plasma membrane, or from the Golgi apparatus; their distribution is strongly in favour of the former possibility.

Later Stages of Differentiation

The adipose cells grow gradually and assume an ovoid shape. The amounts of both cytoplasm and lipid increase moderately, but the Golgi complex and granular endoplasmic reticulum are less evident (Fig. 6.9a). Mitochondria appear to have increased somewhat in numbers. The lipid droplets tend to coalesce into a single droplet, although small lipid inclusions may still occur scattered through the cytoplasm (Fig. 6.9a). Glycogen inclusions appear at this time in aggregates of particles 200–300 Å in diameter, which are massed around the lipid droplets.

At an even later stage of differentiation the adipose cells become spherical. The nucleus is displaced to a peripheral position by the ever-increasing lipid contents of the cell, and finally becomes crescentic in shape. The lipid is concentrated centrally in a huge droplet, with attendant small droplets around it. The number of endoplasmic cisternae is further decreased, while mitochondria are numerous, varying from round to filamentous and having few, incomplete cristae. The plasma membrane continues to show pino-cytotic activity and vesicles occur in large numbers. In mature adipose cells glycogen is sparse or absent.

The adult adipose cell has a characteristic signet ring shape. Its increase in size is probably due largely to the accumulation of lipid, with perhaps some increase in the area of cytoplasm. No correlation was observed between any cell organoid and the accumulation of lipid. It is true, however, that as the adipose cell develops, the granular endoplasmic reticulum decreases in extent. In contrast, mitochondria and small vesicles increase in number with lipid storage, and pinocytotic activity by the plasma membrane is very evident, although none of these features appears to be unequivocally the centre of lipid synthesis.

Secretory Activity in Adult Animals

Thyroid gland—Resting and Secreting

The thyroid gland of normal rats is composed of oval or circular follicles surrounded by a richly vascularized capsule of connective tissue. The follicle cells range from cuboidal to short columnar, and are frequently indented at their base by the perifollicular capillaries, and at their apices they bulge into the central colloid. The colloid is finely granular, with a constant moderate adielectronicity. It abuts directly on to the apical plasma membrane of the follicular cells.

The nucleus of the follicular cells is roughly spherical, with occasional indentations. The nuclear membrane has few pores and is without ribosomes on its outer surface. The nucleoplasm is granular and surrounds areas of dense and more compact granules. Nucleoli are not prominent. The granular endoplasmic reticulum occurs through the cytoplasm in the form of dilated cisternae enclosing a homogeneous material with an electron density like that of the colloid (Fig. 6.9b). The reticulum is generally without a conspicuous ordered pattern, but may appear in parallel arrays. The cisternae at the cell apex are smaller than those at the base and may be incompletely covered with ribosomes, although the basal cisternae bear dense concentrations of RNA particles. The whole reticulum is probably in the form of a richly branching network.

The Golgi complex is relatively small and lies in a juxta-nuclear position, either apical or lateral to the nucleus. It is composed mainly of small vesicles 500–1750 Å in diameter and stacks of flattened sacs are rare (Fig. 6.9b). The vesicular contents are of variable electron density, the contents of the larger vesicles being the most dielectronic. Mitochondria are abundant and evenly distributed, often lying close against the wall of the endoplasmic reticulum. Mitochondria are absent from the superficial apical layer of the cytoplasm. Generally they are long and sinuous, but small $0·2\ \mu$ mitochondria occur and the cristae may be orientated in any direction between transverse and longitudinal, but such cristae are not prominent against the adielectronic matrix in which small numbers of intramitochondrial granules occur.

The plasma membrane shows regional differentiation. The apical membrane bordering on the colloid has numerous microvilli, irregular in form and distribution. The microvillus may have a finger-like shape approximately $0·35\ \mu$ long and 700 Å broad, or equally have an irregular shape and be linked with other microvilli in web-like structures which are very evident in oblique sections (Fig. 6.10a). Vesicles, 600 Å in diameter, lie within the microvilli and indentations of similar dimensions penetrate into the apical cytoplasm, suggesting either pinocytosis or the extrusion of vesicles. A zone of apical cytoplasm, about $0·5\ \mu$ wide, is devoid of cellular organoids, but does contain spherical vesicles 500–1500 Å in diameter, surrounded by a membrane (Fig. 6.10a).

The lateral cell boundaries have apical "terminal bars" and desmosomes, and run relatively straight from apex to base, with occasional interdigitations. The basal plasma membrane is smooth, but a particular cell may have blunt protoplasmic projections from adjacent cells underlying it. A basement membrane of medium electron density runs uninterrupted beneath the follicular cells.

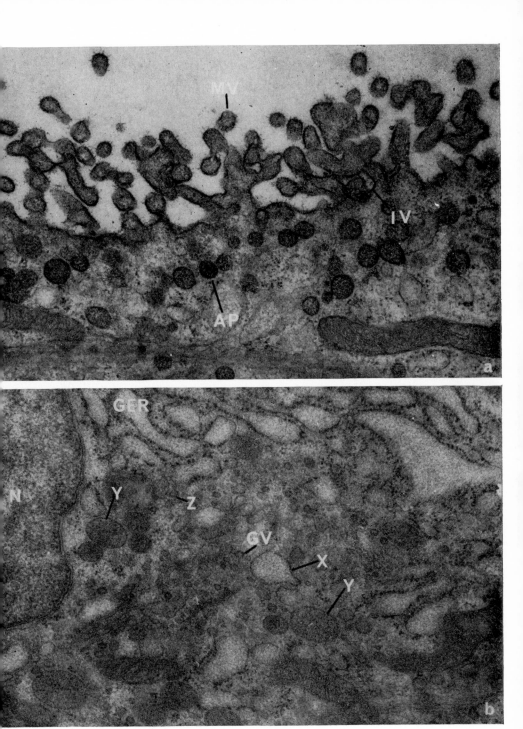

Fig. 6.10. (a) Oblique section of the apex of a thyroid cell from a normal rat. Microvilli (MV) form complex groups with plasma membrane invaginations between their bases (IV). Apical vesicles (AP) are numerous. (Courtesy Dr. S. L. Wissig. ×35,000.) (b) Golgi complex of a rat thyroid cell after TSH stimulation. Golgi vesicles (GV) appear to unite into larger vacuoles (at X) and into colloid droplets (at Y). The possible transfer of material from the granular reticulum to the Golgi complex is at Z. N, nucleus; GER, granular reticulum. (Courtesy Dr. S. L. Wissig. ×51,000.)

Colloid Elaboration

The follicle cells secrete colloid into the follicular lumen at an increased rate during the first few hours after thyrotrophic hormone injection. During this process conspicuous cytological changes can be observed by light microscopy and include the extension of pseudopodia from the follicle cells into the colloid, and the presence of droplets in the apical cytoplasm, although these may extend basally beyond the nucleus.

By electron microscopy, the following features of stimulated follicle cells can be observed. Compared to normal cells, the Golgi complex is expanded, due to proliferation of its vesicular components which cluster along the apical and lateral borders of the nucleus. The Golgi complex is surrounded by small colloid droplets which blend morphologically with the Golgi vesicles, so that the two cannot be distinguished from each other (Fig. 6.10b). In addition, fine particles 75 Å in diameter occur between the Golgi membranes. Progressively larger colloid droplets extend from the Golgi zone and nucleus toward the apical region of the cell (Fig. 6.10b). The large droplets are crowded beneath the apical plasma membrane, which is thrown into broad pseudopodia enclosing colloid droplets (Fig. 6.11a). Colloid droplets have a bounding membrane 70–80 Å thick which encloses particles 75 Å in diameter; these particles are therefore identical to those present in the Golgi complex. Small and medium sized colloid droplets are relatively adielectronic and have many dense particles, whereas large droplets are more dielectronic and contain fewer particles. The very largest droplets have a meshwork of fine fibrils in their contents and therefore are similar to the luminal colloid. The colloid droplets are probably released from their membranes by the fusion of these with the plasma membrane, resulting in a continuous apical plasma membrane, as in merocrine secretion.

The Golgi complex is surrounded by an extensive granular endoplasmic reticulum. Ribosomes are distributed over the whole surface of the membranes, except for small areas of it which face the Golgi membranes (Fig. 6.10b). At these points the reticular membranes give off small smooth surfaced vesicles by budding. This suggests the transfer of material (the protein constituent of the thyroid hormone) from the endoplasmic reticulum to the Golgi complex. In stimulated thyroid cells the endoplasmic reticulum still has the same large dilated pleomorphic cisternae, irregularly orientated, which are observed in normal cells, suggesting that the increased activity of this organoid requires only more rapid use of pre-existing structures (Fig. 6.11b).

Secretion by the thyroid, therefore, resembles that of other exocrine cells. Colloid droplets, the protein of which is perhaps derived initially from the endoplasmic reticulum, appears first in the Golgi vesicles and eventually grows and passes into the apical cytoplasm. The droplets are finally released into the luminal colloid from large pseudopodia by merocrine mechanism.

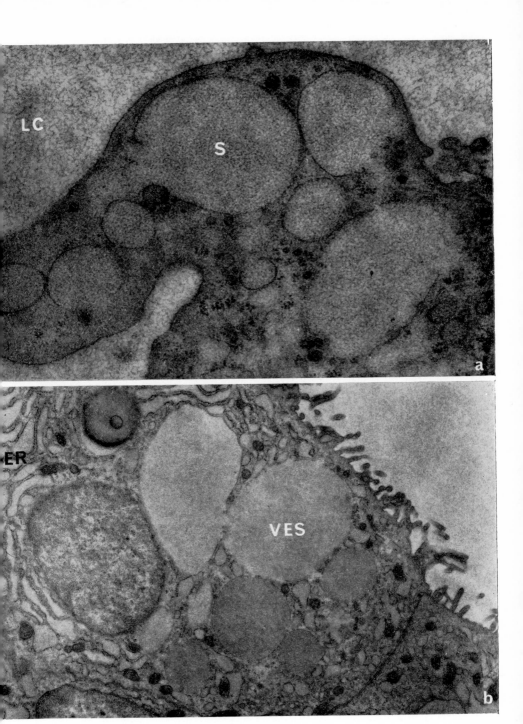

FIG. 6.11. (a) Pseudopodium from the apical cytoplasm of a rat thyroid cell after TSH stimulation. The intercellular colloid secretory droplets (S) have the same structure as the luminal colloid (LC). (Courtesy Dr. S. L. Wissig. ×41,000.) (b) Rat thyroid cell after stimulation with TSH. The large apical secretory vesicles (VES) and flattened basal endoplasmic cisternae (GER) are characteristic of this state of the gland. (Courtesy Dr. S. L. Wissig. ×10,000.)

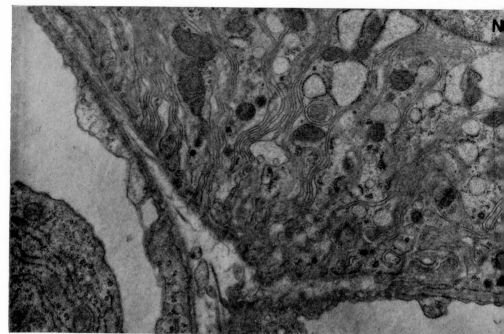

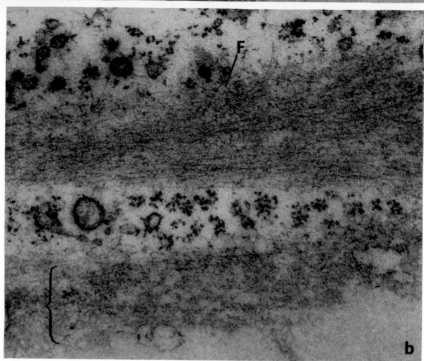

FIG. 6.12. (a) Base of a rat thyroid cell after stimulation with PTV (propylthiouracil). The formation of increased numbers of cellular interdigitations is a characteristic response to this treatment. (Courtesy Dr. S. L. Wissig. × 15,000.) (b) Cultured mouse fibroblast; log phase. The cell surface is bracketed, intercellular fibres occur at F, and polyribosomes are common. (Courtesy Drs. B. Goldberg and H. Green. × 55,000.)

The injection of propyl-thiouracil induces severe thyroid hyperplasia, the follicles collapse with the depletion of the colloid due to its resorption by follicular cells, from which it presumably enters the perifollicular capillaries. During this process apical microvilli increase greatly in height, number and complexity. The microvilli and adjacent cytoplasm are full of pinocytotic vesicles. Throughout the cytoplasm the vesicular-like cisternae of the endoplasmic reticulum increase in volume and number. The bases of the cells, usually smooth, become elaborately modified by numerous interdigitations and branchings, and these often contain large endoplasmic cisternae (Fig. 6.12a).

The colloid appears to be removed from the follicular lumen by pinocytosis, and to be deposited subsequently in neighbouring endoplasmic cisternae, within which it reaches the bases of the cells. Only rarely is the endoplasmic reticulum observed opening directly on the basal surface, and therefore it is assumed that the colloid normally diffuses from the cell in a soluble form.

Collagen Formation by Fibroblasts

A number of electron microscope studies have been made on collagen formation and the observations obtained have resulted in two alternative theories of fibrillogenesis being proposed. One theory states that the collagen is an intracellular formation which is subsequently shed in fibrous form into the extracellular space, whereas the other theory states that the collagen is secreted as an amorphous substance without visible organization and that this takes on the typical periodicity of native collagen after its secretion. Recent observations have shown that established mouse fibroblast lines are capable of *in vitro* collagen synthesis, and an electron microscope study of these cell cultures has demonstrated clearly that the soluble collagen is secreted and that the theory of the extracellular formation of collagen is correct.

The cultured mouse fibroblasts pass through two distinct phases during their development. First, there is a phase of exponential growth (log phase) starting 12 hours after culture and continuing until the third day. By day 6, the cultures enter upon the second phase (stationary or secretory phase) when growth virtually stops and the culture consists of about 10^6 cells.

The interphase cells during the log phase are flattened and stellate in shape, and the plasma membrane occasionally shows villous or bulbous projections. Surface invaginations and vesicles, with limiting membranes similar to the plasma membrane occur deep in the cytoplasm and are evidence of pinocytosis by the fibroblasts. The plasma membrane sometimes appears as a wide, moderately adielectronic zone of amorphous material due to the fact that cells are generally fusiform in cross-section and oblique sections of the plasma membra arene inevitable under such circumstances (Fig.

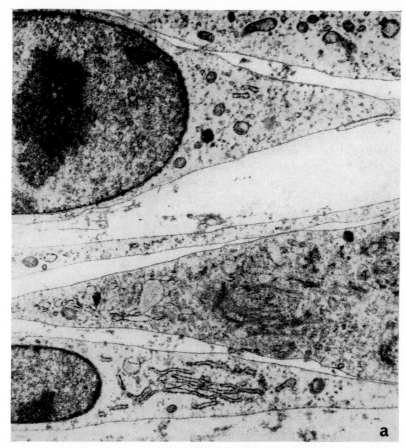

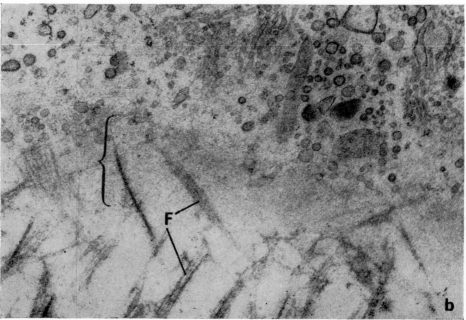

FIG. 6.13. (a) Cultured mouse fibroblast; stationary phase. This is a vertical section through the culture and the plasma membrane is cut at 90° to its surface. (Courtesy Drs. B. Goldberg and H. Green. × 9000.) (b) Cultured mouse fibroblast; stationary phase. In this section horizontal to the culture, the plasma membrane is bracketed and the fibres (F), with and without periodicity, appear to continue from cytoplasm to extracellular space. (Courtesy Drs. B. Goldberg and H. Green. × 26,000.)

6.12b). The nuclei are oval or elongate, with large nucleoli, but are otherwise unexceptional.

The granular endoplasmic reticulum is poorly developed and consists of small isolated profiles containing dielectronic material. The Golgi complex is also small, comprising a few flattened sacs and vesicles lying in a juxtanuclear position. Free ribosomes, often arranged in clusters, are abundant and form a predominant element in the cytoplasm. Mitochondria are small and spherical, with simple septate cristae and dielectronic matrices. The cytoplasm also contains bundles of parallel fibrils 50 Å thick, which occur most often in the endoplasm, although bundles are occasionally observed near the nucleus or elsewhere in the cytoplasm. Hydroxyproline tests on the cultures show these fibrils are not aggregates of the collagen molecules.

In the stationary phase, the cultures are many cells deep, with cellular extensions overlapping very extensively. In horizontal section this overlapping results in the oblique cutting of the plasma membrane, which consequently appears as an amorphous zone around most of the periphery of the cell. Fibrils with or without periodicity, appear to run across this amorphous zone, as though being shed from the ectoplasm (Fig. 6.13b). Observations such as these are the basis for the theory that intracellular fibril formation and subsequent shedding of these into the extracellular space is the mode of origin of the native collagen. Sections of the cultures in the vertical plane, however, always show a definite, 70 Å, plasma membrane, non-periodic intracellular fibrils, and non-periodic and periodic extracellular fibrils which do not connect with the ectoplasm (Fig. 6.13a).

In the stationary phase cells, the mitochondria are long and sometimes form complex branched structures. The endoplasmic reticulum and Golgi complex are both well developed and are structurally related. The number of profiles of the granular endoplasmic reticulum is greatly increased and forms a continuous system of cisterae distended with large amounts of non-fibrous material of moderate adielectronicity (Fig. 6.14a). The attached ribosomes form curved chains and other systems of about 10–12 particles, and free ribosomes are less frequent than in the log phase cells, being peripherally located in the cell.

The Golgi complex and the agranular endoplasmic reticulum form a complex interconnecting system in the cells during the stationary phase. The Golgi complex is juxta-nuclear but extends out between the elements of the granular reticulum. The complex contains multiple paired membranes enclosing narrow lumina and numerous clusters of circular, tubular and saccular profiles (Fig. 6.14b). Some of the smooth surfaced profiles in the Golgi region are continuous with the agranular reticulum, which occurs elsewhere in the cell, especially at or near the plasma membrane. Many vesicles lie beneath the plasma membrane and some appear to be in contact with the latter, or open on to it (Fig. 6.14c).

The mode of collagen synthesis and secretion appears to be as follows. Tropocollagen is synthesized and sometimes accumulated in the cisternae

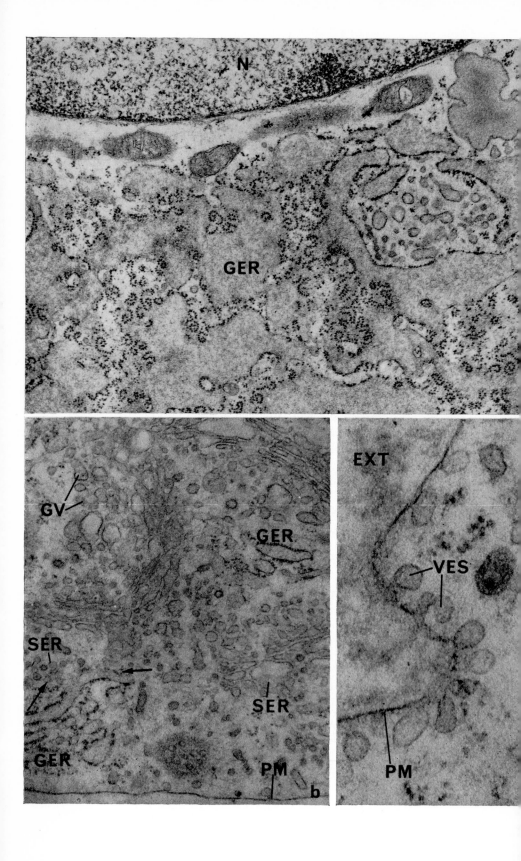

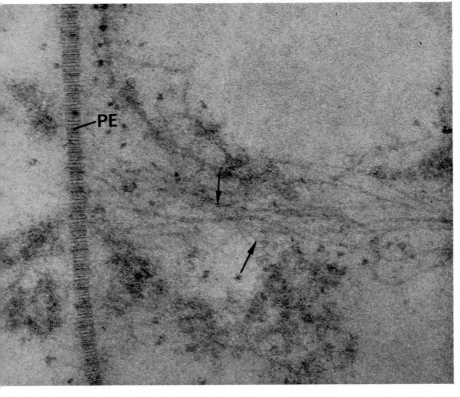

FIG. 6.15. Cultured mouse fibroblast; stationary phase. Non-periodic (arrows) and periodic (PE) fibres are present in the extracellular space. (Courtesy Drs. B. Goldberg and H. Green. × 93,000.)

of the granular reticulum. The material is then passed to the agranular reticulum either (a) by transfer through the lumina of the Golgi complex, or by the continuous supply of membranous elements from the complex to the reticulum, or (b) by a process of ribosomal detachment from the granular reticulum. By way of either of these two organoids the agranular reticulum receives the tropocollagen and buds off vesicles which approach the plasma membrane. The fusion of the vesicular membrane and the

FIG. 6.14. (a) Cultured mouse fibroblast; stationary phase. Characteristic of this state is an extensive, branching granular reticulum (GER) the cisternae of which contain a moderately adielectronic material. N, nucleus. (Courtesy Drs. B. Goldberg and H. Green. × 25,000.) (b) Cultured mouse fibroblast; stationary phase. The large Golgi complex is intimately associated with the granular reticulum (arrows). PM, plasma membrane; GV, Golgi vesicles; SER, smooth reticulum continuous with the granular reticulum (GER). (Courtesy Drs. B. Goldberg and H. Green. × 37,000.) (c) Cultured mouse fibroblast; stationary phase. Vesicles (VES) derived from the agranular reticulum appear to discharge their contents into the extracellular space (EXT). PM, plasma membrane. (Courtesy Drs. B. Goldberg and H. Green. × 101,000.)

plasma membrane permits the discharge of the tropocollagen into the extracellular space where it forms first non-periodic fibrils ranging from 40 to 160 Å in diameter (Fig. 6.15). Subsequently, thick 400 Å fibres with a periodicity of 550 Å and the asymmetrical banding pattern of native collagen appear (Fig. 6.15). The thin fibrils tend to be concentrated near the cell surface and are considered to be the growth points for the thick fibres. Collagen secretion is, therefore, of the merocrine type and native collagen formation is an extracellular event.

Spermatogenesis

Undoubtedly one of the most extensive changes in cellular morphology occurs during spermatogenesis, especially in spermiogenesis. The following is a general account of spermiogenesis derived from studies of both vertebrate and invertebrate material, but whenever significant differences occur between the two groups, they are detailed.

Nuclear Changes

The nuclei of spermatids are initially spherical but later become oval and finally elongate into sperm nuclei with hooked, ovoid, spiral or other bizzare shapes. Concurrent with the change in shape, the structure and electron density of the nucleoplasm alter. In the early spermatid of many vertebrates, the nucleoplasm is homogeneous and composed of small granules or filaments of moderate adielectronicity. Later, this homogeneity is replaced by a random distribution of coarse adielectronic rods or granules, apparently due to the aggregation of the original smaller bodies. The granules and rods may be in reality cross-sections of gyres or helically twisted filaments. The intergranular spaces are gradually obliterated as the dense granules grow by accretion (Fig. 6.16a–c). The nucleolus may break up, or become indistinguishable from the remainder of the dense nuclear material.

In many invertebrates the process of nuclear condensation starts near the nuclear membrane adjacent to the centrioles. The nucleoplasm, when observed in a nucleus cut longitudinally, forms long adielectronic filaments, which in cross-section are revealed as either true filaments or as sheets. The sheets may later roll up into tubes or form meandering reticular structures, or join to give an orderly series of polygons (Fig. 6.16d–f). All the filaments and sheets lie in parallel with each other. At a late stage of spermiogenesis, these complex forms may be obliterated by conversion of the nucleoplasm into a homogeneous, very adielectronic mass.

The Acrosome

In the spermatid, the Golgi complex consists of an aggregation of vesicles with a peripheral group of flattened sacs lying in parallel. During differentiation of the acrosome the vesicles coalesce into a single large vacuole

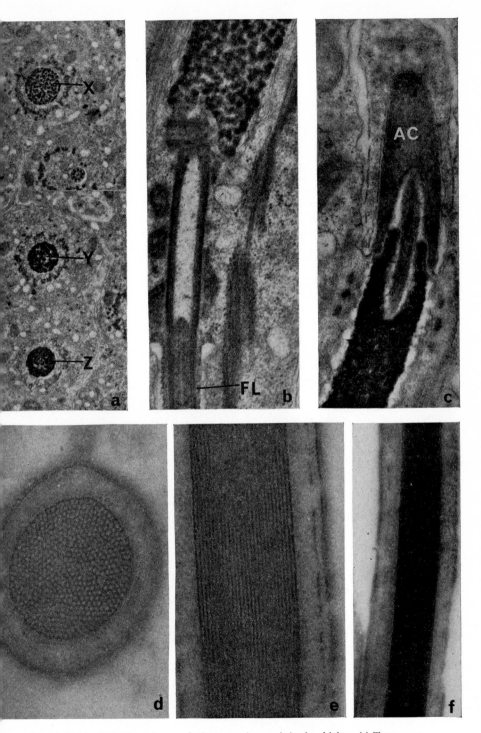

Fig. 6.16. (a)–(c) Nuclear changes during spermiogenesis in the chicken. (a) Transverse
section, the arrows X, Y, Z show increasing accretion of chromatin granules in the sperm
nuclei. (b) and (c) Longitudinal sections, showing the granular nature of the chromatin
and its condensation into a massive nucleus. AC, acrosome; FL, flagellum. (Courtesy
Dr. T. Nagano. (a) × 12,000. (b) × 40,000. (c) × 35,000.) (d)–(f) Nuclear changes during
spermiogenesis in the grasshopper. (d) Transverse section showing the honeycomb
structure of the chromatin. (e) Longitudinal section showing the filaments aligned in
parallel. (f) Longitudinal section of the late sperm showing condensed (massive) nucleus.
(Courtesy Dr. G. Yasuzumi. (d) × 51,000. (e) × 58,000. (f) × 41,000.)

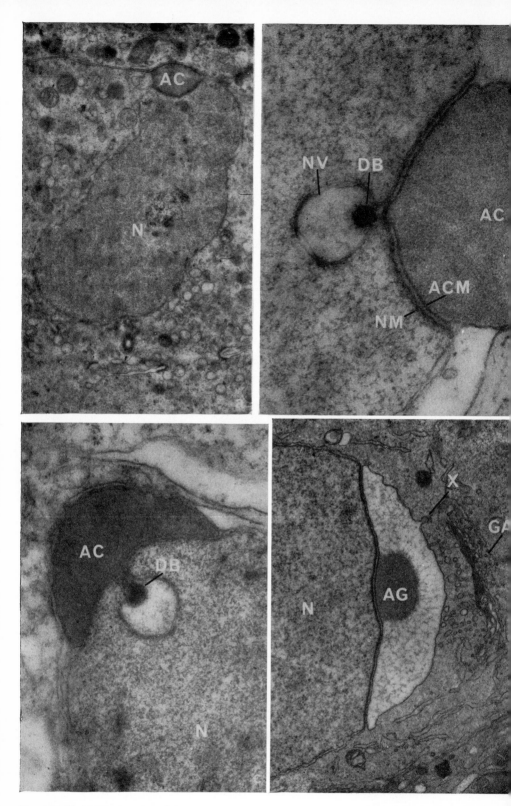

FIG. 6.17. (a)–(c) Development of the acrosome and perforatorium in the chicken. (a) The acrosome (AC) is cl
applied to the nuclear membrane. (b) An invagination of the nucleus (NV) contains a dense bead (DB). A
acrosome membrane; NM, nuclear membrane. (c) The acrosome is moon-shaped and contains an enlarged
bead, which eventually elongates to form the perforatorium. (Courtesy Dr. T. Nagano. (a) ×19,500. (b) ×52
(c) ×53,000.) (d) Acrosome of the mouse sperm with acrosomal granule (AG). Golgi vesicles are budded of
added to the acrosome, as at X. (Courtesy Drs. K. Porter and M. Bonneville. ×15,300.)

(Fig. 6.17a–d). This vacuole is at first irregular in shape, but later becomes rounded on one side and flattened on the other, which is closely applied to the nucleus. Depending on the species the vacuole may be empty, have a fine granularity (Figs. 6.17b, c; 6.18b) or contain distinct adielectronic proacrosome granules (Fig. 6.17d). With elongation of the nucleus and the migration of the cytoplasm from around it, the acrosome is gradually forced over the anterior pole of the nucleus and flattened (Fig. 6.17c, d). Finally, a symmetrical double cap is formed, the lumen of the acrosome persisting as a narrow space enclosed by inner and outer membranes which are continuous at the margins of the "cap" (Fig. 6.17c). In species in which the acrosomal vacuole is empty or contains material of a fine granularity, the acrosomal material eventually acquires a moderate electron density, to an extent which makes distinction of the three layers of the head cap difficult. Where proacrosomal granules are present, an acrosomal granule arises by fusion of these. While still quite small, the acrosomal vesicle becomes attached to the nucleus, growing and spreading over its surface. Meanwhile the acrosomal granule comes to lie against the vesicle membrane on the side towards the nucleus, sometimes indenting the nucleus itself. The Golgi complex migrates away from the acrosomal vesicle and the latter collapses over the nucleus to form the head cap with the acrosomal granule in the centre (Fig. 6.17d).

In some invertebrates, e.g. *Lumbricus,* the Golgi complex (dictysome) lies lateral to the nucleus. The acrosomal vesicle, containing some smaller vesicles but no adielectronic granule, is formed by the dictyosome. The acrosome leaves the dictyosome to move into an acrosome carrier consisting of a tube closed at one end and containing a vacuole (Fig. 6.18a). The acrosome carrier containing the acrosome moves to the anterior end of the nucleus and deposits its load. The acrosome eventually elongates to form a head cap with a tip more adielectronic than the remainder. Acrosome carriers also occur in other invertebrates, e.g. the locustid, *Malenopus differentialis.*

The Perforatorium

In the spermatozoa of rodents, the domestic rooster, some amphibia and invertebrates, a structure additional to the acrosome occurs between the latter and the anterior pole of the nucleus. This is the perforatorium. In the house cricket, *Acheta domestica,* the first evidence of a perforatorium is the appearance of a space between the nuclear membrane and the closely applied acrosome (Fig. 6.18b). The acrosome invaginates at its base and the impression deepens until the whole acrosome forms a cone (Fig. 6.18c). In the large space between acrosome and nucleus, an amorphous material develops next to the acrosomal membrane and condenses into a dense fibrous cone with a pointed tip, the perforatorium (Fig. 6.18d–f). Subsequently, the two sides of the acrosome grow in below the base of the perforatorium and eventually meet and fuse (Fig. 6.18d–f). The final

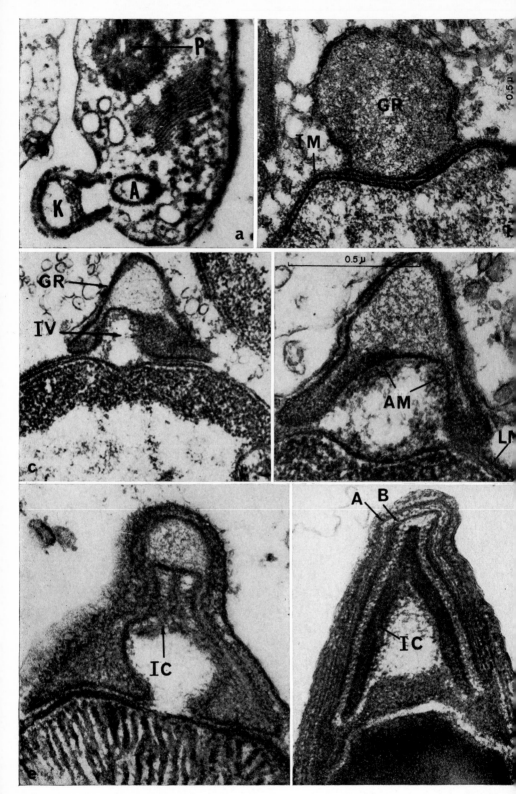

FIG. 6.18. (a) Acrosome (A) and acrosome carrier (K) from the spermatocyte of an earthworm. P, mitochondrial n kern. (Courtesy Dr. A. J. Dalton.) (b)–(f) Development of acrosome and perforatorium in the house cricke Acrosomal granule (GR) attached to the nucleus; IM, interstitial membrane. (c) Cell in mid spermiogenesis conical acrosome; IV invagination. (d) Slightly later stage with amorphous material (AM) in the invagination. (e spermatid with the inner cone (IC) of the perforatorium forming and the lateral sides of the acrosome co together. (f) Mature sperm; A, outer membrane of acrosome; B, inner membrane of acrosome; IC, perforato

Note also the development of the chromatin from granules to filaments to a solid mass. (Courtesy Dr. J. S. Ka

appearance of this region is, therefore, of a dense, fibrous, open-ended cone, the perforatorium, lying enclosed in another cone having a solid base, both structures being very close to the anterior end of the nucleus (Fig. 6.18e). The perforatorium apparently develops in relation to, or under the influence of, the acrosome and not the nucleus. In vertebrates such as the rooster and the toad, the perforatorium arises between the nucleus and the acrosome and is never completely encircled by the latter. In the rooster, the perforatorium develops from a dense granule lying in a depression in the nucleus, the granule eventually forming a fibrous rod.

The Manchette

Situated near the caudal pole of the nucleus and extending towards, but not to, the head cap, is a series of parallel tubes joined together laterally. They extend as a sheet about one third of the way round the circumference of the spermatozoon, between the plasma membrane and the nucleus. This structure is thought to be homologous with the manchette, the origin and function of which is unknown (Fig. 6.19a).

The Centrioles, Neck and Middle Piece

Early in the differentiation of the spermatozoon, the two centrioles are situated in the peripheral cytoplasm. The developing flagellum is intimately related to one of them. During spermatid elongation, the centrioles and flagellum move inwards, followed by the plasma membrane, and take up their position at the caudal pole of the nucleus. Simultaneously, cytoplasm from the anterior end of the spermatid is displaced caudally, forming a broad cuff around the base of the nucleus and backwards for a few microns around the proximal end of the flagellum (Fig. 6.19a). This is the neck and start of the middle piece. The cuff is separated from the flagellum by a narrow cleft, due to a deep invagination of the plasma membrane up to the base of the flagellum. The cuff contains mitochondria, which often assume a complex internal structure.

The two centrioles have a structure similar to the basal bodies of ciliated cells, being about 4000 Å long, 1600 Å in diameter and having the usual 9 triplet fibres surrounding a dielectronic core. The proximal centriole lies at right angles to the sperm's length, sometimes in a deep concavity at the base of the nucleus, whereas the distal centriole lies in the long axis of the sperm. The distal centriole and the flagellum are continuous, although the latter has only the usual 9 + 2 axial fibre complex typical of cilia.

In the spermatozoa of some vertebrates such as the domestic rooster, the two centrioles are still evident in the neck, and are orientated as in the late spermatid (Fig. 6.19a). The limit of the middle piece is indicated by an adielectronic ring centriole (presumed to be derived from part of the distal centriole), and at this level the central filaments of the axial complex of the flagellum have their origin. Ring centrioles are not always recognizable as such in all animals, e.g. toad. In the rooster, the nine peripheral fibres of the

9

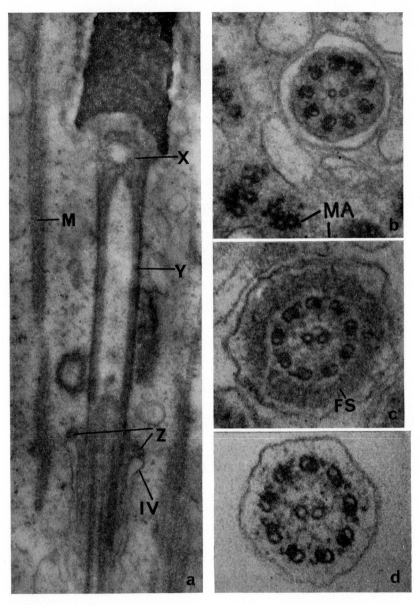

Fɪɢ. 6.19. (a) Longitudinal section of the chicken spermatozoon. The proximal centriole is at X, the centriole giving rise to the flagellum at Y, and the ring centriole (part of the distal centriole) at Z. MA, manchette of microtubules; IV, invagination of the plasma membrane round the flagellum. (Courtesy Dr. T. Nagano. × 50,000.) (b)–(d) Transverse sections at different levels of the flagellum of the chicken spermatozoon. (b) Proximal main piece, 2+9+9 filaments and manchette (MA). (c) Main piece 2+9 filaments and fibrous sheath (FS). (d) End piece 2+9 filaments only. (Courtesy Dr. T. Nagano. (a) × 94,000. (b) and (c) × 130,000.)

axial complex in the proximal part of the middle piece are surrounded by a ring of nine dense bodies, one to each fibre (Fig. 6.19b). This region has, therefore, a $9+9+2$ configuration. In the principal piece of the tail, the $9+2$ axial complex is surrounded by a fibrous sheath which appears to be continuous all round (Fig. 6.19c).

In other vertebrates only the proximal centriole is present in a recognizable form in the late spermatozoon. The organization of the neck, middle and tail regions of the sperm of these vertebrates is best illustrated by reference to mammals. In mammals, the two centrioles of the early spermatid migrate to the nucleus and take up positions as previously described. The proximal centriole retains its morphology during the subsequent stages of spermeogenesis, but the distal one loses its characteristic form. Dense material accumulates round the periphery of the distal centriole, and either by expansion of the original structure, or by the laying down of new material, the distal centriole gives rise to a funnel-shaped body (Fig. 6.20a). This funnel completely surrounds the proximal centriole, for its upper rim is closely applied to the nuclear membrane. In cross-section the funnel is composed of nine distinct columns of adielectronic material separated by narrow spaces, and the dark material eventually develops periodicity (Fig. 6.20a).

The dense fibres of the funnel are continued into the middle piece to form a ring of nine coarse fibres outside the $9+2$ axial complex. The periodicity of these fibres in the neck region is lost, and the fibres are largest in the middle piece, having a radiate, petal-like shape, the broadest part of which is outermost (Figs. 6.20a; 6.21a). These coarse fibres project down into the principal piece of the tail, gradually becoming thinner and terminating at different levels. In many species the coarse fibres opposite axial fibres one, five, and six, are larger than the others. Coarse fibres occur in species other than mammals, e.g. *Passer domesticus, P. montanus*, and *Helix pomatia*.

In the middle piece, the coarse fibres are surrounded by a relatively long band of mitochondria, the mitochondrial helix, made up of single mitochondria pressed close together to form a continuous spiral (Figs. 6.20a–d; 6.21a). In some other vertebrates and invertebrates, the mitochondrial helix is very complex in its internal structure and is derived from the spermatid mitochondria by extreme and complicated changes in their morphology. In the principal piece of the tail, the coarse fibres are enclosed in a fibrous sheath (Figs. 6.20d; 6.21a). This is made up of semicircular ribs, which are joined at their ends to two longitudinal columns. These longitudinal columns run the full length of the principal piece and are in direct line with the two central fibres of the axial filament complex (Fig. 6.21a). At the junction of the rib and the column, there may be a thickening, giving the sheath an oval, rather than a circular outline (Fig. 6.21a). The ribs do not run straight between one column and the other, but branch and anastomose (Fig. 6.20d). The ribs and columns end abruptly at the junction of the principal piece and end piece of the tail.

FIG. 6.20. (a) Tridimensional (A) and sectional (C) drawings of human spermatozoon. (B) shows appropriate cross-sections. (b)–(d) Longitudinal sections from cat spermatozoon from points equivalent to those labelled *b*, *c*, and *d* in (C). ((a) Courtesy Dr. D. Fawcett. (b)–(d) Courtesy Drs. K. Porter and M. Bonneville. (b) ×11,400. (c) ×70,000. (d) ×11,400.)

The end piece of the tail resembles a cilium, for it consists of only an axial complex enclosed by a plasma membrane and a very thin layer of cytoplasm (Fig. 6.21a). The axial complex of the flagellum is not always simple throughout, however. The doublet peripheral fibres may have arms, as in several mammals, other vertebrates (Fig. 6.19b–d), and the sperm of the sea urchin, *Psammechinus* (Fig. 3.24a). The interior of the subfibre *a* may be adielectronic and apparently solid, whereas subfibre *b* may still appear as a hollow tube (Fig. 6.19d). Such features, however, are more common in the middle piece and principal piece of the flagellum than in the end piece. There may be other irregularities also, for example in the number and disposition of the axial filaments themselves and in the coarse fibres outside them.

Undulatory Membrane

In amphibia the spermatozoa have a thin, ribbon-shaped band of dense fibrous substance projecting perpendicularly from the side of the tail fibres. This undulating membrane arises from a mantle which forms around the proximal centriole and is attached to the base of the nucleus. At the proximal end of the tail, the undulating membrane appears as a thick band extending out only a short distance from the flagellum (Fig. 6.21b). Caudally, however, the dense material is reduced to a thin sheet in its middle region, but is still thick along its free and its attached margins (Fig. 6.21b). The entire structure is invested by an extension of the plasma membrane of the tail. This undulating membrane always lies in the same place as the two central fibres of the axial complex of the flagellum.

Oocyte Development and Yolk Formation

The salient features of oocyte maturation are the formation of the polar bodies and the accumulation of yolk. The latter process has been the subject of continual controversy, yolk production having been attributed at various times and by various authors to the nucleolus, the mitochondria, the Golgi complex, the ground cytoplasm or the microsomes, or indeed any combination of two or more of these. Electron microscopy has finally demonstrated the participation of at least some of these cell organoids in this important aspect of oocyte maturation.

Invertebrate

Crayfish, *Cambarus, Orconectes* and *Procambarus* species. The crayfish ovary is surrounded by a connective tissue sheath which also forms the ovarian stroma. At any given time the oocytes of one ovary are at approximately the same size, but younger stages are always present. Each oocyte has a single layer of amoeboid follicular cells.

The oocytes are polymorphic, due to mutual compression during growth. The nucleus is relatively large with an abundance of dense chromatin

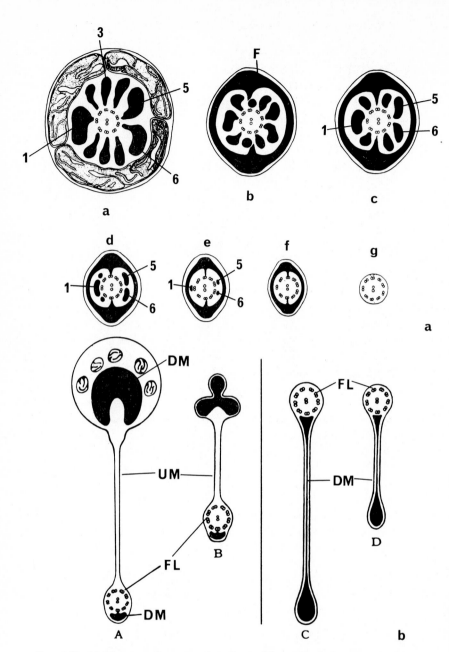

F<small>IG</small>. 6.21. (a) Diagram of cross-sections from different levels in rat spermatozoon flagellum. *a*, middle piece; *b*, upper end of principal piece; *c* to *g*, sequential termination of the nine coarse fibres, first 3 and 8, then 4 and 7, 2 and 9 and finally 1, 5 and 6. F, fibrous sheath. Coarse fibres 1, 5, and 6 are numbered. (Courtesy Dr. D. Fawcett.) (b) Diagram of cross-sections of the sperm tails and undulating membranes of A and B the salamander and C and D the toad. A and C are in the major part of the tail, B and D a few microns from the tip. In salamander the flagellar axis is in the free edge of the membrane, while in toad it is the dense rod and dense material which are in the undulating membrane. (Courtesy Dr. D. Fawcett.)

disposed in a network. Adjacent to nuclear membrane, which is of typical structure, are nucleoli composed of a fine granular substance aggregated into the form of wide anastomosing strands. Small clusters of granular material lie near the nucleoli, suggesting the shedding of material by the latter (Fig. 6.22a). In certain regions of the nuclear membrane granules similar to those of the nucleoli appear to be passing through nuclear pores, after which they aggregate in the perinuclear cytoplasm. The outer nuclear membrane gives off outpocketings of agranular endoplasmic reticulum (Fig. 6.22a) which lie among the nucleolar extrusions in the perinuclear cytoplasm, while further into the ooplasm, wide cisternae of agranular endoplasmic reticulum become branched. Finally, stacks of granular endoplasmic reticular cisternae are derived from the agranular branched cisternae (Fig. 6.22b). The stacks have numerous ribosomes on their surface and many free ribosomes lie between the individual members of the stack. The stacks may be composed of as many as sixteen units and these units are interconnected by narrow agranular intercommunicating and branched endoplasmic cisternae. The agranular and granular endoplasmic reticula therefore form a single branching system of cisternae running throughout the ooplasm and form the basis of an active transport system.

As the stacks of granular endoplasmic reticulum become further differentiated, discrete adielectronic particles appear in the interior of the cisternae, presumably synthesized under the influence of ribosomes (Figs. 6.22b; 6.23a). In the intermediate regions of the ooplasm, stacks are loaded with intracisternal disc-shaped granules, 600–1000 Å long and 200–400 Å wide. When the granules attain a certain density within a stack, they apparently "flow" out of the granular endoplasmic reticulum and along the agranular portions. In regions where several agranular cisternae unite, granules tend to accumulate and form expanded, roughly spherical cisternae (Fig. 6.23a). Within these swollen bodies the granules eventually change into a finely granular proteinaceous yolk body (Fig. 6.23b). In the large oocytes the cortical protoplasm is filled with yolk masses of both the proteainaceous and lipid types. At this stage the stacks and interconnecting system of cisternae become disorganized and restricted in distribution. The fatty yolk globules appear in the cytoplasm before the protein yolk and their origin is obscure.

The crayfish oocytes have numerous mitochondria, many filamentous in form and pleomorphic. Their cristae sometimes branch and anastomose, and in some regions aggregate into tightly packed parallel groups resembling a honeycomb. The Golgi complex is present as a crescentric shaped mass of flattened sacs and associated vesicles. Occasionally, granules similar to the intracisternal granules occur in the interior of the Golgi sacs, probably having passed into the Golgi complex through interconnections between it and the endoplasmic reticulum. These two cell organoids do not appear to take any direct part in the formation of yolk, although presumably

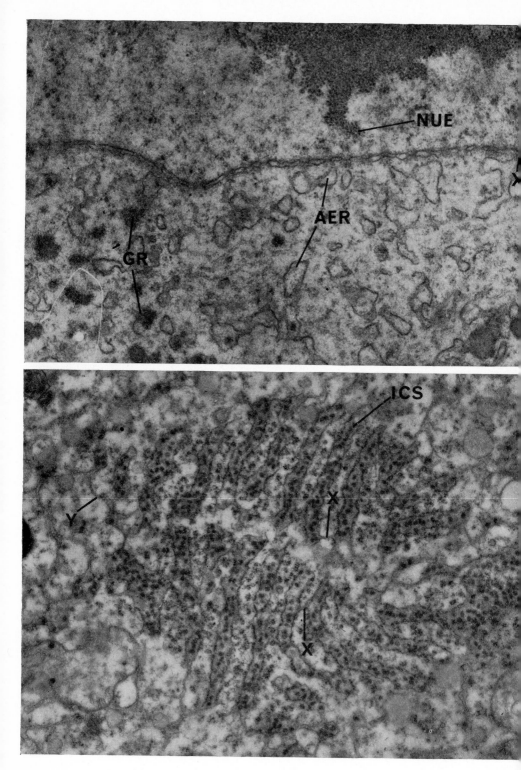

FIG. 6.22. (a) Young oocyte of the crayfish. NUE, nucleolar extrusion passing through pores; AER, agranular reticulum closely associated with the nuclear membrane (at X); GR, granular masses probably derived from the nucleolar extrusions. (Courtesy Drs. H. W. Beams and R. G. Kessel. ×32,000.) (b) Young oocyte of the crayfish. Stacks of parallel endoplasmic reticulum which interconnect (at X), and contain intracisternal granules (ICS). At Y are smooth reticular membranes interconnecting one granular stack with another. (Courtesy Drs. H. W. Beams and R. G. Kessel. ×20,000.)

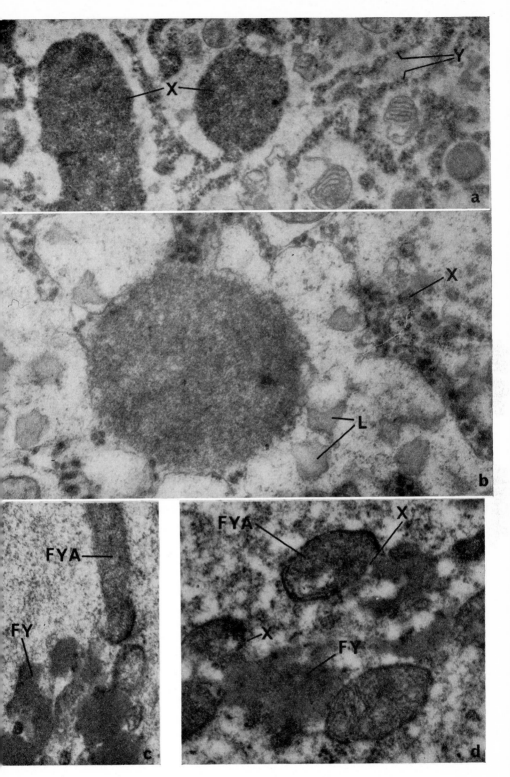

6.23. (a) Crayfish oocyte; initial stage of protein yolk formation. Expanded cisternae containing intracisternal ules in aggregates appear at X and interconnecting tubules also containing granules at Y. (Courtesy Drs. H. W. ns and R. G. Kessel. ×13,000.) (b) Crayfish oocyte; later stage of protein yolk formation. A homogeneous body ting from the dissolution of the intracisternal granules, some of which are still evident at X. L, lipid. (Courtesy H. W. Beams and R. G. Kessel. ×42,000.) (c) and (d) Ooctye from *Rana pipiens* tadpole. Formation of fatty . FYA, fatty yolk mitochondria; X, points at which the fatty yolk is secreted from the mitochondrion; FY, fatty yolk. (Courtesy Dr. R. T. Ward. (c) ×35,000. (d) ×55,000.)

the mitochondria provide the energy necessary for the synthetic processes involved in yolk formation.

Yolk Formation in Rana pipiens *Oocytes*

The young oocytes of *Rana* measure about 100 μ in diameter and have a spherical nucleus with a smooth nuclear membrane. Granular nucleoli lie in the peripheral nucleoplasm. The cytoplasm contains abundant filamentous mitochondria and a few endoplasmic cisternae. In addition, fatty yolk centres are present and consist of vaguely delineated dense droplets, some very adielectronic granular bodies and less adielectronic sharply bounded spheres. The vaguely delineated droplets are perhaps derived from the breakdown of filamentous mitochondria into beads containing a few cristae. Within these bead-like mitochondria a dense material accumulates and is apparently extruded through an opening in the mitochondria to form a vaguely delineated droplet (Fig. 6.23c, d). Mixed with the droplet are masses of very adielectronic granules, thought to be the protein remnants of the mitochondrial membranes, after the lipid content of the mitochondria has been extracted and added to the fatty yolk spheres. Protein yolk formation is always preceded by fatty yolk synthesis.

When the oocyte has reached 175 μ in diameter, the nucleus loses its smooth contour and the nuclear membrane becomes folded. The nucleoli appear to fragment and give rise to small groups of granules. Nuclear material passes through the pores of the nuclear membrane and becomes condensed as streams of adielectronic material which unite into large masses in the perinuclear cytoplasm (Fig. 6.24a). Following the extrusion, mitochondria increase greatly in number, and this increase is perhaps dependent on the extrusion. At this stage, in addition to the fatty yolk spheres, protein yolk is also present. This yolk is in the form of plates, not observed less than 500 Å thick, or less than 0·2 μ across opposite vertices of the hexagonal faces. Because these protein yolk bodies are usually obliquely sectioned, they frequently appear as rods with a variety of lengths and widths. Whatever their shape, the protein yolk always lies completely enclosed within a mitochondrion, usually at one pole (Fig. 6.24b, c). The plates appear to arise within the space of a single crista, so that the mature yolk bodies are bounded by a narrow clear zone and a membrane resembling a crista membrane (Fig. 6.24b, c). The mature protein yolk has a crystalline lattice structure, the space between the adielectronic lines of granules averaging 70–85 Å. More than one yolk plate may occur within a single mitochondrion, and plate-containing mitochondria tend to be grouped together. The formation of these protein yolk plates requires a very great increase in the amount of mitochondrial matrix.

During the formation of the intramitochondrial protein yolk and fatty yolk, another type of cellular inclusion appears immediately below the plasma membrane. The inclusions are spherical bodies of medium electron

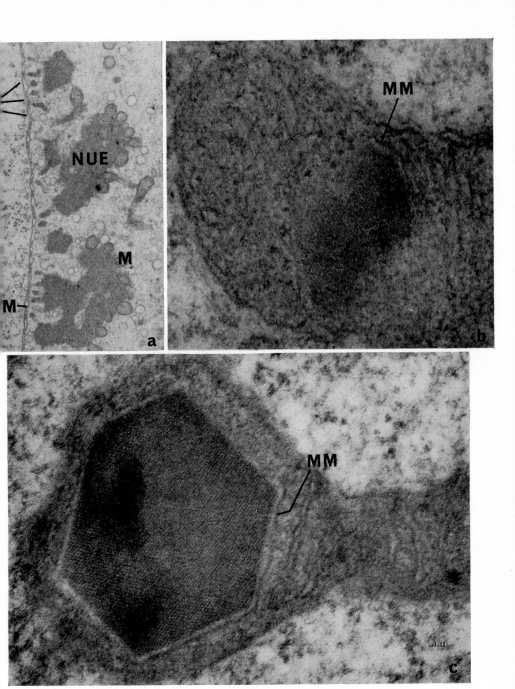

FIG. 6.24. (a) Nucleolar extrusions which appear to initiate yolk formation in *Rana pipiens*. NUE, nucleolar extrusions in the cytoplasm; NM, nuclear membrane; X, nucleolar extrusions passing through nuclear pores. (Courtesy Dr. O. L. Miller. × 13,000.) (b) and (c) Oocyte from *Rana pipiens* tadpole. Intramitochondrial yolk platelets showing a lattice pattern are present. MM, mitochondrial cristae membrane. (Courtesy Dr. R. T. Ward. (b) × 162,000. (c) × 100,000.)

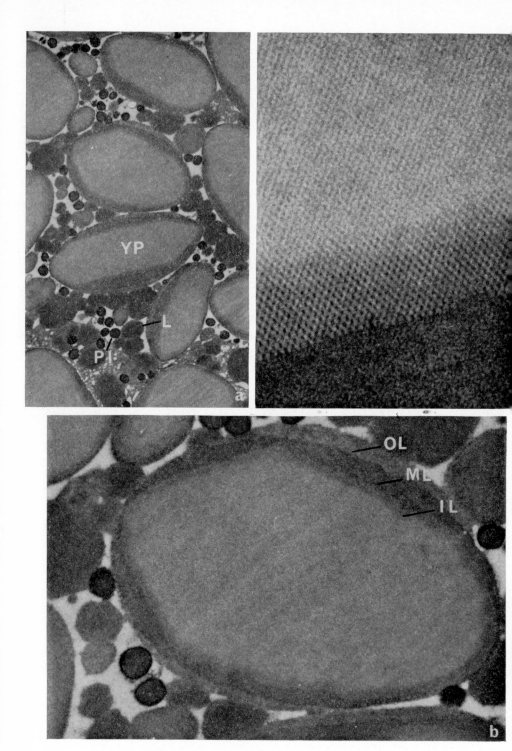

FIG. 6.25. (a)–(c) Mature yolk from *Rana pipiens* tadpole. (a) Low magnification; PI, pigment granule; L, lipid. (b) Single platelet at high magnification to show outer (OL), middle (ML), and inner (IL) layers. (c) Matrix and outer layer showing the crystalline lattice. (Courtesy Dr. R. T. Ward. (a) × 6500. (b) × 19,000. (c) × 233,000.)

density, the so-called cortical granules, the origin of which is not known. The plasma membrane and overlying follicle cells also undergo changes at this time. The follicle cells pull away from the oocyte, but remain attached in places through microvillus-shaped structures. Simultaneously, the

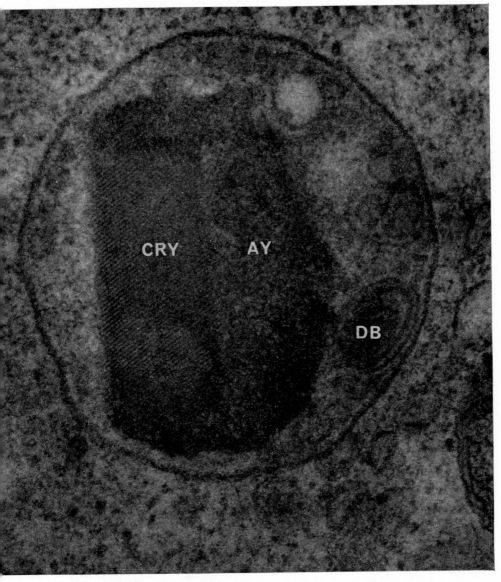

FIG. 6.26. Oocyte from young *Rana pipiens* adult. A second mode of yolk formation is observed in young frogs as compared to tadpoles. Yolk precursor complex is shown and consists of AY, amorphous material; CRY, crystalline yolk apparently derived from AY; DB, dense bodies which become added to the yolk precursor and complex are apparently derived from mitochondria. (Courtesy Dr. R. T. Ward. × 120,000.)

plasma membrane pushes out microvilli all over its surface, and at a late stage these may measure up to 1·67 μ long and 800 Å in diameter. The oocyte microvilli interdigitate with those of the follicle cells to give a prominent zone, the zona radiata. The zone radiata is surrounded by follicle cell processes plus intercellular spaces, a region formerly considered to be the vitelline membrane or chorion.

In the later stages of oocyte development, yolk platelets are synthesized in the peripheral cytoplasm, while the original yolk plates grow and are displaced inwards towards the nucleus. In oocytes of 1·0 mm or more in diameter yolk plates completely fill the cytoplasm and may measure up to 3·7 × 5·8 μ. The plates are always enclosed in a membrane and possess three distinct layers; a centre with a lattice structure, a granular middle layer of considerable electron density, and an outer layer of less electron density (Fig. 6.25a, b). It is not clear what relation the middle and outer layers have to the original mitochondrial matrix, and they form an incomplete layer over the plates, the outer layer sometimes being absent.

In mature oocytes the ooplasm contains, in addition to yolk, pigment granules, 0·3 μ in diameter, which first appear peripherally and then spread throughout the ooplasm. From the observations given above, it is clear that protein yolk has an intramitochondrial, possibly intracristal, origin, and fatty yolk is derived by the breakdown of mitochondria in such a way that the lipid is extracted from the mitochondrial membranes, leaving behind the protein content.

The foregoing observations are derived from studies of oocytes from tadpoles, whereas recent investigations of young frog ovaries have revealed another mode of yolk platelet formation. In this second route, multivesicular bodies, apparently derived from mitochondria, accumulate within themselves a dense amorphous material (Fig. 6.26). This material is increased by the addition of yolk precursor complexes and eventually crystallization occurs until the amorphous material is completely replaced. An hexagonal outline does not occur until the complexes are 1·0 μ across their vertices, compared to 0·1 μ for the platelets within mitochondria. This additional route of platelet formation appear to be the major one in adult frogs, although intramitochondrial yolk formation also occurs. The two modes are in no way interconnected.

Further Reading List

1. FAWCETT, D. W., The Structure of Mammalian Spermatozoon, *Int. Review of Cytology*, Vol. 7, edit. BOURNE, G. H. and DANIELLI, J. F., Academic Press, London, 1957.
2. KUROSUMI, K., Electron-microscope Analysis of the Secretion Mechanism, *Int. Review of Cytology*, Vol. 12, edit. BOURNE, G. H. and DANIELLI, J. F., Academic Press, London, 1961.
3. HADEK, R., Structure of the Mammalian Egg, *Int. Review of Cytology*, Vol. 18, edit. BOURNE, G. H. and DANIELLI, J. F., Academic Press, London, 1965.

PART II

THE DIVIDING CELL

CHAPTER 7

INTRODUCTION TO CELL DIVISION

CENTRAL to the process of growth and reproduction in living systems is cell division. The types of cell division involved in these two processes are, however, fundamentally different. Growth involves somatic cell division, or mitosis, which can be defined as a single division of the nucleus and cytoplasm resulting in two daughter cells with the diploid number of chromosomes and identical gene complements. Reproductive cells are the product of germ cell division, or meiosis, which can be defined as two divisions of the nucleus and cytoplasm, resulting in four cells which have the haploid number of chromosomes and dissimilar gene complements.†

The process of mitosis is more completely understood and has been more widely studied than meiosis, mainly because cells in mitosis are easy to isolate, early stages of embryogenesis being readily available. Before detailing either type of cell division, however, it is worth while considering why cells divide and what the significance and structure of the chromosomes are.

Cell division is essentially the avoidance of ageing. The growth of any particular cell is limited and a point is reached when growth ceases and senescence begins, unless division ensues. Without growth there is no division, but this is not to say that division is caused by growth. It is true that the nuclear sphere of influence is apparently limited and excessive cytoplasm leads to a disturbance in nucleo-cytoplasmic relationships which may be fatal, but the limiting factor is not the size of the nucleus (DNA content), but the nucleolus. The limiting factor is one of communication, the cytoplasm requiring constant information (RNA of the messenger and transfer types), and the nucleolus presumably has only a certain capacity for producing the necessary code materials. The nucleolus is the intermediary between the genes and the cytoplasm, and acts as a valve. The potential for cell growth is renewed with nuclear reproduction and division, being in fact doubled, the two daughter cells having twice the capacity for growth of the parent cell. At some point during cell division, therefore,

---

† Exceptions to the above are found in some protozoa and other cells, in which amitosis, conjugation and endomixis occur. Amitosis involves only the simple constriction of the cell into two, without complicated nuclear changes. Conjugation may be considered as a form of sexual reproduction, since although the number of individuals is the same at the end as at the beginning of the process, it leads to a phase of active asexual multiplication. Endomixis is the breakdown of the macronucleus and its reconstruction by the micronucleus.

physiological reproduction occurs, a doubling of all the functional potentialities of the cell. It is the nucleolus which commences as a single structure, disappears during division and reappears as two separate entities after division, a cycle which is correlated with the cessation of growth during division and the reappearance of synthesis and growth after division. Nucleolar reproduction, therefore, occurs during division, whereas DNA reproduction occurs before division, a fact which has now been amply substantiated.

A second reason why cells divide is because the segregation of an organism into semi-independent units leads to efficiency. Differentiation and specialization confer adaptability and a better prospect for survival, and also mean that the organism has a built-in repair and maintenance system which does not impose an unnecessary physiological burden because it can be applied only when and where necessary. The replacement of worn out or obsolescent parts is in itself both a protection and a means of avoiding ageing.

Finally, cell division is necessary for the perpetuation of the species. Meiosis leads to an over-production of reproductive cells, which is often pronounced in the male. Such over-production is a form of insurance against natural hazards which can take a great toll of the species without necessarily obliterating it. Furthermore, meiosis allows biparental inheritance and variation, which is of such importance from the point of view of evolution, continuation of the species, and the evolution of new species.

The appearance of chromosomes during the process of cell division is generally accepted without question, but are these structures necessary? Genes are not necessarily assembled into chromosomes, e.g. bacteria and viruses, just as all animals are not cellular. The advantage of chromosomes lies in the packaging of large numbers (10^4–10^7) of genes and in their attachment to a small number of kinetochores (2–20). It is the kinetochores which are responsible for the movements of the chromosomes during division, and the fewer of these there are the more ordered can be the separation of the chromosomes.

Chromosome Structure

The morphology of the chromosomes is best seen at metaphase or anaphase, at which time they appear as cylindrical bodies of various lengths and stain intensely with basic dyes and with histochemical methods for demonstrating DNA.

Each chromosome has characteristics which are constant throughout the individual and these characteristics depend on the position of the kinetochore and the secondary constrictions. If the kinetochore is terminal or almost terminal, the chromosome has virtually a single arm and is termed acrocentric; if the kinetochore is off centre but not terminal, then the

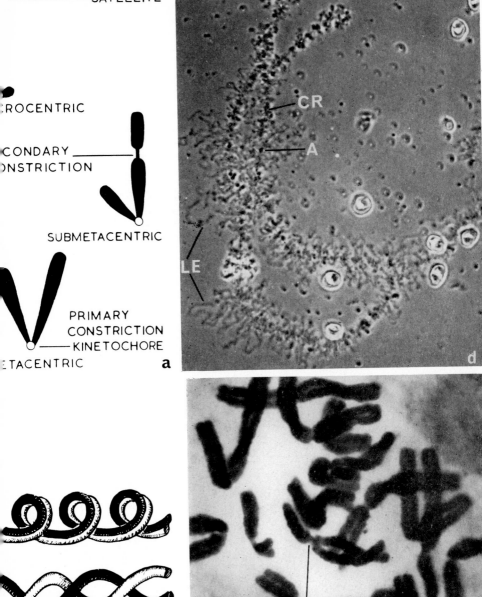

SATELLITE

CROCENTRIC

CONDARY
ONSTRICTION

SUBMETACENTRIC

PRIMARY
CONSTRICTION
KINETOCHORE
TACENTRIC   a

CR

A

LE

d

K

c

b

Fig. 7.1. (a) Drawing of the three types of chromosomes classified on the basis of kinetochore position. (Original.) (b) Prometaphase chromosomes of *Triturus* showing the bipartite character of the chromosomes. K, kinetochore. (Courtesy Dr. H. G. Callan. × 1600.) (c) Drawing showing the two types of chromosome coiling, paranemic above and plectonemic below. (Original.) (d) Lampbrush chromosomes with lateral expansions (LE) and chromomeres (CR) on the axis (A). (Courtesy Dr. H. G. Callan. × 490.)

chromosome has unequal arms and is submetacentric, while if the kineto-chore is central and the arms equal, the chromosome is metacentric (Fig. 7.1a, b). The kinetochore is called the primary constriction, and secondary constrictions may also occur which have a variety of lengths (Fig. 7.1a). An additional feature in some chromosomes is the satellite, a round or elongate body with a diameter equal to or less than the chromosome and attached to the chromosome by a delicate chromatin filament (Fig. 7.1a).

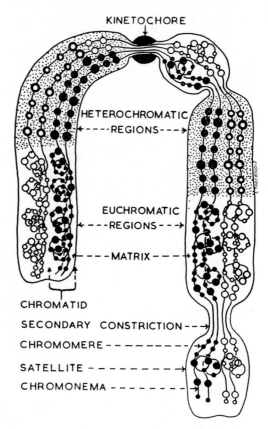

FIG. 7.2. Drawing of the structure of a chromosome as observed by various techniques of light microscopy. (Original, after Drs. A. Engstrom and J. B. Finean.)

With special techniques the internal structure of the chromosomes can be observed. The chromosomes consist of filaments, one, two, or four, depending on the stage of cell division. These filaments, or chromonema, are coiled (Fig. 7.2), whether plectonemically (wound round each other and inseparable unless unwound) or paranemically (coiled filaments lying side by by side and freely separable without unwinding), is not clear (Fig. 7.1c). The coils may be classified as either major, with a diameter about equal to the chromosome diameter, and minor, which are superimposed on, and lie perpendicular to, the major coils, and are gyres of small diameter (Fig. 7.2). The degree of coiling varies with the stage of cell division, being most loose at interphase and increasing to a peak at metaphase and anaphase.

The chromosomes may not have a uniform density after staining, for different regions stain more or less strongly and are called positive and negative heteropyknotic, respectively. Furthermore, the chromosomes have heterochromatic regions which remain tightly coiled throughout interphase and are thought to contain DNA and RNA, while other regions, euchromatic, uncoil and swell during interphase and apparently contain DNA and histone (Fig. 7.2). The heterochromatic and euchromatic regions are continuous and the fomer is generally, but not necessarily, positively heteropyknotic. Another structure of the chromosome is the chromomere, a bead-shaped swelling on thin chromosomes (Fig. 7.2). These regions are considered to be either tightly coiled regions of the chromonema, or condensations of nucleo-protein.

A distinctive type of chromosome occurs during the maturation and prophase of oocytes in fish, amphibians, reptiles and birds. The chromonema has many fine lateral projections which have given rise to the name lampbrush chromosome (Fig. 7.1d). The bivalent chromosomes consist of two homologues held together by chiasmata (cross-over points), the axis of each chromosome consisting of a row of chromomeres and the lateral projects, which are loops, occurring in pairs. The chromomeres are tightly coiled regions of DNA, and the loops represent laterally extended portions of the chromonemata coated with protein and RNA. Material is synthesized by the loops and is released to the nucleus and cytoplasm at about the time that yolk formation begins in the oocyte. The lampbrush chromosomes become reduced in size during late prophase.

Mitosis

Mitosis can be divided into two stages, first the preparative stage, and second, the distributive stage. Although the two stages merge imperceptibly and no point in time or definite event can be designated as the mid-point between the stages, the division is a useful one and is adopted here as the basis for a detailed description of mitosis.

Preparative Stage

The preparative stage occurs during interphase and must be distinguished from cell growth as such. These preparations occupy a large portion of interkinesis, e.g. interkinetic time in *Amoeba* is 24 hours, with the replication of the chromosomes taking up 16 hours. The essential events in preparation are as follows:

1. The doubling of the chemical constituents of the chromosomes, that is, DNA and histones. In addition, the kinetochores must also be doubled.

The DNA content must not only be doubled in amount, but also organized into two equal bodies, the chromatids, which can be separated by splitting. The reduplication of the chromosomes by the template mechanism, e.g. the chromatid from the previous division acting as a template for the organization of the chemical substances necessary for the second chromatid, raises a number of problems. How are the two chromatids related? If they are relationally coiled, as they seem to be, how are they split? Chromatids may become separated in the middle or in a number of places before separating at their ends. Final separation appears to be by rotation of the chromatids at their ends, due to some unknown force. Additionally, the distribution of the old and newly synthesized DNA between template and new chromatid poses a problem. Most evidence suggests that the chromosomes replicate in a conservative way, i.e. the parent unit retains its integrity and all the new DNA goes to form the daughter chromatid. The situation is not fully resolved, however, and the semi-conservative method of replication may occur, with the distribution of the old and new DNA equally between the parent and daughter chromatids.

2. The reduplication of the mitotic centres. During interphase the centres are duplex, consisting of two fully formed rod-like centrioles, each of which has a bud (daughter centriole) lying at right angles to its length. During division the daughter centrioles grow to full size and then separate from the parent. By metaphase, there are four mature centrioles, and in telophase each of these forms a bud, so that after cytokinesis the centriole is again duplex. The reduplication of the centrioles and their division precedes the replication of the genetic material, although the two events are independent of each other. The centres appear to be self-reproducing systems and must, therefore, code their own structure, although how this is carried out is not known.

3. The synthesis of the proteins necessary for the mitotic apparatus (spindle and asters). These substances are definitely not synthesized at division, when all synthesis is depressed and metabolism is low. It must therefore be present, though unassembled and unorganized, during late interphase.

4. Energy requirements for the actual division processes appear to be met beforehand, because as already stated, metabolism is low and respiration and glycolysis decline during division. It has been proposed that a high energy fuel is stored in an energy reservoir during interkinesis and utilized during division. This high energy fuel has not been identified and does not appear to be ATP. Regarding energy, therefore, division is like a functional enucleation, metabolic events controlled, directed or initiated by the nucleus cease or are depressed, all of which probably hinges on the changes in the nucleolus at this time.

The occurrence of the above events during interkinesis makes the identification of the starting point of mitosis very difficult. There are some morphological indicators, such as a rapid increase in nuclear volume, and some physiological signs also, e.g. the cessation of DNA synthesis, and somewhat later of RNA synthesis, and the sudden change in cytoplasmic viscosity leading to the gelation of the mitotic apparatus. These events, however, are not sharply defined and it is not clear whether or not a signal is given to trigger off mitosis itself.

Distributive Stage

The distributive stage of mitosis can be divided into phases, namely, prophase, metaphase, anaphase and telophase, although it must be kept in mind that these phases are parts of one continuous process.

The total time taken for mitosis is generally between half an hour and 3 hours, with relatively few exceptions. The length of time involved depends to some extent on both cell size and temperature; an increase in temperature speeds up the process. The range in the duration of some of the phases is shown in the table below.

DURATION OF PHASE (min)

	Minimum	Maximum	Typical range
Prophase	2	270	14–102
Metaphase	0·3	175	13–44
Anaphase	0·3	122	5–26
Telophase	1·5	140	3–110

(From Mazia, D. Mitosis and the Physiology of Cell Division, *The Cell*, Vol. 3, Academic Press.)

Prophase

During this phase the mitotic apparatus is assembled and the chromosomes become visible and make their first movements (Fig. 7.3). In early prophase the chromosomes appear within the nucleus as slender threads with several orders of coiling, minor, major, and super coils (Fig. 7.4a). These threads thicken progressively, due to the acquisition of phospholipids and some RNA, perhaps derived from the nucleolus. These acquired substances are carried by the chromosomes throughout mitosis and released before the next interphase, but the significance of this process is not understood. The chromosomes also shorten during this time, presumably due to further coiling. The mechanism responsible for this continued coiling is not known for certain and has been variously assigned to either the collection of a matrix around the central thread, or to the helical properties of DNA itself. Condensation, as this coiling process is known, continues into metaphase and even into anaphase in some cases. Such condensation is important in view of the future activities of the chromosomes. In such a contracted state the chromosomes can make clean movements without risk of entanglement and subsequent incorrect separation of the chromosomes. Furthermore, this shortening minimizes the resistance of the chromosomes to the mitotic apparatus and so facilitates movement.

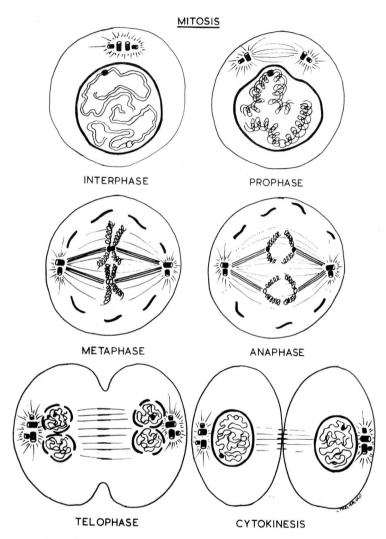

FIG. 7.3. Diagram showing the various stages of mitosis. (Original.)

Some chromosomes are observably double at prophase (Fig. 7.4b) and those which in appearance are not, must actually be so. The halves of the chromosome, the chromatids, are, however, still one at the kinetochore, the region of attachment to the spindle fibres. The kinetochores are, however, probably duplex, at any rate functionally, and are characterized by their location on a particular chromosome, their self-reproducing ability and the

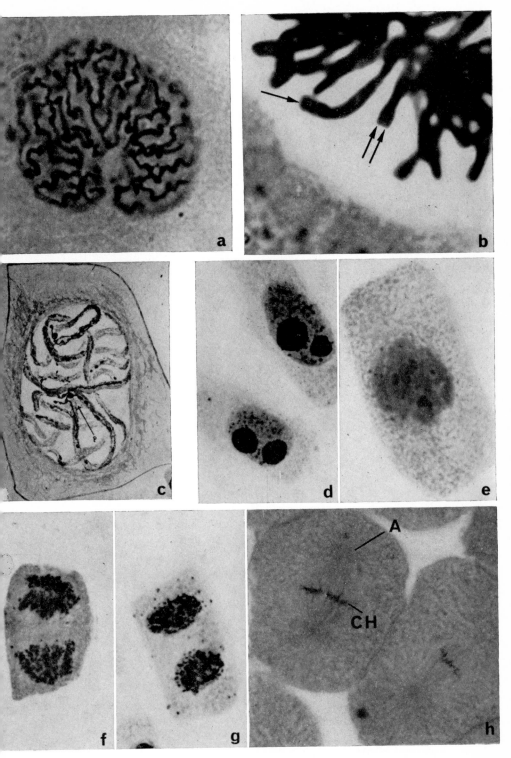

FIG. 7.4. (a) Prophase in *Amblystoma* larval epidermis. (Original. ×1200.) (b) Prophase chromosomes showing their duplex nature (arrows) (chromatids). (Original. ×2500.) (c) Nucleolonema in prophase, *Allium cepa*. (Courtesy Drs. C. Estable and J. R. Sotelo. ×1550.) (d)–(g) Sequence of photographs showing the passage of an unknown silver staining substance between the nucleolus and the cytoplasm during mitosis in onion root tip cells. (d) Interphase; (e) prophase; (f) anaphase; (g) telophase. (Courtesy Drs. N. Das and M. Alfert. All photos ×900.) (h) Metaphase in whitefish blastula. A, aster; CH, chromosomes. (Original. ×400.)

presence of DNA. Despite the double nature of the chromosome and kinetochore, these structures act as one in this stage.

During prophase, the pars amorpha region of the nucleolus disperses, but the nucleolonema continues (Fig. 7.4c). Previously the nucleolar material was considered to be predominantly RNA which became transferred to the chromosomes during prophase, but more recent evidence shows that the RNA content may be as low as 10 per cent of the dry weight of the nucleolus. Furthermore, a specific nucleolar substance, as yet unidentified chemically, goes to the cytoplasm during prophase and at the end of mitosis is again associated with the chromosomes and the nucleolus (Fig. 7.4d–g). The tightly woven type of nucleolonema characteristic of interphase begins to unfold during prophase. It spreads throughout the nucleoplasm and becomes closely associated with the chromosomes. Lengths of this thread run either parallel to the long axis of the chromosomes, or are slightly coiled about them, with connecting strands running between the chromosomes.

A conspicuous event during prophase is the separation of the centres. The centriole is already double in interphase, but early in division the centres appear to repel each other, perhaps due to the growth of the central spindle fibres, and so move apart around the periphery of the nucleus (Fig. 7.3). The centres, however, are always in contact, first by the centrodesmosome and later by the central spindle fibres. On reaching opposite sides of the nucleus, the centrioles cease movement and the poles of the mitotic apparatus are established. Towards the end of prophase the connection between pole and chromosome is formed, the so-called half-spindle fibres. Additionally, fibre-like structures radiate out from the centrioles towards the plasma membrane on the side away from the spindle; these are the astral rays (Fig. 7.3).

Late in prophase, the nuclear membrane breaks down and apparently disappears. In some cells the nuclear membrane persists, for example when the spindle forms inside the nucleus, or in those cases in which the spindle fibres appear to pierce the nuclear membrane and contact the chromosomes inside. The nuclear membrane, therefore, is no barrier to the spindle fibres and the movements of the chromosomes in the succeeding phase are not timed by the breakdown of the nuclear membrane.

The final stage of prophase is called prometaphase, at which time the chromosomes may move to the inner side of the nuclear membrane even before the latter disintegrates. After the dissolution of the membrane, the chromosomes move and become aligned on a well-defined equatorial plate midway between the poles. The chromosomes do not go directly to the metaphase plate but move in an irregular fashion back and forwards between the poles and the equator before finally settling down. The synaptic pairs are, therefore, pulled apart and come together again and each sister chromatid is attached to a different pole, although no satisfactory explanation has been advanced to show how sister kinetochores become attached to different poles in this manner. These movements suggest that the chromosomes are under the influence of the centres at this time.

Metaphase

The metaphase plate and the confining of the kinetochores to a single plane are the characteristic features of metaphase (Figs. 7.3; 7.4h). The arrangement of the chromosomes on the plate ranges from that in which all chromosomes are peripheral, forming a ring round the equator, to that in which all chromosomes are centrally clumped within the spindle. Generally, small chromosomes tend to be central and large ones peripheral. The particular arrangement found in any one cell is perhaps due to the relationship between the central spindle and the half-spindle fibres, which gives the spindle a duality which may be biochemical as well as functional.

The equatorial position of the chromosomes is probably due to the establishment of an equilibrium state, because the sister kinetochores are attracted equally to opposite poles, the strength of the pull to the poles being proportional to the distance from that pole. The chromosomes, however, are not yet ready to split, and so the forces of attraction to opposite poles are balanced by the mutual attraction of the sister chromatids, resulting in an equatorial disposition of the chromosome (Fig. 7.4h).

The mitotic apparatus is fully formed during metaphase. The apparatus is an individual structure without a limiting membrane and occupies 10–50 per cent of the volume of the cell as a whole (Fig. 7.5a). Large particles and structures such as mitochondria are completely excluded from the spindle, despite the lack of a bounding membrane. The apparatus is organized into highly orientated fibres, which are elastic, and its gel-like character is due to the polymerization of RNA and mainly acidic proteins with lipids. Intermolecular S–S links and other linkages involving sulphur are involved in binding the proteins together (Fig. 7.5b), but other bonds are also present. ATPase, which can split only ATP and IMP (adenosine and inosine triphosphate, respectively) also occurs in the spindle.

During metaphase the nucleolonema is still longitudinally and intimately associated with the chromosomes. The structure grows throughout its length and by terminal sprouting. It apparently also undergoes division or is reduplicated, for each chromatid has its associated nucleolonemal strand (Fig. 7.5c).

Anaphase

Anaphase is the stage during which the actual separation of the sister chromatids is brought about (Figs. 7.3; 7.5d, e). The transition from metaphase to anaphase is marked by an apparent signal, to which all chromatids respond simultaneously; the kinetochores of the chromatids "jump" apart. The chromosomes move in a straight line towards the poles at a linear or

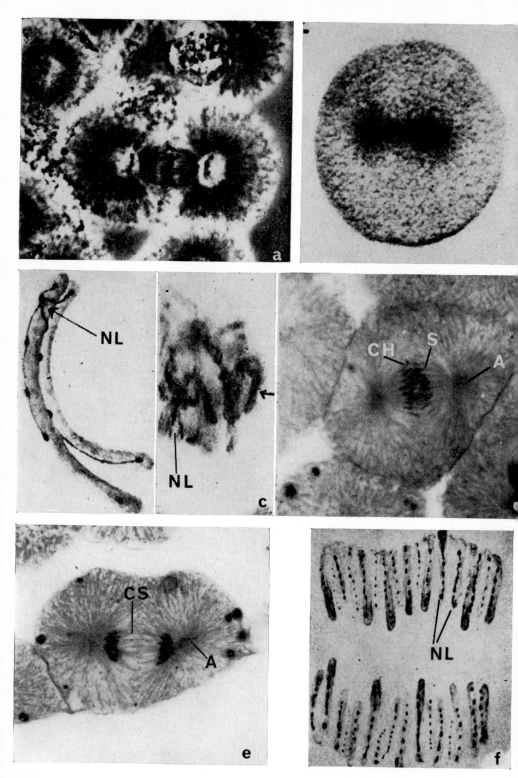

Fig. 7.5. (a) Isolated mitotic spindle of the sea-urchin egg. (Courtesy Dr. D. Mazia.)
(b) High protein SH contents in the mitotic spindle of the sea-urchin egg. (Courtesy
Dr. D. Mazia.) (c) Nucleolonema (NL) during metaphase in *Notoscordum*. (Courtesy Drs.
C. Estable and J. R. Sotelo. × 1850.) (d) Early anaphase in whitefish blastula. A, aster;
CH, chromosomes; S, chromosome to pole spindle fibres. (Original. × 400.) (e) Late
anaphase in whitefish blastula. A, aster; CS, central spindle fibres. (Original × 400.)
(f) Nucleolonema (NL) at anaphase in *Notoscordum*. (Courtesy Drs. C. Estable and
J. R. Sotelo. × 2950.)

decelerating rate and never at an accelerating rate. Generally, all chromatids move together, regardles of size, with the kinetochores leading the way and the chromatid arms trailing. On separation, the chromatids are generally called sister chromosomes (Fig. 7.5e).

The separation of the sister chromosomes is brought about by two factors. First, the central spindle elongates and the mass of the spindle increases, probably due to hydration plus the incorporation of more of the originally performed molecular materials. Second, the half-spindle fibres contract to about one-fifth of their original length in some cases. The observations that the chromosomes move individually to the poles, that two poles are required for movement and that sister chromosomes move to opposite poles, support the idea that specific and individual pole to chromosome connections or interactions exist, so that the chromosomes are either pushed or pulled to the poles. Most of the evidence suggests that the chromosomes are pulled to the poles by the half-spindle fibres shortening, either due to a mechanism analogous to muscle contraction, or to the loss of molecules by the fibres to the background matrix, resulting in shortening without loss of the pole to chromosome connection. Possibly the kinetochore actively participates by gliding along the half-spindle fibres.

The nucleolonemal strands longitudinally associated with the chromatids during metaphase separate with the latter during anaphase, so that each chromatid takes a segment of nucleolonema with it (Fig. 7.5f). Towards the end of anaphase the astral rays expand greatly and reach the cell surface. The rays do not exclude large particles from between them, as does the spindle, and run individually through the cytoplasm (Fig. 7.5e).

At the end of anaphase, the sister chromosomes are finally separated into two equal groups, one at each pole of the spindle. The two groups may be farther apart than the distance between the poles at the start of anaphase, due to the lengthening of the spindle during this stage.

Telophase

At telophase the chromosomes which are crowded together at the poles become less densely stained (due to loss of RNA?), and return to their interphase condition either by swelling to form chromosomal vesicles which fuse, or by uncoiling and clumping into chromosome groups (Figs. 7.3, 7.6a). Additionally, during this stage a material which has RNA characteristics, and is probably derived from the chromosomes and the poles, begins to move to the equator; it is probably endoplasmic reticulum with associated ribosomes (Fig. 7.6b–e).

The nucleolus is reconstructed at this time. The nucleolonemal strands associated with the individual chromosomes become thicker and shorter. They eventually come together into the typical ravelled skein of interphase (Fig. 7.6f). The pars amorpha reappears around the nucleolonema and appears to be gathered along all the chromosomes before being concentrated.

The final phase of this stage is the reconstruction of the nuclear membrane which may either be derived from the remnants of the former nuclear membrane, or be a newly synthesized structure.

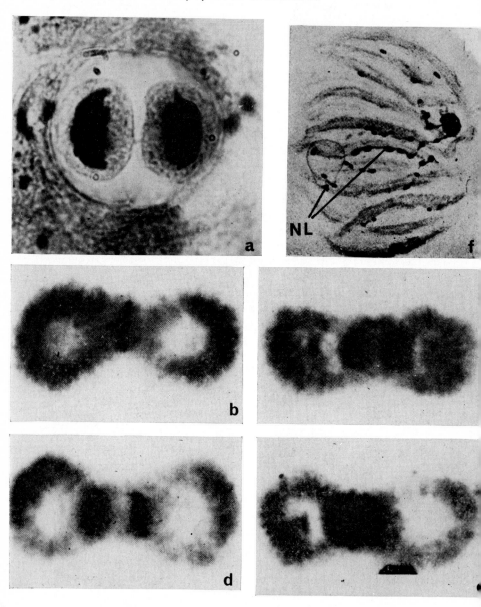

FIG. 7.6. (a) Telophase and cytokinesis in *Ambystoma* larval epidermis. (Original. × 1200.) (b)–(e) Sequence of photographs showing the movement of RNA from the poles to the equator of the spindle. (b) metaphase; (c) early anaphase; (d) late anaphase; (e) end of anaphase. (Courtesy Dr. D. Mazia.) (f) Nucleolonema (NL) at telophase in *Notoscordum*. (Courtesy Drs. C. Estable and J. R. Sotelo. × 2400.)

Cytokinesis

Although cytokinesis, or division of the cytosome, may not follow nuclear division, thereby giving rise to a syncytium, it generally commences during telophase and ends some time after the nuclear events are completed.

The division of the cytoplasm is by furrowing, that is, a constriction arises at the equator of the cell, forming a depression which deepens progressively until separation of the daughter cell results (Fig. 7.3). The plane of this furrow in the majority of cells is perpendicular to the mid-point of the spindle. Cytokinesis with unequal daughter cells occurs in some invertebrates, due either to asters of unequal size or a bulging of the cytoplasm to one end of the cell. The position of the furrow clearly indicates a connection between it and the mitotic apparatus, but, in addition, a relationship between the mitotic apparatus and the time of cytokinesis has also been established. Quite early in cell division, the time and site of the furrow are determined, and after that point in time cytokinesis becomes autonomous, continuing even if the spindle is removed. The centrioles appear to be the determining factor in cytokinesis, for both spindle fibres and chromosomes are inessential. The mode of communication between the centrioles and the furrow is not understood. It may be due to a chemical substance diffusing from the poles, the two fronts on meeting defining and initiating the furrow, or may be due to a physical connection between the astral rays and the plasma membrane, the former crossing at the equator with the result that as the spindle grows, the points of attachment come closer together, relaxing the plasma membrane in the equatorial region.

Other theories of the mechanism of cytokinesis involve (a) the expansion of the plasma membrane, either by the unfolding of the original membrane or by addition of new plasma membrane to both poles and furrow, due to synthesis or from the endoplasmic reticulum, (b) a ring of gel-like proto-plasm in the equatorial cortical region of the cytoplasm, which possesses contractile properties, (c) amoeboid movements, suggested by the appearance of bubbling at the surface of the furrow, which often occurs just prior to and during cytokinesis, and the observation that factors inhibiting amoeboid movement also inhibit cytokinesis. In all, no one theory has a predominance of supporting evidence, and two or more of them may be involved sequentially or together.

Meiosis

Meiosis, like mitosis, can be divided into two parts, the preparative stage and the distributive stage. Meiosis is closely related to both mitosis and fertilization, being always preceded by the former and leading to the latter. No convincing explanation of the change-over of gametocytes from mitosis to meiosis has been proposed. The change is not a sudden one, rather successive mitoses of the gametocytes become more and more meiotic in so far as the time of spindle formation relative to chromosomal contraction, the extension of prophase and the length of the metaphase chromosomes, are concerned. One major difference between cells undergoing meiosis rather than mitosis is that in the former RNA synthesis continues after DNA synthesis has ceased, whereas in the latter RNA and DNA synthesis cease at almost the same time. It has been suggested that a high RNA/DNA ratio results in mitosis and a low ratio in meiosis. Specific chemical substances, e.g. hormones, may also initiate meiosis, but whether directly or indirectly is unknown.

Preparations for Meiosis

This aspect of meiosis has been little investigated, but presumably the events which occur in the pre-division stage are similar to those of mitosis. This stage must include the synthesis of DNA and other chemical constituents of the chromosomes, the synthesis of the materials of the spindle, the reproduction and growth of the centres, and the storage of energy. In meiosis, however, it is not known whether all or only some of these processes occur before the first nuclear division, or in the interval between the first and second nuclear divisions. As the interphase period is generally short and in some cases non-existent, most synthesis, reduplication and energy storage must occur some time between the last mitosis of the gametocyte and the beginning of meiosis.

Distributive Events

Characteristic features of the distributive events in meiosis are the occurrence of two each of prophase, metaphase, anaphase and telophase, and the length of the prophase, which necessitates the subdivision of this stage into five.

Prophase I

The onset of meiosis is indicated by an increase in nuclear volume and the appearance of the chromosomes as coiled threads. This stage is called the preleptotene, or premeiotic, spiral prophase stage.

Leptotene

The tightly coiled chromosomes unravel and are wholly devoid of spirals in the early part of this phase (Fig. 7.8a). Generally, these long filaments are well separated from each other and randomly orientated (Figs. 7.7; 7.8a). In some cells, however, the chromosomes lie with their proximal ends arranged in parallel close to the nuclear membrane, or polarized with respect to the centrioles, while their distal ends splay out into the nucleoplasm; this is the bouquet stage. Later the chromosomes have bead-shaped regions strung along their chromonema; these are the chromomeres. The larger chromomeres are constant in location and size for any particular chromosome, and are in reality regions of the chromonema more tightly coiled than elsewhere. At this time the chromosomes of some species are clearly double, indicating that replication of DNA occurs before leptotene, or very early in that stage.

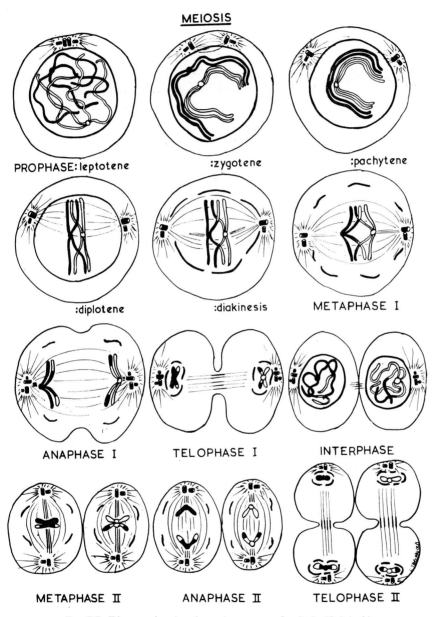

FIG. 7.7. Diagram showing the various stages of meiosis. (Original.)

10

The nucleolus is still evident in leptotene, and is attached to the nucleolar zone of the nucleolar chromosomes. The nucleolus continues to synthesize RNA and proteins during the early phases of prophase.

Zygotene

By the beginning of zygotene, the chromosomes have shortened and become wider, due to increases in the diameter of the spirals (Figs. 7.7; 7.8b). The pairing of the homologous chromosomes, one homologue of each pair being from the maternal parent and one from the paternal, begins, being accomplished in a variety of ways. The pair may unite at one end and pairing then proceeds in a regular fashion down to the other end, or pairing may occur simultaneously at a number of places along the homologues and spread out from these centres. The pairing is exact, chromomere to chromomere, but the forces involved are not understood.

Pachytene

The pairing of the homologues is completed by the beginning of pachytene (Figs. 7.7; 7.8c). The chromosome pairs (tetrads or bivalents) continue to contract and finally form short, coarse filaments which may be relationally coiled. The number of chromosomes appears to be reduced to the haploid number, but each bivalent is in reality a tetrad composed of four chromatids, two sister chromatids for each homologue.

At some point between pachytene and the next stage, diplotene, the chromosomes swop genetic material. The interchange is between homologous chromatids, never between sister chromatids, and is called crossover. At a particular point, the chiasma, a transverse break occurs simultaneously on two homologous chromatids, the segments are interchanged and fuse in their new positions. The other two homologous chromatids remain intact. At least one chiasma is formed for each bivalent and generally more chiasmata form on the longer chromosomes than on the shorter ones, although the number is not proportional to length. More than one chiasma may be made between the same pair of homologous chromatids, or after crossing with one chromatid of its homologous chromosome a particular chromatid may cross with the other, sister, chromatid of that chromosome. A crossover suppresses the occurrence of other chiasmata in immediately adjacent areas of the chromatid so that chiasmata do not generally lie close together; this is called interference.

Diplotene

During this stage the attraction between the bivalents is replaced by a repulsion (Figs. 7.7; 7.8d). The chromosomes part except at the point of crossover and so form figures which are characteristic of the number and position of the chiasmata. In bivalents with one non-terminal chiasma a cross is formed, in those with one terminal chiasma a rod is formed, while those with terminal chiasmata on both arms form rings (Fig. 7.8d).

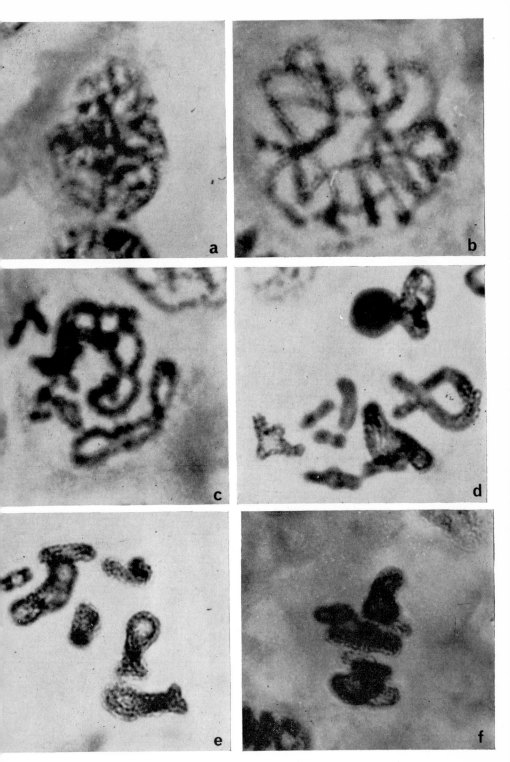

FIG. 7.8. (a)–(e) Prophase stages in the male germinal cells of the amphibian, *Batrachoseps*. (a) Leptotene; (b) zygotene; (c) pachytene; (d) diplotene; (e) diakinesis. (Original. All photos × 1500.) (f) Metaphase I in the male germinal cells of the amphibian, *Batrachoseps*. (Original. × 1500.)

10*

Throughout diplotene the number of chiasmata is gradually reduced by terminalization, i.e. the displacement of the chiasmata along the length of the chromosomes toward the ends until they are released. This process may continue until anaphase.

Diakinesis

The process of terminalization continues and the chromosomes contract and spiral to a degree even more marked than in mitosis (Figs. 7.7; 7.8e). The nucleolus, which has decreased during diplotene, disappears and the rapid increase in chromosomal basophilia at the same time suggests that nucleolar material is incorporated into the chromosomes, although this has been questioned.

The bivalents tend to lose their random distribution in the nucleoplasm and migrate to the periphery where they lie close to the nuclear membrane. With the disintegration of the nuclear membrane, the stage of diakinesis is ended.

Metaphase I

Each bivalent has two kinetochores, and at metaphase the bivalents move to the metaphase plate with the two kinetochores lying one each side and equidistant from the equator (Figs. 7.7; 7.8f). The distance of the kinetochores from the equator depends on the position of the proximal chiasmata. The number and position of the chiasmata, plus the length of the chromosomal arms, determine the shape of the bivalents at this time. Half-spindle fibres connect the kinetochores to the poles, the centrioles having migrated to their polar positions and formed a spindle during the preceding prophase.

Anaphase I

The bivalents (tetrads) separate into two dyads, each dyad going to a different pole, with the kinetochore leading (Fig. 7.7). During the polewards movement the chiasmata slip off the ends of the chromatids, the process being rapid when the chiasma is terminal, but more slow with the more intermediate chiasmata (Fig. 7.7). Longer chromatids generally take longer to separate than shorter ones.

The maternal and paternal dyads are randomly segregated during anaphase, and, in addition, a reduction division occurs at this time, in the sense that the number of chromosomes going to the daughter cells is only half that of the present cell.†

---

† The terms reduction division and equation division must be used with care, for they can refer, as in this text, to the number of chromosomes, but may also be used to refer to the segregation of genes. For example, take a pair of homologous chromosomes which have the alleles A and B and a and b, with the two dominant genes on one chromosome and the two recessives on the other. The linear order of these genes is, kinetochore A, B, and kinetochore a, b. If one of the non-sister chromatids forms a single chiasma between the A and B locus, then one dyad at

The chromosomes which go to the poles are not, however, identical with the original maternal and paternal chromosomes, due to the swopping of parts of chromosomes during crossing over.

Telophase I

After anaphase I the meiotic cells undergo one or other of the following sequences: (a) the anaphase dyads, with little change in length or coiling, go into the second, equation, division. The daughter chromatids appear to repel each other and so acquire a V- or X- form, (b) the telophase dyads elongate by loosening their coils, the nuclear membrane reforms, and the chromosomes gradually assume the characteristics of interphase (Fig. 7.7). No nucleolus is formed and the interphase is generally of short duration. Cytokinesis follows, in either case, to give two daughter cells, known as the secondary spermatocyte in males and the secondary oocyte in females.

Prophase II

This stage and the following metaphase II, anaphase II and telophase II resemble mitosis. In prophase the dyads are clearly shown to consist of two chromatids joined at the kinetochore. The chromatids are not coiled relationally and are longer than at telophase I. The spindle begins to form, with the centrioles moving to the poles and the nuclear membrane, where it exists, begins to break down (Fig. 7.7).

Metaphase II

The haploid chromosomes of each daughter nucleus move to the equatorial plate. The kinetochores come to lie on the plate and are double. The half-spindle fibres join each half of the kinetochores to a different pole, and the full spindle is formed (Fig. 7.7).

Anaphase II

The dyads separate, one chromatid (now designated a chromosome) moves to each pole, so that each daughter nucleus still has a haploid number of chromosomes; this is then an equational division (Fig. 7.7).

---

anaphase I will be A.B and A.b, the other a.b, and a.B. Under these circumstances the A locus would have undergone a reduction division, as all dominant A genes would go to one pole and all recessive a genes to the other. The genes of the B locus, however, would have undergone an equation division, as a B.b combination would go to each pole. In the following division the A.A or a.a combinations would be subject to an equational division, and the B.b locus to a reductional division.

Telophase II

The chromosomes uncoil and swell to give the characteristic form of the chromatid at interphase. The nuclear membrane reforms and the nucleolus reappears. These nuclear events are followed by cytokinesis to give a final result of four cells, each with the haploid number of chromosomes (Fig. 7.7). These cells are called the spermatids in the male and the ootids in the female. All the spermatids will subsequently develop into spermatozoa, but only one of the four ootids will become a functional ovum, the other three becoming the degenerate, polar bodies.

Further Reading List

1. HUGHES, A., *The Mitotic Cycle,* Butterworths, 1952.
2. MAGIA, D., Mitosis and the Physiology of Cell Division, *The Cell*, Vol. 3, edit. BRACHET, J. and MIRSKY, A. E., Academic Press, London, 1961.

CHAPTER 8

THE ULTRASTRUCTURE OF THE CELL
IN DIVISION

ELECTRON microscopy of the cell in division is still in its infancy, and none of the wealth of morphological detail exists concerning the cell in this condition, as it does for the cell at interphase. Three factors are responsible for this state of affairs and they are, namely, (a) the problem of good fixation: (b) the problem of sampling, and (c) the problem of reconstruction in three dimensions.

As has already been stated, routine fixation of the interphase cell gives excellent preservation of the cytosome, but is sometimes not equally satisfactory for the nuclear structures, especially the chromosomes. This inadequacy of fixation is even more conspicuous in dividing cells, in which the nuclear components and division apparatus comprise the major part of the cell volume. Furthermore, the spindle fibres, asters and kinetochores have proved very difficult to preserve in a form which can be subjected to high resolution studies. This difficulty is understandable in view of the transitory nature and kinetic qualities of these structures and of cell division as a whole.

It is impossible, therefore, to detail the fine structure of mitosis or meiosis through the various stages. Indeed, little would be gained by so doing, for the essential features of these stages are no better illustrated, nor more comprehensible as the result of greater resolution and magnification. Inevitably the intriguing morphological problems of cell division, such as the genesis of the spindle fibres, or the sequences of changes leading to fibre–kinetochore linkage, will eventually be investigated and solved. At present, however, the main aim of electron microscopy is centred on the elucidation of the ultrastructure of those features of the cell in division which have eluded light microscopy. It is the general ultrastructure of the dividing cell which will be dealt with in this text, and observations from mitosis and meiosis have not been distinguished except where this is essential.

Nuclear Membrane. Its Dissolution and Reconstruction

The dissolution of the nuclear membrane follows the same basic pattern, with slight variations, in all cells so far studied. The first evidence of the

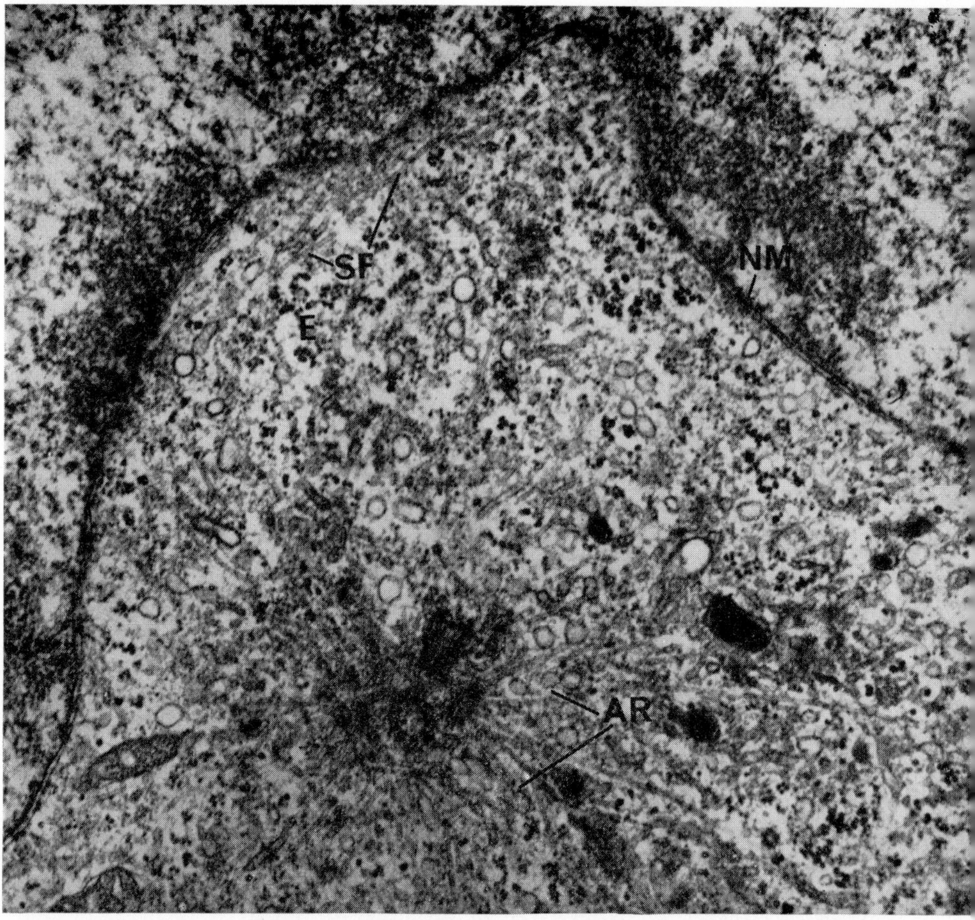
SF
E
NM
AR

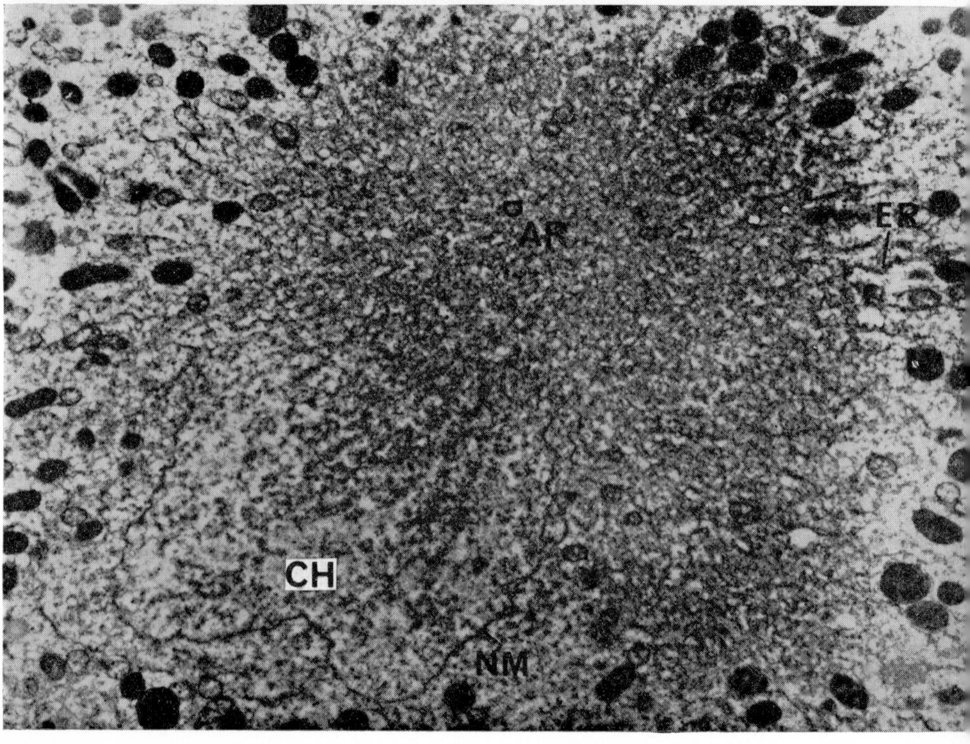
AR
ER
CH
NM

process is the formation of numerous identations of the membrane at points opposite the growing astral rays (Fig. 8.1a, b). The astral fibres contact the nuclear membrane, which may be deeply indented at that particular point, and later the fibres pass through spaces which develop. Whether the initial breakdown of the nuclear membrane at the poles is due to the mechanical forces of the growing astral rays is not clear, and perhaps some other influence diffusing from the fibres of the spindle or some other structure, may be the major influence. Following the penetration of the astral rays, the intermembranous space of the nuclear membrane becomes irregular in width and the inner and outer membranes becomes fused and pinch off large vesicles, which lie at the nuclear cytoplasmic interface (Fig. 8.1b). These vesicles, in a variety of sizes, migrate out into the cytoplasm and sometimes into the nucleoplasm; in either case they become indistinguishable from agranular endoplasmic reticulum.

In some nuclei the equatorial region of the membrane persists in its typical form until early in metaphase when it disintegrates into vesicles. In yet other nuclei, e.g., mitotic erythroblasts, the membrane leaves the surface of the contracting chromosomes and fragments, some of the fragments remaining as relatively long sections and migrating to the cell periphery, while others break up further into vesicles 150–200 Å in diameter (Fig. 8.2a). In insect spermatocytes, mitochondria lie in clumps or crescents against the nuclear membrane during prophase (Fig. 8.2b). At the point of contact between these two structures, a gap appears in the nuclear membrane and the limiting membrane of the mitochondria may be continuous with the nuclear membrane, or alternatively, the nucleoplasm and mitochondrial matrix may be in direct contact. In other regions of the nucleus, where mitochondria are not present, the membrane consists of a thickened zone of diffuse material and vesicles. In insect spermatocytes, therefore, mitochondria appear to be involved in nuclear membrane breakdown. The end result of all the processes listed above is the same, namely, the vesiculation of the nuclear membrane into structures resembling agranular endoplasmic reticulum.

Two fundamentally different modes of reconstitution of the nuclear membrane have been described. In the first mode, which is by far the commonest, the chromosomes in telophase, and occasionally in anaphase, become surrounded by vesicles very similar to agranular endoplasmic reticular vesicles lying throughout the cytoplasm (Fig. 8.2c). These vesicles fuse together at the surface of individual chromosomes to form a double membrane which has a very irregular appearance. Later the membranes

---

FIG. 8.1. (a) Centrioles, astral rays (AR) and spindle fibres (SF) lying in a depression of the nuclear membrane (NM). HeLa cell. (Courtesy Drs. E. Robbins and N. K. Gonatas. × 26,000.) (b) The well-developed astral rays (AR) include not only spindle fibres but also endoplasmic reticulum (ER) and sections of nuclear membrane (NM). CH, chromosome. Sea-urchin egg, *Strongylocentrotus*. (Courtesy Dr. P. Harris. × 5000.)

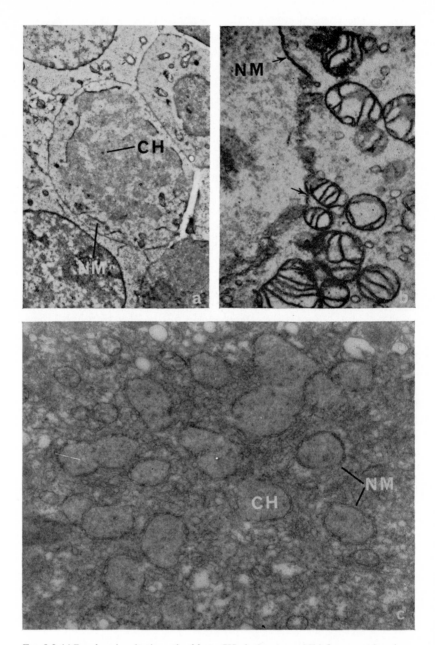

Fig. 8.2. (a) Prophase in mitotic erythroblasts. CH, chromosome; NM, fragmented nuclear membrane. (Courtesy Dr. O. P. Jones. × 5600.) (b) Intimate mitochondrial–nuclear membrane association (arrow) during nuclear membrane dissolution in the secondary spermatocyte of the locust. NM, nuclear membrane. (Courtesy Dr. R. Barer. × 14,000.) (c) Reformation of the nuclear membrane after division. Individual chromosomes (CH) are surrounded by a membrane (NM). (Courtesy Dr. P. Harris. × 19,000.)

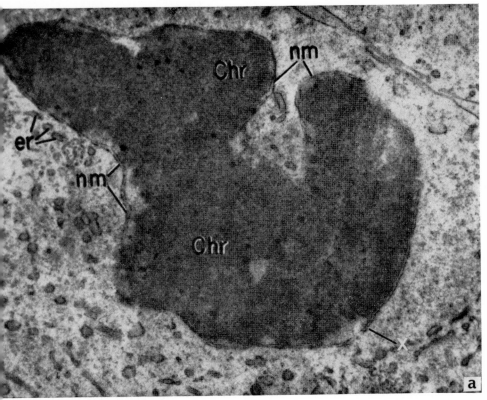

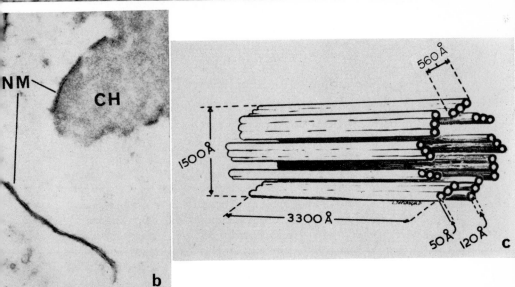

FIG. 8.3. (a) Reconstructed nuclear membrane lifting off the chromosomes (at X) in the spermatocyte of the locust. (Courtesy Dr. R. Barer.) (b) *De novo* origin of the nuclear membrane at the surface of the chromosomes in mitotic erythroblasts. NM, nuclear membrane; CH, chromosome. (Courtesy Dr. O. P. Jones. × 15,000.) (c) Diagram showing the tridimensional structure and dimensions of a centriole. (Original.)

round the chromosomes are more regular and have pores 900–1000 Å in diameter. The chromosomes are compacted progressively during telophase and, by swelling, inevitably connect, so that the membranes surrounding adjacent chromosomes fuse until all are surrounded by a continuous nuclear membrane. During the process of fusion, individual membrane elements may become trapped inside the nucleus. The new nuclear membrane is at first very irregular in outline, for it still follows the contours of the chromosomes at the periphery of the consolidating mass of chromatin (Fig. 8.2c). Later, however, the membrane lifts off the chromosomes and assumes an oval contour, perhaps due to the formation of the nucleoplasm (Fig. 8.3a). In this type of nuclear membrane reformation, therefore, the membrane is apparently derived from what must be considered cytoplasmic vesicles indistinguishable from agranular endoplasmic reticulum.

In the second mode of reformation, as observed in mitotic erythroblasts, the chromosomes are themselves the source of the new membrane. In telophase, intrachromosomal vesicular bodies form just internal to the chromosome–cytoplasm boundary (Fig. 8.3b). These vesicles are membrane-bound and accumulate in large numbers. The new nuclear membrane arises at many points round the periphery of the chromosomes, due to the fusion of the intrachromosomal vesicles, and this process generally starts distal to the interzonal spindle fibres. Eventually the chromosomes and their individual membranes fuse, as in the first mode of reformation, and a continuous nuclear membrane results. Although, therefore, the origin of the vesicles is different in the two modes, in both cases it is chromosomes which are first enclosed in a membrane and the reconstituted nuclear membrane is a completely new structure, as far as can be seen at present.

The Structure and Replication of the Centriole

The centriole and the basal body of cilia and flagella are in reality homologous organelles and are therefore almost identical in structure. The centriole of the light microscope is seen in electron microscopy as a duplex structure, always consisting of a fully formed centriole with a small, partially formed, daughter procentriole lying at right angles to it.

The parent centriole is a cylindrical body 1500–1600 Å in diameter and 3000–5000 Å long (usually 3300 Å) (Figs. 8.3c; 8.4a). The cylinder is composed of nine complex fibres running parallel to the long axis, and embedded in a finely granular adielectronic mass (Figs. 8.3c; 8.4a). Each complex fibre is made up of from two to four subfibres, with three fibres, a triplet, being the most common. These subfibres have dielectronic cores, 120–130 Å in diameter, and adielectronic walls 50 Å thick. The three subfibres of a triplet lie in contact, so sharing common walls at these points, with the result that the length of the three subfibres along their longest axis is only 560 Å, instead of 560–590 Å (Fig. 8.3c). The subfibres are coded as *a*, *b*, *c*, reading from the centre outwards, and subfibres of adjacent triplets may be joined,

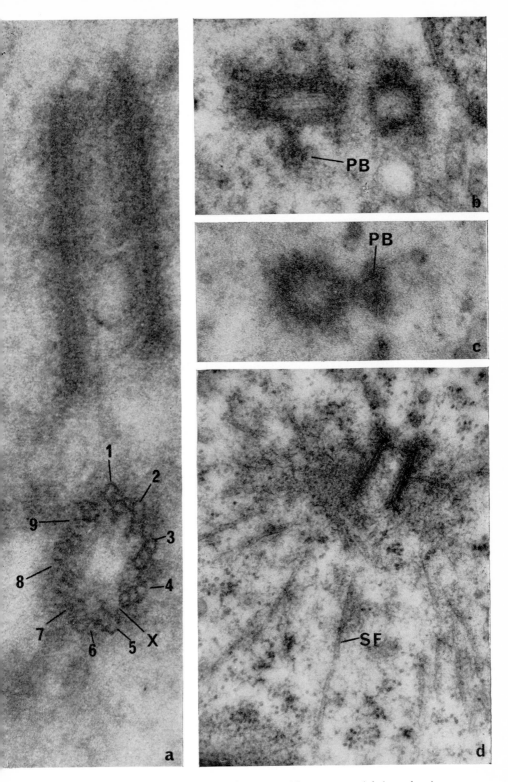

FIG. 8.4. (a) Centrioles from human lymphosarcoma. The upper centriole is cut longitudinally, the lower transversely. Note the nine groups of triplet fibres and the bridging
fibres between the *a* and *c* subfibres (at X). (Courtesy Dr. W. Bernhard. × 200,000.)
(b) and (c) Pericentriolar bodies (PB) as observed in relation to centrioles cut longitudinally in (b), and transversely in (c). (Courtesy Dr. W. Bernhard. All photos × 87,000.)
(d) Centriole with attached spindle fibres (SF) from a chick spleen cell. (Courtesy Dr. J.
Andre. × 60,000.)

a to *a*, or *a* to *c* connections being the most frequent (Fig. 8.4a). Connecting subfibres *a* and *c* on the inner side of each individual triplet is a dense "line", the triplet base (Fig. 8.4a), with a dense, RNA positive granule, the foot (Fig. 8.4a). A straight line can be drawn through the centre of the three subfibres of a triplet, demonstrating that their long axes must all be in one plane. This axis is inclined at 30–40° to the circumference of the centriole, giving the whole a pinwheel appearance.

The centre of the centriole is moderately adielectronic, generally having a dielectronic core 200 Å in diameter (Fig. 8.4a). Occasionally, a cartwheel structure, with an indistinct hub and nine radiating spokes projecting to the triplets, is seen in this central region. In the centre and in contact with the triplet foot is a spirally wound fibre, which present evidence strongly suggests is DNA. The cartwheel structure and the region of origin of the daughter centrioles apparently designate the proximal end; the distal end has a "plate" with eight-fold symmetry, the octagonal end structure, and gives rise to the ciliary fibres, the astral rays, and the spindle fibres (Fig. 8.4d). In some centrioles additional structures, named pericentriolar bodies, are present. The bodies are diffuse polymorphic structures about 700 Å in diameter, and are joined to the centriole by a narrow stalk. The pericentriolar bodies generally occur in a circular zone about as wide as the distance between the centriole and the daughter centriole (Fig. 8.4c).

The daughter centriole lies opposite the proximal end of the parent and is separated from it by a distance of about 700 Å. The procentriole is cylindrical, with a diameter of 1500 Å and a length of 700 Å (Fig. 8.5a). In all other respects it has the same structure as the parent. The daughter centriole grows outwards away from the parent, so that the original procentriole is the proximal end of the fully formed centriole. Apparently such replication potential as the centriole possesses is located in the proximal end.

The Mitotic Spindle and Asters

In interphase, the centriole lies close to the nucleus in a region of granular and amorphous cytoplasm which is without any of the larger cell organoids. In this region, and arising from the centrioles, are a few fine fibres, 150–200 Å in diameter, with adielectronic walls and a dielectronic core (Fig. 8.7b). Favourable sections show faint striations on the fibres, which suggests that they may be coils. During aster formation in prophase, a compact mass of agranular endoplasmic vesicles grows around the centriole (Fig. 8.5b). The vesicles are roughly spherical near the centriole and become progressively more narrow and elongated towards the periphery of the mass, where they are radially orientated (Fig. 8.6a). Within this mass and growing from the centriole, the spindle fibres increase in number and length, sometimes forming bundles. Between the fibres and vesicles are numerous ribosomes. The bundles of fibres and radial endoplasmic vesicles represent the gel of light microscopy.

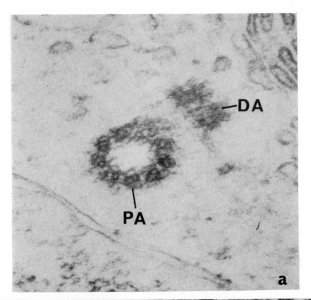

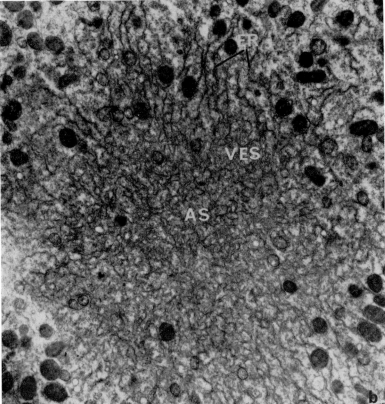

Fig. 8.5. (a) Parent (PA) and daughter (DA) centrioles in a cell of the snail, *Viviparus*. (Courtesy Dr. J. G. Gall. × 110,000.) (b) Aster (AS) at prometaphase in the egg of the sea-urchin, *Strongylocentrotus*. The vesicles (VES) and endoplasmic elements (ER) are clearly part of the aster, but large organoids such as mitochondria are excluded from this region. (Courtesy Dr. P. Harris. × 7600.)

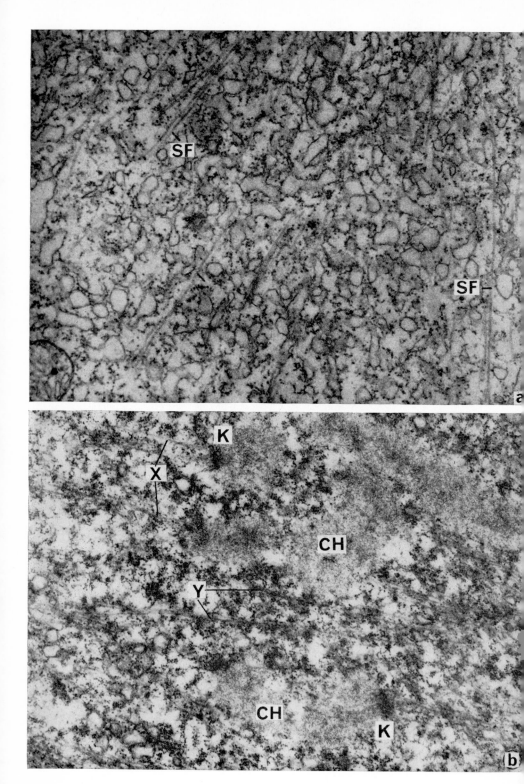

FIG. 8.6. (a) Bundles of spindle fibres (SF) radiating from the aster and centrioles in a sea-urchin egg. Vesicles and ribosomes are prominent features. (Courtesy Dr. P. Harris. × 31,000.) (b) Pole-to-chromosome (at X) and pole-to-pole fibres (at Y) in a sea-urchin egg. CH, chromosome; K, kinetochore. (Courtesy Dr. P. Harris. × 21,500.)

The growing spindle fibres eventually indent the nuclear membrane, forming finger-shaped invaginations within which are fibres either singly or in groups. Some fibres penetrate the nuclear membrane, even before it has broken down, but the majority remain outside. With the separation and migration of the centrioles the mass of vesicles and fibres increases until it is finally seen on both sides of the nucleus. When the nuclear membrane fragments, this gel invades the nucleoplasm and forms a full spindle consisting of bundles of pole-to-pole fibres running between the chromosomes, pole to kinetochore fibres, also in bundles of 10 to 20, agranular endoplasmic vesicles of irregular size and shape, many free ribosomes, and lengths of cisternal reticulum lying at the periphery and parallel to the surface of the spindle (Fig. 8.6b). The interzonal region, which appears during anaphase and telophase, has a different appearance from the remainder of the spindle. It is a dielectronic zone with an indistinct boundary, and is composed of a few fibres, vesicles and granules in an amorphous background (Fig. 8.7a). The regions around the chromosomes and the asters still have great masses of vesicles and therefore appear more dense than the interzonal region. During telophase, the pole to chromosome fibres shorten but their diameter remains the same as previously. There is no evidence of coiling or folding and the fibres still end at the kinetochore. When the chromosomes become polar and individually surrounded by a new nuclear membrane, they lie in a disorganized mass of vesicles in which fibres are not evident. In the interzonal region the pole-to-pole fibres are gathered together by the advancing furrow and may persist until well into the next division cycle.

The Chromosomes

The information concerning the ultrastructure of the chromosomes in the dividing cell is little greater than that for the resting cell; the same problem of three-dimensional reconstruction applies in both cell phases. The chromosomes during division become individual localized bodies, which are revealed by electron microscopy as adielectronic granular or fibrous structures, 10,000–30,000 Å in diameter, although they may appear as dielectronic areas after certain fixatives. These chromosomes are made up of the same basic components as their interphase counterparts. The proto-chromonema measures 30–90 Å in width and has been observed by some researchers as sheets in sperm nuclei. It has been claimed that the proto-chromonema varies in diameter from 45 Å to 70 Å to 100 Å between early prophase and metaphase in the spermatocytes of the grasshopper, but such changes have not been recorded generally. Subchromonema and chromonema have somewhat larger diameters than in interphase and measure 200–500 Å and 500–2000 Å respectively. This increase in diameter is presumably due to spiralization. Studies of chromosomes during cell division have not resulted in any solution of the manner in which the DNA

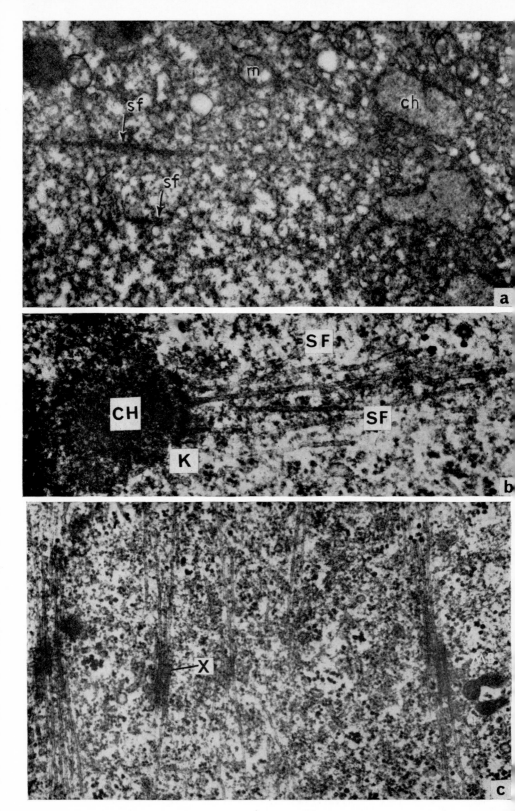

Fig. 8.7. (a) The interzonal region of the spindle in the late anaphase stage of a sea-urchin egg. Ch, chromosom surrounded by reforming nuclear membrane; Sf, increased density of the spindle fibres in the mid-region; M mitochondrion. (Courtesy Dr. P. Harris. × 15,000.) (b) A kinetochore (K) with attached spindle fibres (SF CH, chromosome. HeLa cell. (Courtesy Drs. E. Robbins and N. K. Gonayas. × 76,000.) (c) Increased densi (at X) in localized regions of the spindle fibres in the mid-region of the spindle. HeLa cell. (Courtesy Drs. I Robbins and N. K. Gonatas. × 41,000.)

fibres are organized or how they are related to the various orders of coiled fibres seen in electron micrographs.

Studies of meiotic chromosomes at the synaptic stage have revealed some new structures. The chromosomes at this time have a core or axial complex of three filaments, a tripartite complex. The central filament of the complex is 100–200 Å thick and is separated from the 250–300 Å thick lateral filaments by a space 150 Å wide. The tripartite complex, therefore, measure 900–1100 Å, is slightly spiraled and is surrounded by a diffuse mass of fine, coiled fibrils. Where two chromosomes are in synapse, a synaptinemal complex forms, a pentapartite complex. The pentapartite conditions is presumably due to the fusion of the adjacent lateral filaments of the two synapsed tripartite complexes, but this conclusion is disputed because these structures have recently been observed in spermatids.

Located at the chromosome surface are the kinetochores which generally appear as very adielectronic plates, 500 Å thick and 1500 Å in diameter. In favourable circumstances, the plates are resolved into 100 Å fibrils, very tightly packed, and these fibrils may be continuous with the 100 Å filaments of the chromosomes (Fig. 8.7b). Spindle fibres fuse to the outer side of the adielectronic plates, but details of the actual junction are lacking. Some kinetochores are crater-like and occasionally two centres of chromosome convergence are seen lying close together, presumably one kinetochore for each chromatid.

Nucleolus

There are few observations on changes in the ultrastructure of the nucleolus during cell division. In interphase the nucleolus is roughly spherical in shape and consists of a tangled thread 1000 Å in diameter, composed in turn of coiled filaments 50 Å thick, the whole surrounded by a less dense amorphous substance, the pars amorpha. In the mitotic prophase stage of mammalian cells, the nucleolus becomes irregular in shape, often assuming the form of a dumb-bell. A reversal of electron density apparently occurs, the thread-like nucleolonema showing up as less dense than the pars amorpha, but interpretation of this stage is difficult. Other mitotic stages do not seem to have been seen or recorded.

During spermatogenesis in mice, the spermatogonial nucleolus has the shape and structure characteristic of interphase. In spermatocytes, however, the nucleolus becomes irregular in shape and nucleolus-associated body arises. This latter is slightly more adielectronic than the nucleoplasm and is made up of twisted filaments 15–30 Å in diameter, forming a compact tangled mass. The associated body often lies on the nuclear membrane, filling the space between the latter and the nucleolus. Unlike the nucleolus, this body is composed of DNA. During the spermatid stages, the nucleolus forms a very adielectronic mass within the nucleus and, with the increasing adielectronicity of the chromatin, the nucleolus as such becomes indis guishable from the rest of the massive nucleus.

Cytokinesis

Early in anaphase, the dividing cell lengthens, especially in the interzonal region between the separating chromosomes, and the continuous spindle fibres in this zone show points of increased electron density (Fig. 8.7c). During telophase, this interzonal region becomes progressively narrower, a process which is usually accepted as the first indication of the cleavage furrow (Fig. 8.8). The plasma membrane in the furrow shows increased electron density, which is also visible in the adjacent cytoplasm. As at this time, however, the newly formed nuclei, which lie transversely in the cell, are still solid masses of chromatin and have considerable rigidity, they may be responsible for expanding the ends of the cells. Such an occurrence would make the formation of the central constriction a passive process, rather than an active one.

The continuous spindle fibres in the interzonal region continue to increase in density and eventually form an adielectronic fibrillary plate in the equatorial plane; this is the mid-body, from which the continuous spindle fibres radiate out towards the two daughter nuclei (Figs. 8.9; 8.10c). As cytokinesis progresses, a large empty membrane-bound vesicle appears on each side of the mid-body and in some cases the latter is completely encircled by a ring-shaped vesicle (Fig. 8.9a). Subsequently, small vesicles arise in the equatorial plane of the cell and number some hundreds. These vesicles are apparently associated with smooth endoplasmic reticulum which commences near the nuclear membrane, runs parallel to, but some distance from, the plasma membrane, turns to run parallel to the equator and is reflected back towards the nucleus along the margins of the spindle (Fig. 8.9b). It is suggested that this smooth endoplasmic reticulum gives rise to the vesicles, because these differ from the larger ring-shaped vesicles encircling the mid-body.

The final stages of cytokinesis appear to be the growth and fusion of all vesicles, both ring and small vesicles, to form a deep furrow, leaving the daughter cells connected by an intercellular bridge (Fig. 8.10a, b). During this furrowing, the plasma membrane in the cleft forms many small microvilli, perhaps as a result of vesicular fusion. The telophase bridge, which is generally excentrically placed, is at first stout, with the mid-body lying in the centre as a fibrillar plate 1000–3000 Å wide (Figs. 8.10c; 8.11a–c). As the bridge lengthens, the central part of the mid-body disc loses its identity and an amorphous ring forms, due to the loss of the former fibrillar nature of the region (Fig. 8.11b). The bridge narrows, but the ring apparently does not alter in diameter and eventually forms a central bulbous body. On one side of this bulbous ring a row of tiny vesicles arises, and it is presumed that their growth and function result in the final separation of the daughter

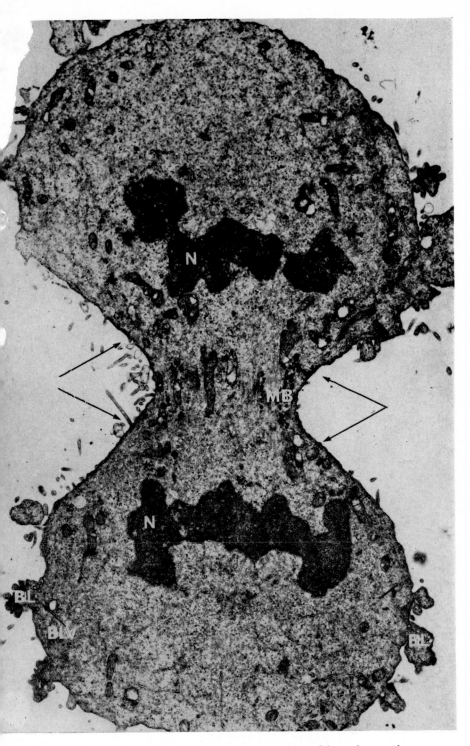

FIG. 8.8. Telophase in an HeLa cell. Note the close apposition of the nuclear membrane to the chromosomes (N), the cleavage furrow (arrows) and associated microvilli, and the bubbling (BL) of the cell periphery. MB, mid-body. (Courtesy Drs. E. Robbins and N. K. Gonatas. × 7750.)

11

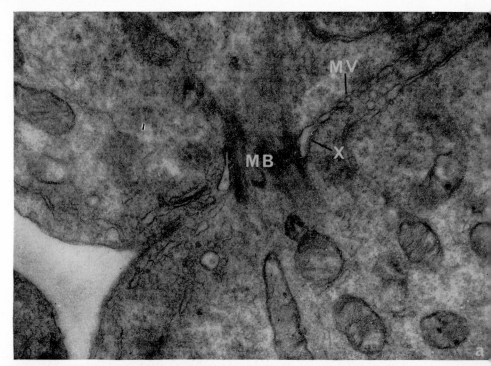

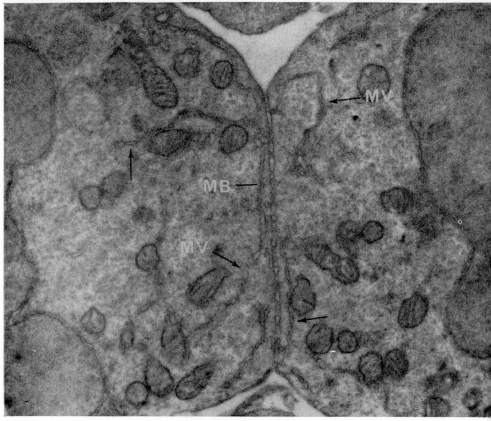

FIG. 8.9. (a) and (b) Early stage of mid-body formation in erythroblasts (a) through the mid-body; (b) same cell but sectioned lateral to the mid-body. MV, multiple vesicles at the equatorial plate; MB mid-body; at X enlarged vesicles adjacent to the mid-body. Note the disposition of the cisternae in relation to the plasma membrane, nucleus, and cleavage plane (arrows in b). (Courtesy Drs. R. C. Buck and J. M. Tisdale. (a) ×36,000. (b) ×18,000.)

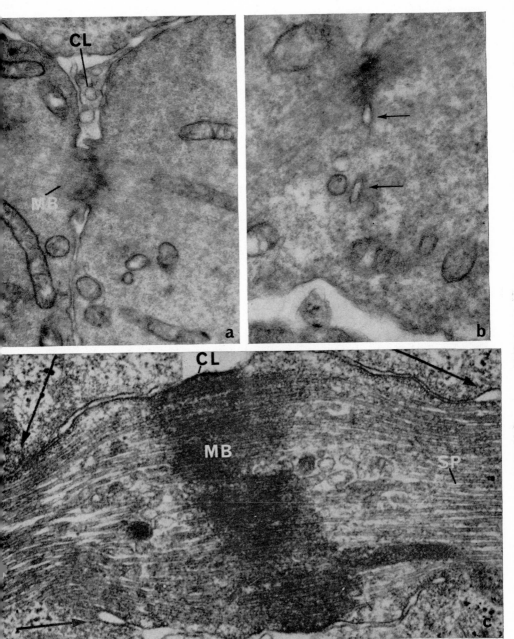

FIG. 8.10. (a) and (b) Mid-body formation (MB) in erythroblasts; late stage. The increased density in the central region of the body is due to increased density of the spindle fibres (see Fig. 8.10c). CL, cleavage furrow. (Courtesy Drs. R. C. Buck and J. M. Tisdale. (a) ×23,000. (b) ×34,000.) (c) Mid-body (MB), cleavage furrow (CL) and continuous spindle fibres (SP) in HeLa cell. (Courtesy Drs. E. Robbins and N. K. Gonatas. ×30,000.)

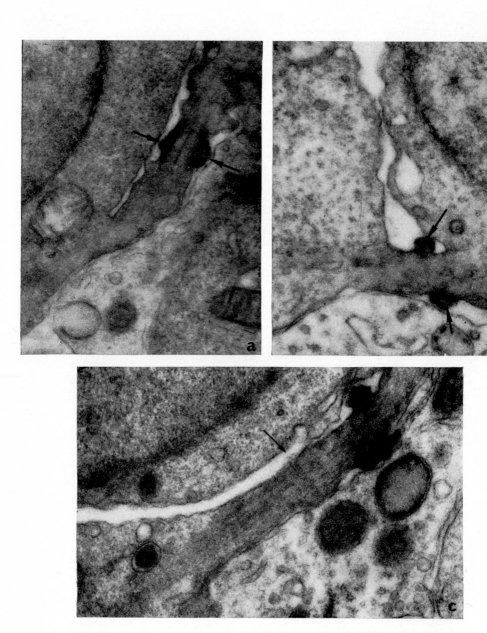

FIG. 8.11. (a)–(c) Lengthening of the telophase bridge in mitotic erythroblasts. (a) Margination of the dense material (arrows). (b) Ring formed from marginated dense material (arrows). (c) Row of small vesicles (arrow) traversing the long mid-body. (Courtesy Drs. R. C. Buck and J. M. Tisdale. (a) × 24,000. (b) × 42,000. (c) × 37,000.)

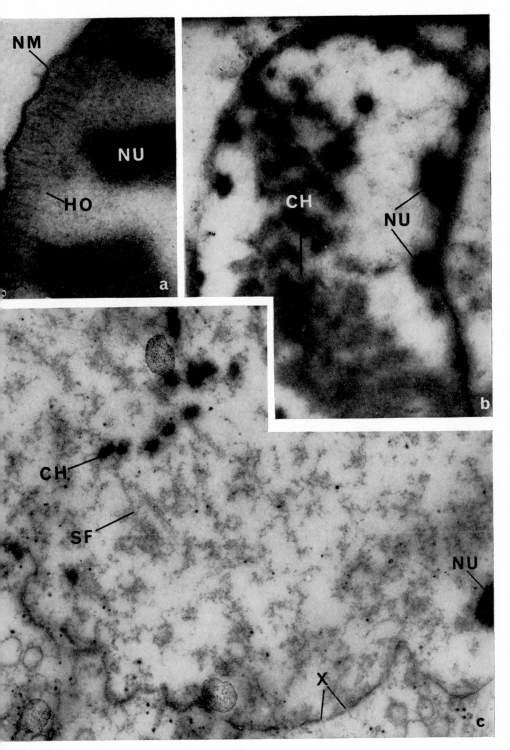

FIG. 8.12. (a) Nuclear membrane (NM), and honeycomb layer (HO) in *Amoeba proteus* at interphase. NU, nucleolus. (Courtesy Dr. L. E. Roth. ×27,000.) (b) Late prophase; the honeycomb layer is absent and the chromatin network evident (CH). *Amoeba proteus.* (Courtesy Dr. L. E. Roth. ×15,000.) (c) Metaphase; CH, chromosomes; SF, spindle fibres; nuclear membrane gaps are present at X. *Amoeba proteus.* (Courtesy Dr. L. E. Roth. ×11,000.)

cells (Fig. 8.11c). The mid-body passes into one of the daughter cells, but its fate and function are quite unknown.

Cell Division in Protozoa

Mitosis in protozoa is unlike that of metazoan somatic cells and has been studied in the ultrastructural level in *Amoeba proteus* and *Pelomyxa carolinensis*, the giant amoeba. The major difference between mitosis in amoebae and metazoan cells is that in the former there is an absence of centres and an incomplete breakdown of the nuclear membrane.

In *Amoeba proteus* the interphase nucleus is flattened and slightly bi-concave, and is bounded by the typical outer double membrane and inner honeycomb type of nuclear membrane (Fig. 8.12a). Nucleoli are numerous in the peripheral nucleoplasm, and the central region has granular material and the helices previously described (Chapter 2). During prophase, the nucleus swells into a sphere and may pinch off finger-shaped evaginations. The honeycomb layer disappears, leaving only the double membrane. The peripheral nucleoli are reduced in number and the centrally situated helices disappear, being replaced by an irregular network of chromatin in a condensed form (Fig. 8.12b). At metaphase, the nuclear membranes are still present but have large discontinuities which allow the admixture of cyto-plasm and nucleoplasm. The chromosomes are small adielectronic masses of granules 5000–8000 Å long and 2000 Å in diameter and are arranged on the metaphase plate (Fig. 8.12c). No kinetochores are evident and the chromosomes appear to be directly connected to bundles of spindle fibres, 150 Å thick, which arise randomly in the cytoplasm (Fig. 8.13a). The nucleus has a few nucleoli, fine filamentous material and ribosome-like particles lying in it.

In anaphase, the daughter nuclei are small and have a concave–convex shape, which is enclosed by an apparently continuous nuclear membrane (Fig. 8.13b). The chromosomes are the same as at metaphase and the nucleoli have not reformed. By telophase the chromatin has returned to the inter-phase condition and nucleoli are again present and peripherally arranged (Fig. 8.13c). After cytokinesis the nucleus has a biconcave shape and the inner honeycomb layer is reformed, although only to about two-thirds of its interphase depth. The nucleoli appear both as granules and sheets, the latter sometimes in contact with the nuclear membrane (Figs. 8.13c; 8.14a). This perinuclear configuration of the nucleoli appears to be correlated with the laying down of the honeycomb layer. Chromatin becomes associated with the nucleoli and helices are frequently found around such bodies (Fig. 8.14b). As helices do not co-exist with condensed chromosomes, they cannot be such chromosomes and are either DNA in a form unique to interphase, or not DNA at all.

Mitosis in *Pelomyxa* differs somewhat from that in *Amoeba*. At interphase the nuclear membrane is like that of the metozoa and does not have a

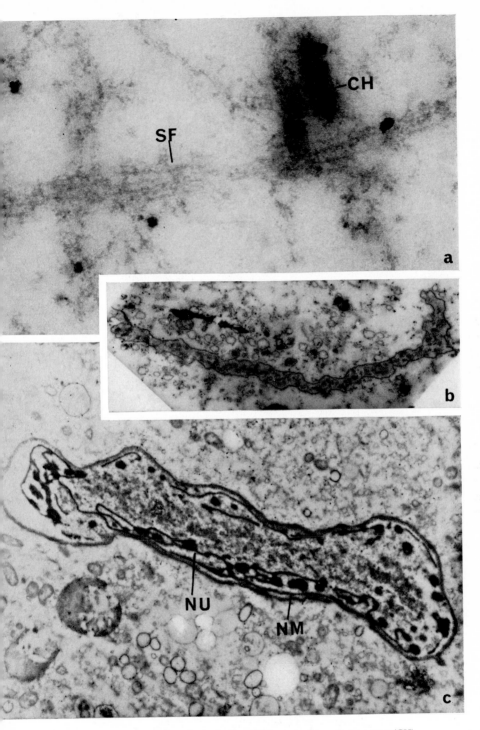

FIG. 8.13. (a) Metaphase; bundles of spindle fibres (SF) attached to a chromosome (CH) (×42,000.) (b) Complete cross-section of a thin, disc-shaped nucleus. (×3200.) (c) Early reconstruction phase; NU, nucleolar material in peripheral nucleoplasm. ×2600.) ((a)–(c) *Amoeba proteus*, courtesy Dr. L. E. Roth.)

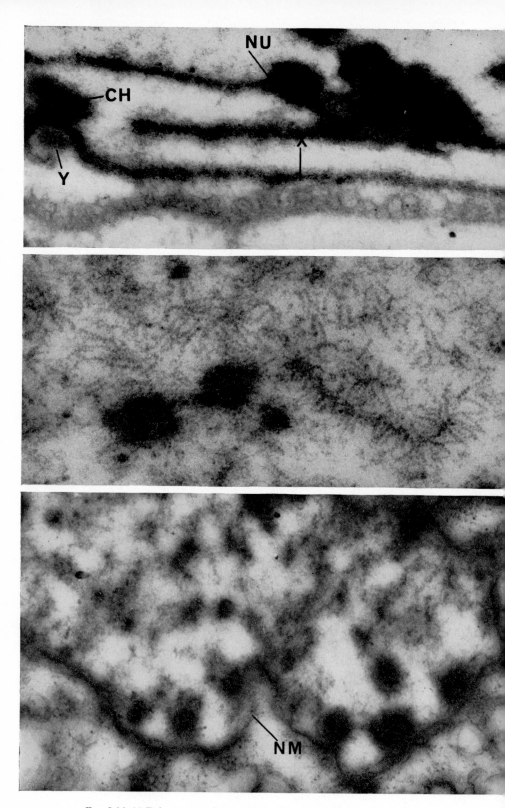

FIG. 8.14. (a) Enlargement of part of a reconstructing nucleus. At X nucleolar material (NU) is closely associated with the reforming honeycomb layer and at Y with chromatin (CH). *Amoeba proteus*. (× 22,500.) (b) Late reconstruction phase. The honeycomb layer and helices are once again present. *Amoeba proteus*. (× 31,000.) (c) Interphase nucleus of *Pelomyxa carolinensis*. No honeycomb layer is present at any time. NM, nuclear membrane. (× 15,000. (a)–(c) courtesy Dr. E. L. Roth.)

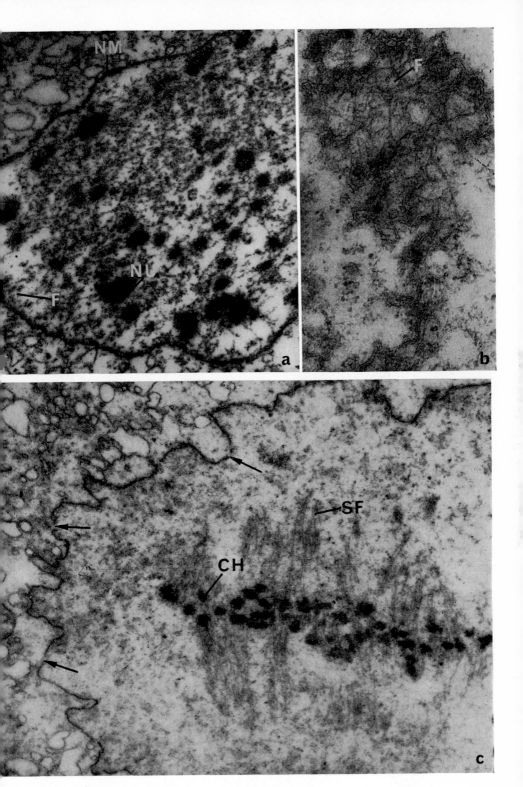

FIG. 8.15. (a) Prophase; nucleoli (NU) have lost their peripheral position and a fibrillar material (F) is attached to the inner aspect of the nuclear membrane. (× 5800.) (b) Prophase; enlargement of part of the nuclear membrane and associated fibrillar material. (× 41,000.) (c) Early metaphase; the chromosomes (CH) are aligned on the equator and the spindle fibres (SF) show little convergence. Arrows point to discontinuities in the nuclear membrane. (× 10,000. (a)–(c) *Pelomyxa carolinensis*, courtesy Dr. L. E. Roth.)

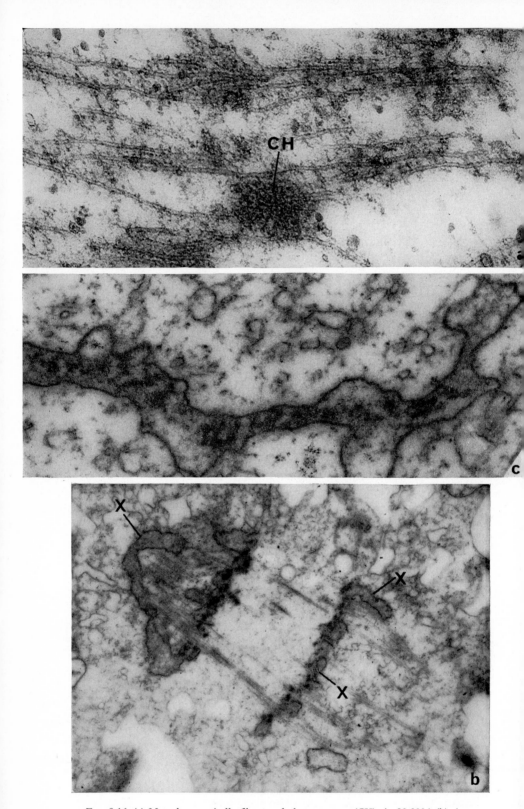

FIG. 8.16. (a) Metaphase; spindle fibres and chromosomes (CH). (×80,000.) (b) Anaphase; remnants of the nuclear membrane are present at X and accompany the chromosomes to the poles. Note the slight densification of the central spindle fibres. (×6800.) (c) Early telophase; the nuclear membrane is continuous, but the nucleus is still plateshaped. (×19,000. (a)–(c) *Peolomyxa carolinensis*, courtesy Dr. L. E. Roth.)

honeycomb layer (Fig. 8.14c). The nucleus has an irregular outline, numerous peripheral nucleoli and sparse central helices. During prophase the nucleus swells into a spherical shape, the nucleoli become randomly situated, and a feltwork of 100 Å fibres becomes layered on the inner nuclear membrane (Fig. 8.15a, b).

During metaphase, the nuclear membrane is broken into sections of various lengths and the nucleoli are lost. By late metaphase the nuclear membrane fragments are found among and parallel to the spindle fibres. The admixture of cytoplasm and nucleoplasm is shown by the presence of ribosome-like particles 300–400 Å in diameter which in interphase appear only in the cytoplasm. The chromosomes, small and numerous, are arranged on a narrow metaphase plate (Fig. 8.15c). Spindle fibres occur in groups attached to the chromosomes and such groups are non convergent and almost parallel, giving a cylindrical, rather than a conical, mitotic apparatus. The fibres are 140 Å thick and have an indistinct banding at 60 Å intervals. Associated with the fibres is a cloud of fine material, 20–60 Å in diameter and not regularly orientated (Fig. 8.16a).

At anaphase, the nuclear membrane remnants lie either close to the chromosomes or precede them to the poles. Continuous spindle fibres are present in the interzonal region and pass between the chromosomes to converge somewhat towards the nuclear membrane elements (Fig. 8.16b). Chromosome to pole fibres, added to the continuous fibres, form a packed mass between the chromosomes and the nuclear membrane which precedes them. The interzonal region is more dielectronic than the general cytoplasm (Fig. 8.16b). The chromosomes are aligned to form plates, due to all the chromosomes apparently moving at the same rate. After the chromosomes have completely separated in telophase, the daughter nuclei have a plate-like shape, with the nuclear membrane closely applied to the chromosomes (Fig. 8.16c). Spindle fibres, freed of the chromosomes, occur in compact bundles in the cytoplasm and have little associated fibrillar material around them.

Further Reading List

1. RHOADES, M. M., Meiosis, *The Cell*, Vol. 3, edit. BRACHET, J. and MIRSKY, A. E., Academic Press, London, 1961.
2. HARRIS, P. and MAZIA, D., The Finer Structure of the Mitotic Apparatus, *The Interpretation of Ultrastructure*, edit. HARRIS, R. J. C., Academic Press, London, 1962.

CHAPTER 9

SUMMARY

THE structure of the cell, which became generally accepted as the result of light microscope and other studies, was of a two-phase system, nucleus and cytoplasm. These two phases contained within them individual formed elements, such as nucleoli or chromosome, mitochondria or paraplasms, embedded in a semi-fluid medium. It was, of course, realized that the two phases functioned as an integrated whole, though the principal functions of each were essentially different, and that the individual organoids and other bodies, despite their discrete nature, combined to a common end. Structurally, however, the cell still appeared as a heterogeneous system, and a common denominator for the variety of components which comprised the cell was not evident.

Electron microscopy has altered this earlier conception drastically and revealed that the apparent heterogeneity of the cells is in reality a repetition in a variety of forms of a limited number of basic components. Let us consider these components themselves and then see how they have suggested a new conception of the cell.

The basic structural units of the cell are: (a) the membrane, (b) the fibre or microtubule, (c) the granule. The lipoprotein membrane, with or without pores, is the basic component which has attracted most attention. The advantages of this membrane are principally its highly labile nature and its supervisory function. The membrane takes the form of flat or folded sheets, complete shells, tubes, and an endless variety of other polymorphic forms, which are apparently interconvertible. These structures act as mechanical boundaries or supports between different phases, and as semi-permeable membranes controlling the exchange between one phase and another and as a conducting system. The universality of these membranes resulted in the unit membrane hypothesis, which stated that all cell membranes had a lipoprotein composition and were 75 Å thick, this thickness being made up of three components, protein–lipid–protein, each approximately 25 Å thick. Any differences in thickness or absence of a tripartite structure were attributed to the technique used, or inherent mechanical factors of the electron microscope itself.

This theory had considerable appeal, mainly because it gave a structural foundation to the functional interrelationship which was known to exist between distinctive and individual cell organoids. All these organoids were now shown to be membrane-composed, and temporary or permanent fusion between them, or the passage of parts of one organoid to another, were eminently possible (Fig. 9.1). A natural consequence of the unit membrane hypothesis was the idea of membrane flow, that is, the constant genesis of membranes and the structural and functional continuity of

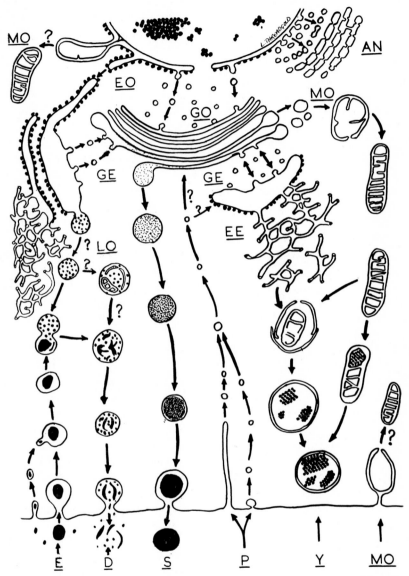

FIG. 9.1. Possible origin and interrelationship of membraneous components of the cell. AN, annulate lamellae; D, exocytosis; E, endocytosis; EE, association of granular and agranular endoplasmic reticulum; EO, origin of endoplasmic reticulum; GE, interchange of vesicles between the Golgi complex and endoplasmic reticulum; GO, origin of the Golgi complex; LO, origin of the lysosomes; MO, origin of mitochondria; P, pinocytosis; S, secretion; Y, yolk formation. (Original.)

membrane-bound organoids. The membrane would act as a conveyor belt, flowing with attached metabolic substances, other compounds and enzymes into the hyaloplasm to give rise to phagocytotic or pinocytotic formations. The inflowing plasma membrane, or the vacuoles, could become part of the endoplasmic reticulum, the Golgi complex, and even perhaps of mito-chondrial and nuclear membranes. In addition, membranes could flow from the cytosome to the exterior, by way of nuclear blebs and the budding off of membrane-limited secretory bodies, lysosomes or vacuoles from the Golgi complex and endoplasmic reticulum; these would eventually fuse with the plasma membrane and discharge their contents (Fig. 9.1).

The inward membrane flow and influx of material could be termed endocytosis and would be the predominant activity of absorptive cells, while the outward flow of membranes could be termed exocytosis and this type of activity would predominate in secretory cells. The lack of frequent observations of continuity between membrane-bound organoids does not argue against this idea of membrane flow, but is only to be expected in a system having dynamic functional continuity (Fig. 9.1).

Recently, however, the unit membrane hypothesis and the idea of mem-brane flow have become less acceptable and, on the face of it, untenable. High resolution studies and precise measurements have shown that all membranes are divisible into two groups. Group 1 contains the plasma membrane and vacuoles derived from it. This is a thick membrane, being 90 Å or 100 Å in diameter† and having asymmetry, that is, the inner (cyto-plasmic) protein component of the tripartite membrane is thicker than the outer (external) protein component. In Group 2 are the membranes of the Golgi complex, the endoplasmic reticulum, the nuclear membrane, the mitochondrion and the lysosome. These membranes vary from 50 Å or 60 Å for mitochondria and granular endoplasmic reticulum, to 60 Å or 70–80 Å for the Golgi complex and agranular endoplasmic reticulum. Whatever their dimensions, however, all membranes in Group 2 have the same morphology, namely, symmetry and a globular middle lipid compo-nent. Clearly the two groups of membranes have different molecular architecture and perhaps chemical composition also.

If the above observations of ultrastructure and size of membranes are correct, as they appear to be, then the general concept of the continuity of all membrane-bound organoids would be incorrect. Only the nuclear membrane, endoplasmic reticulum, Golgi complex and lysosomal mem-branes would be interconvertible, and the numerous recorded observations of physical connections between these structures support this point. The possibility of structural or functional connections between the plasma membrane and the membranes of the Golgi complex or other Group 2 membranes must be questioned. Connections between Group 1 and

---

† All figures are derived from measurements of vestopal-embedded tissue stained with uranyl acetate, but the first figure is from tissue fixed in OsO_4, and the second from $KMnO_4$-fixed material.

Group 2 membranes, and the breakdown of pinocytotic vacuoles or their fusion with Group 2 membranes, have often been hypothesized but less frequently observed. Indeed, it has frequently been suggested that the release of the contents of pinocytotic vacuoles or of lysosomes does not require the dissolution of their bounding membrane, but only a change in the permeability of that membrane. The release of secretory products could be by a similar mechanism, though this is hard to visualize and accept, as it involves alterations in permeability of two membranes, the membrane round the secretory body and that of the plasma membrane, before the release of the product. Furthermore, despite the recorded observations, the origin of mitochondria from the plasma membrane or nuclear membrane and fusion of mitochondrial membranes with other membranes, would seem to be unlikely in view of the difference in thickness between mito-chondrial and other Group 2 and Group 1 membranes.

Despite the difficulties raised by the observations on membrane structure and thickness, it would seem obligatory that structural and functional continuity, however, temporary, should exist between the two groups of membranes in order to ensure proper cellular function. Perhaps these structural differences are not as significant as may appear at first sight. Almost nothing is known of the growth or dissolution of membranes, and it is possible that the conversion of a plasma membrane into a cytoplas-mic membrane, or vice versa, requires only a reorganization of existing molecules, due to changes in ion concentration, pH, electrical charge, loss or addition of enzymes, etc., rather than the genesis of a completely new membrane. Such a facility would not be unexpected in such a labile struc-ture as the membrane. These points require extensive study, using tech-niques to label membrane components and so enable the origin and develop-ment of membranes to be followed at high resolution, as well as other allied physical and chemical methods of investigation.

The second basic structure of the cell is the fibre, or microtubule, the former solid and the latter hollow. The microtubule might be considered as a rolled-up membrane, from a morphological viewpoint, but it has a function different from a membrane. These fibres are often composed of subfibres and exhibit a variety of other subordinate features such as periodicity or spiralization. From a functional viewpoint, the fibres may be classified into two main groups—(a) inert structural fibres, and (b) active fibres which do work, that is, contract or expand.† In the first group are such intracellular fibres as those of the cell web and tonofibrils, the important chromosomal and DNA fibres and perhaps neurofilaments, and such extracellular fibres as collagen and elastin. In the second group are spindle fibres, fibres of the cilium and flagellum and myofilaments. There has as yet not been enough intensive high resolution electron microscopy of some of these fibres, to

† Fibres may be classified on criteria other than those used here. For example, on whether their significance in cell physiology was because of chemical properties (e.g., DNA), or on physical properties, e.g., collagen or myofilaments.

reach an understanding of how they are organized and operate at the molecular level, either as mechanical supports or for mechanical work. Such understanding cannot, of course, be obtained by ultrastructural studies alone, but requires correlated electron microscopy, X-ray diffraction, biochemical and biophysical research.

The third basic unit is the granule, which has generally received less attention than the other basic units. The reasons for this lack of study appear to be an absence of internal structure in the granule, perhaps due to insufficient resolution in the electron microscope, the difficulty of chemical identification, and the less obvious function of granules in cellular activity, when compared to membranes and fibres. Granules may be solid or hollow, and in many cases so-called granules may be sections of solid tubes or of gyres. The granule which has received most attention is the ribosome, both because it has been identified chemically and also because of its role in protein synthesis. The intramitochondrial granules have also attracted study, as have the lattice and other repeating patterns assumed by some granules in forming crystals and other paraplasms. Doubtless, increased electron microscope performance will resolve almost all structures into granules, which can be equated with molecules or aggregates of molecules. However, it is only in that such molecules act together for a common end that they become cytologically significant.

In addition to the unit membrane hypothesis, another consequence of the discovery that many components of the cell were composed of membranes, is the conception of the cell as a three-phase system (Fig. 9.2). Clearly the old two-phase theory of nucleus and cytosome is no longer valid in the face of these new discoveries, and the three-phase theory was evolved to replace it. The three phases are:

1. The external phase. This is the fluid or other environment of the cell, which may penetrate deep into the cytosome, even as far as the nucleus, by way of membrane-limited channels, tubes or vacuoles. The contents of the channels, etc., are always extracellular, even when lying deep within the cell and cut off either temporarily or permanently from the environment from which it is derived. Such deep penetrating structures facilitate exchange between cell and environment and provide a larger surface area for such exchange.

2. The internal phase, including the hyaloplasmic matrix filling the space between other cell organoids and the nucleoplasm, which is in contact with the hyaloplasm by means of the nuclear pores.

3. The membrane phase, which separates phases 1 and 2, and may even separate parts of phase 1 from itself. Not only does this phase act as a mechanical boundary between two environments with different physico-chemical properties, but it helps to maintain the identity of these two phases because of its selective control of communication between them. Furthermore, the membranes act as conveyor belts; for example, the genesis of

granular endoplasmic reticulum by the nuclear membrane and the pushing out of this membrane, with its inherent instructions and information, into the cytosome, is a means of gene control over cytoplasmic activity. Whether the nuclear membrane should be considered a cytoplasmic structure, or the granular endoplasmic reticulum a nuclear derivative, is a matter of controversy. From the viewpoint of embryogenesis and cellular differentiation,

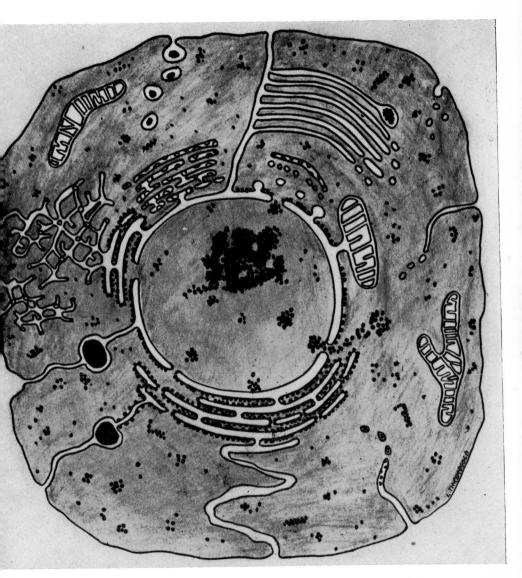

Fig. 9.2. Diagrammatic representation of the cell as a three-phase system; extracellular environment, and intracellular environment separated by membrane systems. (Original.)

the granular endoplasmic reticulum is a nuclear derivative, because it originates from the nuclear membrane; this is true also from the functional viewpoint. In cell division, however, the nuclear membrane appears to arise from pre-existing endoplasmic vesicles lying in the cytosome, although it cannot be denied that these may be derived from the breakdown of the nuclear membrane before or during division. In mitotic erythroblast, amphibian and embryonic cells, at least, the new nuclear membrane appears to be synthesized at the surface of the chromosomes. On present evidence, therefore, it is probably best to view the granular reticulum as a nuclear derivative, and perhaps the agranular endoplasmic reticulum also.

The three-phase view of the cell makes the interaction and exchange of substances between the cell and its environment, and between nucleoplasm and hyaloplasm, much easier to appreciate than in the two-phase system. Additionally, the nucleus is not only no longer apparently isolated within the cytosome, but is obviously and more easily approached by the environment. It is very possible that the nucleus receives stimuli directly from the environment, without such stimuli passing through or being affected by the hyaloplasm. Perhaps more nuclear events are "triggered" by external environmental stimuli, as opposed to cytoplasmic environmental stimuli, than is commonly supposed. Whatever, the true situation, it must be realized that the nucleus is subject to two environments, that which is extracellular and that which is extranuclear but intracellular. The hyaloplasm is similarly under the influence of material and information from two sources, namely, the external environment and the nucleus.

With this three-phase picture of the cell in mind, it is interesting to speculate on the mode of evolution of this complex cell from a more primitive organizational pattern of living substance. As pointed out in the first chapter, protoplasm organized as nucleus and cytosome is not the only form living material assumes. Bacteria do not have a membrane-limited nucleus and their genetic substance is in direct contact with the cytoplasm, although it remains as a localized area within the latter. It has been speculated, therefore, that the primitive cell was somewhat similar to the bacterium in that the genetic material lay approximately in the centre of a protoplasmic mass, but was not separated from that mass by a membrane (Fig. 9.3). During evolution more complex and specialized cells and cell functions arose, due to invasion of more complex environments, and it is postulated that under these circumstances the third phase of the cell, the membrane, became increasingly important. Cells increased their surface area by folding their plasma membrane, the inward folds having the additional benefit of bringing the environment deep within the protoplasm (Fig. 9.3). Such active membranes also resulted in the genesis of membrane-bound organoids which had either permanent or temporary functional connections with the plasma membrane and with the environment by way of their lumina. The other major development was the walling off of the genetic material into an internal conclave, which could still, however, be in close contact with the external environment by way of membrane-limited invaginations. Another consequence of membrane infolding and complexity was an overall increase in cell size. Cytoplasmic areas could be greatly increased without

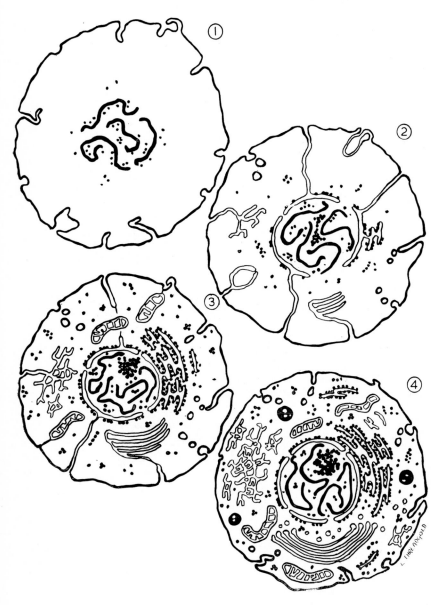

FIG. 9.3. Diagram illustrating one possible route for the evolution of the three-phase cell. Proliferations of the plasma membrane give rise to membraneous organoids and systems, presumably under the influence of the environment. (Original.)

loss of efficient cellular physiological function, because the exchange between protoplasm and environment could still be maintained at the necessary level. Membrane complexity resulted in an increased surface area for chemical work, without a consequent disadvantageous increase in cytoplasmic volume.

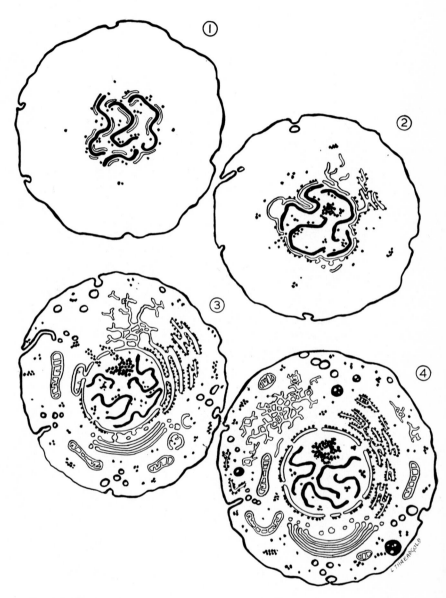

FIG. 9.4. Diagram illustrating an alternative route for the evolution of the three-phase cell. Membrane systems and organoids originate under the influence of the chromosomes and through the continuing need for information between genes and cytoplasm. (Original.)

This theory of the origin of the complex specialized cell is, of course, almost entirely speculative and must be treated with reservation. It has indeed one major weakness, even in the light of present knowledge. The theory supposes that all membrane-bound organoids and structures are derived exclusively from the plasma membrane, although it is known that this differs structurally from most other membranes of the cell. It is possible, of course, that either the plasma membrane or the other membranes have diverged in structure during evolution, especially as they are subject to different environments and have basically different functions. Furthermore, in this evolutionary viewpoint, the nuclear membrane is undoubtedly a cytoplasm derivative, although the evolutionary advantage of a genetic material partially separated from the cytoplasm is hard to appreciate, especially as bacteria are genetically viable without a nuclear membrane.

An alternative theory for the origin of complex membranes is that the genetic material itself is responsible for the membrane-limited organoids, while the plasma membrane is responsible only for such forms as phago-cytic or pinocytotic vacuoles (Fig. 9.4). In a primitive cell the problem of passing information to the cytoplasm exists in the same way, if perhaps not to the same degree, as in a more complex cell. One method of overcoming this problem of communication in an increasingly larger and physico-chemically more complex cytoplasm would be the production of mem-branes (conveyor belts) by the nucleus, or more specifically at the surface of the chromosomes or genes. The more complex membraneous structures, such as the Golgi complex and mitochondria could follow on cell speciali-zation and the restriction of particular organoids to specific functions. Such organoids, being genetically derived, might have built into them a self-replicating code and mechanism, whereby they could grow and reproduce themselves in the cytoplasm, as mitochondria, centrioles and other cell organoids appear to do.

On consideration, it appears more logical that the nucleus should be the originator of membranes, rather than the plasma membrane. The bounding and structural nature of the nuclear membrane could be only an incidental consequence of its primary function as a means of communication. Basically the genes are the controlling factors and initiators of cell differentiation and function, properties which the plasma membrane does not possess. Genes must have the potential to organize molecules into information-bearing patterns, specific genes giving specific molecular patterns and, therefore, distinctive and incontrovertible information. This is a more reasonable supposition than the proposal that membrane growth occurs at the cell surface, and that membranes so derived later become specialized in struc-ture for particular functions under the influence of the environment and the cytoplasm. Membrane origin, formation and differentiation under genetic influence (Darwinism) would fit into the general evolutionary theory better than a supposed environment influence (Lamarkism). The testing of these alternative hypotheses will be of great interest, and doubtless experiments to test their validity will eventually be designed, although it is hard to visualize such experiments at present.

Further Reading List

1. OPARIN, A. I., *Life, its Nature, Origin and Development,* Academic Press, London, 1961.
2. HANSON, D., Evolution of the Cell from Primordial Living Systems. *Quarterly Review of Biology*, Stony Brook Foundation Inc., New York, 1966.
3. KEOSIAN, J., *The Origin of Life*, Chapman & Hall, London, 1964.

INDEX

References to figures in the text are indicated by page references in **bold type**

OTHER TITLES IN THE ZOOLOGY DIVISION

General Editor: G. A. KERKUT

OTHER DIVISIONS IN THE SERIES IN PURE AND APPLIED BIOLOGY

BIOCHEMISTRY

BOTANY

MODERN TRENDS IN PHYSIOLOGICAL SCIENCES

PLANT PHYSIOLOGY